The ARRL Satellite Anthology

Published by
The American Radio Relay League
225 Main Street,
Newington, Connecticut 06111

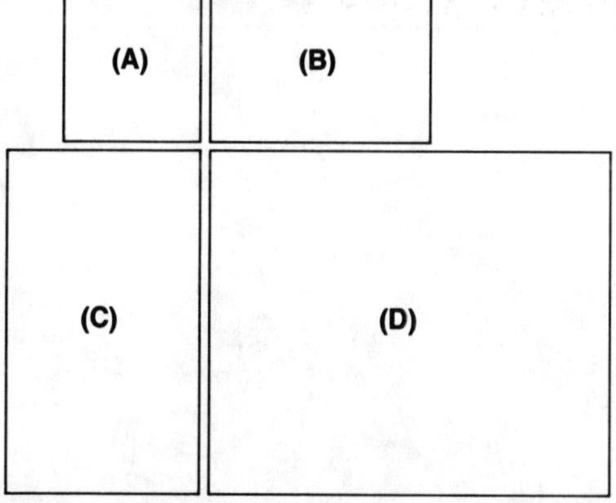

THE COVER

A—Photo courtesy of Grant Zehr, WA9TFB

B—Photo of AMSAT-OSCAR 10 courtesy AMSAT-DL

C—Photo of UoSAT-OSCAR 11 courtesy of the University of Surrey, England

D—Photo courtesy of SRI International, Menlo Park, California

Printed in USA

Second Edition

$8.00 in USA

ISBN: 0-87259-381-9

FOREWORD

It's been over 30 years since the first Amateur Radio satellite was launched. Satellite technology has evolved tremendously since those early days. The amateur satellites of the '80s and '90s have achieved a level of sophistication that rivals multi-million dollar commercial spacecraft. While satellite design has become more complicated, however, satellite *operating* is easier than ever! Today, some satellites can be worked with as little as 20 watts and a simple ground plane antenna.

In this second edition of *The ARRL Satellite Anthology*, we've collected informative articles from *QST* concerning most of the active amateur satellites. You'll learn about their operating features and how you can put them to work for you. If you've never tried satellite operating before, I recommend it highly. You'll enjoy excitement and satisfaction unlike anything you've ever experienced in Amateur Radio. I hope to hear you soon!

David Sumner, K1ZZ
Executive Vice President, ARRL

PREFACE

Communicating with a satellite is a unique experience. It places you in touch with the future of Amateur Radio and of humanity itself. It's not so much the technology that makes a satellite contact impressive, it's the sheer nature of what you are doing! You're engaging in a form of vicarious space travel, communicating with a craft hurtling through an airless void. Believe it or not, through the assistance of your earthbound equipment, you're participating in mankind's first footsteps to the planets and the stars!

With the progress of amateur satellite technology, more hams have been able to enjoy satellite communications. AMSAT OSCAR 13, for example, has been a source of operating pleasure for several years. Its powerful transmitters, sensitive receivers and high, elliptical orbit make it accessible with modest equipment. By the same token, the Microsats have broken new ground with digital packet communications and image transmissions. Despite their diminutive sizes and low-earth orbits, they have become favorites among satellite-active hams throughout the world. The Russian RS (Radio Sputnik) satellites and the Japanese Fuji-OSCAR 20 have also increased the popularity of amateur satellite communications.

As you read the collection of articles in this second edition of *The ARRL Satellite Anthology*, one point should come through loud and clear: satellites are for *everyone*. The time has come to dispel the myth that satellite operating is difficult and expensive. Like any other facet of Amateur Radio, satellite operating costs as much as you're willing to spend! It's true that some "birds" are easier to work than others, but with the variety of satellites presently in orbit, it's a sure bet that there's at least one satellite you can access! When hams take the time to research the current state of amateur satellite technology, they're often surprised to discover that they already own the equipment necessary for satellite communications. (If you can key the push-to-talk line on your 2-meter FM transceiver and listen on 10 meters, you're already equipped to make CW contacts through the RS-10 satellite!)

Now is the time to get acquainted with satellites. New birds are already in development and they'll be in orbit soon. With each new satellite there is a leap forward in technology, making it even easier for you to use them. At AMSAT we're always looking ahead—and we see an exciting future! The day will soon come when amateur satellites will be accessible with little more than hand-held transceivers. And as mankind explores the planets, you can be sure that Amateur Radio will be along for the ride. In our lifetimes, or the lifetimes of our children, hams will be communicating with each other from outposts on the moon and Mars.

So don't just read these articles, get busy putting the ideas to work! Every day the satellites are passing overhead, inviting you to use them. If you take a little time to explore their capabilities, you won't be disappointed. The excitement of a satellite QSO is beyond measure, and as an Amateur Radio operator you possess the ability to take part in that excitement—from your own station. If you'd like to receive more information about Amateur Radio satellites and AMSAT, send a self-addressed, stamped envelope to AMSAT, PO Box 27, Washington, DC 20044.

Doug Loughmiller, KO5I
Executive Director, AMSAT
February 1992

Contents

Update

As you read through the second edition of *The ARRL Satellite Anthology*, you'll notice that we have retained several articles from the first edition that date as far back as 1985. Despite the age of some of these articles, we felt that the information they contained was still very useful in the '90s.

In these older articles you'll see repeated references to Phase 3C. Some of the articles speak of this satellite in the *future* tense since it had not been launched at the time of their publication. As you may know, Phase 3C was successfully launched and became AMSAT-OSCAR 13.

AMSAT-OSCAR 13 is essentially a replacement for AMSAT-OSCAR 10—although it does contains a number of new features and improvements. In terms of working OSCAR 13 versus OSCAR 10, the ground station equipment and techniques are very similar. Therefore, we've retained several articles that are oriented to OSCAR 10 in the hope that you will put the information to good use in working OSCAR 13! (OSCAR 10 is still alive at press time, but it is often difficult to use and control.)

NOTE: Addresses and other information concerning authors, organizations and manufacturers may have changed since these articles were originally published. Be sure to verify the information *before* sending correspondence or money. In addition, the postal rates mentioned in some articles have *increased* in recent years. Please take this fact into account when ordering literature and other materials.

Steve Ford, WB8IMY
Assistant Technical Editor

Introducing Phase 3C: A New, More Versatile OSCAR

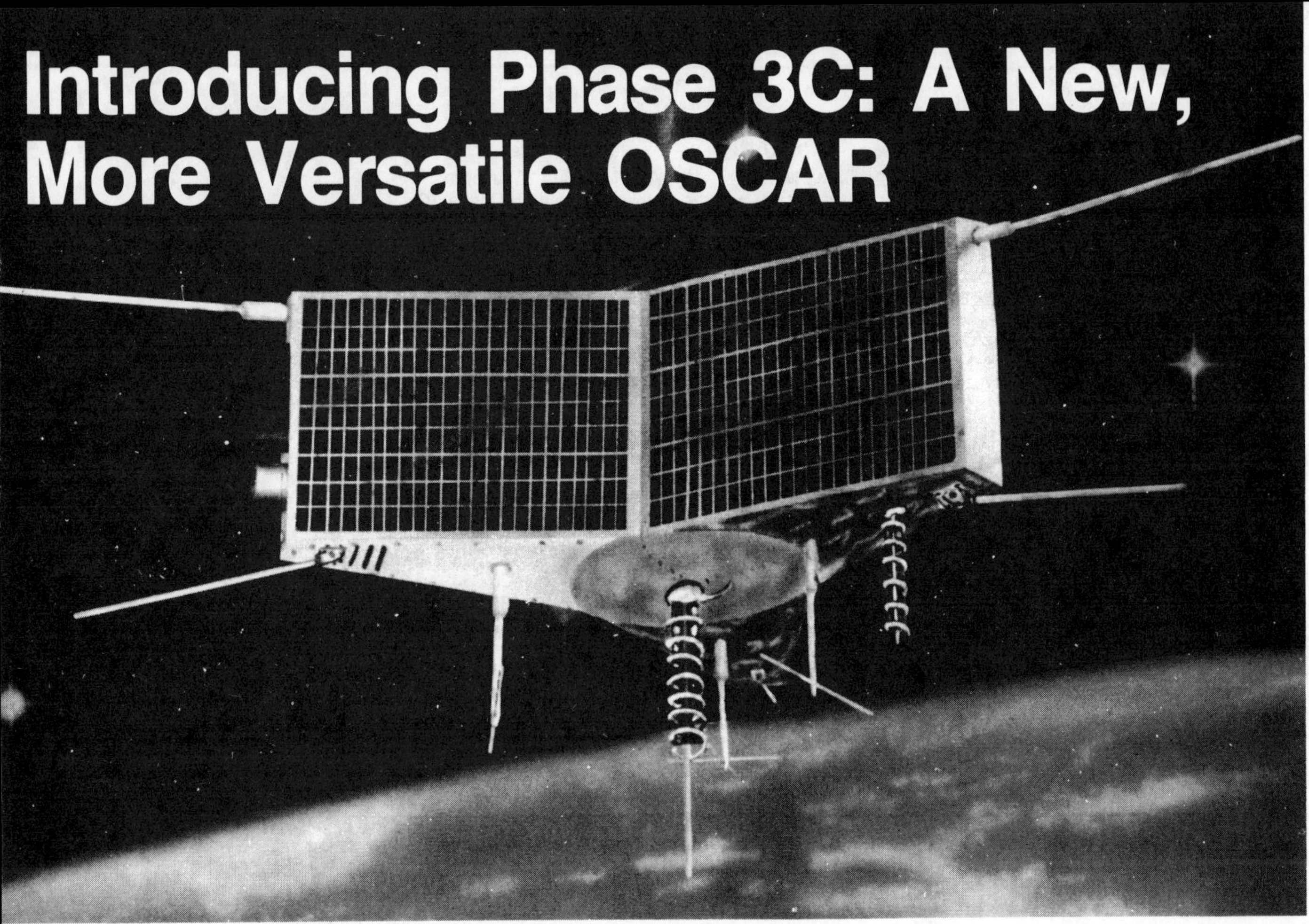

Easily accessible and easy to use, Phase 3C offers many operating alternatives to those of previous Amateur Radio satellites.

By Vern Riportella, WA2LQQ
PO Box 177
Warwick, NY 10990

What has been around for more than 25 years, has been used by tens of thousands of hams, including a US President and a king, and now stands poised for a new series of breakthroughs? Since this is an article about OSCAR, you probably guessed the answer right away![1]

But suppose I made the question slightly more difficult. Did you know the latest OSCAR is ready for launch and will permit intercontinental QSOs on voice, CW, SSTV or packet?

It's a fact. As you read this, the newest OSCAR may have already been placed in orbit. A new Amateur Radio satellite will be plying its way across the heavens, providing superb VHF and UHF communications to those who know how to use it. Surprisingly, using the new OSCAR will be easier than ever—even though it's by far the most complex and versatile OSCAR ever launched.

OSCARs Are Easier Than Ever To Use

The new ease of operation results from several significant factors, including noteworthy improvements in the area of user support. For example, tracking OSCARs used to be a chore. Now, computer programs make tracking a breeze. Some of the newer systems automatically point your antennas. And if your radios can be interfaced to a computer, there are programs to tune your radios to compensate for Doppler shift. You just sit back and enjoy the QSOs!

Furthermore, an improved network of OSCAR Elmers is being established to ensure you get the help you need when getting started. The equipment needed to work any OSCAR is readily available. Many quality VHF and UHF transceivers can be found on the new- and used-equipment markets. (I still use a vintage TS-700S I purchased 12 years ago for OSCAR work.) Antennas and preamps proliferate in magazine ads and on flea-market tables. Moreover, OSCAR users are a resourceful group and often enjoy renewing the "home-brew" legacy in their own shacks. Many homemade helical antennas are regularly used for OSCAR operation. In sum, Phase 3C will be easier to use. Taking advantage of technological advances, the new OSCAR will provide more payback in user satisfaction than any of the earlier amateur satellites.

What is Phase 3C?

Phase 1 OSCARs were simple battery-powered RF beacons usually placed in low orbits (the first was launched in 1961). They had typical life spans of only a few weeks to a few months. Phase 2 OSCARs were more sophisticated. They carried solar cells and batteries for longer life spans. Most important, Phase 2 OSCARs carried repeaters, or, as they are properly called, *transponders*. Phase 2 satellites such as AMSAT-OSCARs 6, 7 and 8 provided useful VHF/UHF communication between amateurs separated 3000 miles and, on occasion, more. Using AMSAT-OSCAR 7, contacts between the East Coast and

Table 1

Phase 3C Operating Modes and Frequencies

Mode	*Uplink Band*	*Downlink Band*	*Notes*
B	70 cm (435 MHz)	2 m (145 MHz)	AO-7 and AO-10 favorite
S	70 cm (435 MHz)	13 cm (2401 MHz)	New; first use on Phase 3C
JL	2 m & 24 cm (1269 MHz)	70 cm (435 MHz)	New; first use on Phase 3C
RUDAK	24 cm (1269 MHz)	70 cm (435 MHz)	New; first use on Phase 3C

Beacons Mode B: General beacon 145.812; Engineering beacon 145.985 MHz
Mode JL: General beacon 435.651; Engineering beacon/RUDAK downlink : 435.677 MHz
Mode S: Beacon: 2400.325 MHz

Mode B

Uplink	*Downlink*	
	145.985 MHz	Engineering beacon
435.420	145.975	Passband limit, upper
435.430	145.965	
435.440	145.955	
435.450	145.945	
435.460	145.935	
435.475	145.925	
435.480	145.915	
435.490	145.905	
435.500	145.895	
435.505	145.890	Passband center
435.510	145.885	
435.520	145.875	
435.530	145.865	
435.540	145.855	
435.550	145.845	
435.560	145.835	
435.570	145.825	Passband limit, lower
	145.812	General beacon

Mode JL

L Uplink	*J Uplink*	*Downlink*	
1269.330		436.005 MHz	Passband limit, upper
1269.340		435.995	
1269.345	144.425	435.990	J sub-band limit, upper
1269.355	144.435	435.980	
1269.365	144.445	435.970	
1269.375	144.455	435.960	
1269.385	144.465	435.950	
1269.395	144.475	435.940	J sub-band limit, lower
1269.400		435.935	
1269.410		435.925	
1269.420		435.915	
1269.430		435.905	
1269.440		435.895	
1269.450		435.885	
1269.460		435.875	
1269.470		435.865	
1269.475		435.860	Passband center
1269.480		435.855	
1269.490		435.845	
1269.500		435.835	
1269.510		435.825	
1269.520		435.815	
1269.530		435.805	
1269.540		435.795	
1269.550		435.785	
1269.560		435.775	
1269.570		435.765	
1269.580		435.755	
1269.590		435.745	
1269.600		435.735	
1269.610		435.725	
1269.620		435.715	Passband limit, lower
1269.710	RUDAK up	435.677	Engineering beacon/RUDAK downlink
		435.675	
		435.665	
		435.655	
		435.651	General beacon

Mode S

Uplink	*Downlink*	
	2400.325	Beacon
435.601	2400.711 MHz	Passband limit, lower
435.605	2400.715	
435.610	2400.720	
435.615	2400.725	
435.619	2400.729	Passband center
435.620	2400.730	
435.625	2400.735	
435.630	2400.740	
435.635	2400.745	
435.637	2400.747	Passband limit, upper

RUDAK

Uplink	*Downlink*	
1269.710	435.677 MHz	Single channel

Although this table might suggest the passbands are divided into many 10-kHz channels, this is not the case; there are no "channels" as such. The table merely shows the correlation of uplink and downlink frequencies across a continuous spectrum of available frequencies with certain "guideposts" illustrated for convenience.

Hawaii could be accomplished under some conditions.[2]

By 1976, however, designers sought to provide regular intercontinental linkups and longer periods of coverage. They recognized that aside from the recreational aspects of Amateur Radio, OSCARs could play a vital role in public-service emergency communications. But, emergency communicators cannot wait for a satellite to appear; a communications channel has to be available nearly always. Recognizing this fundamental public-service requirement, together with the existing Amateur Radio community's appetite for longer access and ease of use, the OSCAR designers began to raise their sights above the low earth-orbiting (LEO) Phase 2 OSCARs.

At first, the designers considered a geosynchronous satellite, but soon realized the inherent limits. For one thing, it would be expensive, and only one could be built. Because it would be expensive, it had to be the product of a large consortium of Amateur Radio satellite groups. But, if the satellite were geosynchronous, its communications area would cover less than one third of the earth's surface. Some countries would be left out. How could the geosynchronous satellite be positioned to serve the contributors equitably?

The answer is the series of Phase 3 satellites. By using a type of orbit pioneered by the Soviets called *Molniya*, a kind of semi-synchronous orbit could be achieved. The Molniya orbit is elliptical instead of circular, and has a period of about 12 hours. For much of the orbit the satellite remains high above the earth (nearly 36,000 km;

22,000 miles) to provide a footprint as large as that of a geosynchronous satellite. Then the bird plummets close to earth only to rise toward its apogee (high point) elsewhere. In this way, Phase 3C provides benefits of broad coverage that can be distributed among a worldwide user population. In other words, the Phase 3 Molniya orbit gives the next best thing to intercontinental coverage all of the time: intercontinental coverage *much* of the time. The Molniya orbit spreads that coverage equitably across the globe, obviating difficult decisions on positioning a geosynchronous satellite's footprint.

By 1980, the first Phase 3 bird, Phase 3A, sat on the launch pad in French Guiana. From there, it was to fly into a Molniya orbit from which it could serve a worldwide community of OSCAR users clamoring for the fun of satellite DX. Many looked forward to working rare DX without regard to the vagaries of F_2 propagation. Others sought to make obsolete the hurried QSOs so common on the low-orbiting Phase 2 satellites that quickly whizzed from horizon to horizon.

The Phase 3A project ended in disaster, however, when an errant launcher was destroyed, dropping its payload into the Atlantic ocean. The product of years of work—transponders, computers, everything—literally went down to the sea in chips!

Not to be bested by "outrageous fortune," the AMSAT team went back to work to develop Phase 3B in 1983. Phase 3B became AMSAT-OSCAR 10 upon its successful insertion into orbit. Since then, nearly 150 countries have been heard on AO-10, and numerous firsts have been achieved. Now, the stage is set for the latest, most powerful and capable OSCAR yet: Phase 3C, the third in its generation.

Phase 3C Subsystems

Phase 3C is a self-contained system. It carries all the resources it will need to operate in space for 5 years or more. The satellite's four major subsystems are: communications, power, control and propulsion.

The Communications Subsystem

The Phase 3C communications subsystem consists of four transponders. Each of these functions as a cross-band repeater. (See Table 1.) You transmit on the uplink frequency and listen on the downlink frequency. Because you transmit and receive on different bands, you can transmit and receive simultaneously (full duplex operation), and even listen to your downlink signal delayed up to a third of a second—an experience that is unnerving to those who've not experienced it before!

The Mode B and JL transponders are linear. That means the signal appearing in the uplink receiver is transmitted on the downlink so that SSB, CW, SSTV and various digital waveforms are faithfully reproduced. Moreover, the transponder passbands are wide enough to accommodate several contacts at once. That means European amateurs can chat with those in South America, while hams in Africa can chat with North Americans and others in between at the same time, albeit on different frequencies within the passband.

The Mode-S transponder is an experimental UHF-to-UHF transponder designed primarily for a single FM channel. It can handle up to four SSB stations, providing they each stay below the hard-limiting threshold of the transponder. RUDAK—the English translation: *Regenerative Repeater for Digital Amateur Communication*—is a new type of packet-radio repeater. It uses the most advanced form of digital modulation (phase shift keying, PSK) and techniques to create an efficient digital communications channel.

The antennas on Phase 3C are an assortment of VHF and UHF designs. Coverage of the 2-meter band is accomplished using two antennas. The 2-meter high-gain array, a so-called ZL Special, consists of three two-element beams phased in such a way as to produce right-hand circular (RHC) polarization.[3] This array has a gain of about 6 dBic (decibels referenced to a circularly polarized isotropic source), and a 3-dB beamwidth of roughly 100°. An omnidirectional 2-meter antenna is used for conditions where the high-gain beam is inappropriate. This antenna is linearly polarized, has as much as 2 dBi gain and a toroidal pattern.

The UHF antennas on Phase 3C are common types. On 70 cm, a monopole is also used for the same reasons as the 2-meter monopole, and it gives comparable performance. The 70-cm high-gain array consists of three phased dipoles over a groundplane, and produces 9.5 dBic gain with a theoretical 3-dB beamwidth of 67°. The 24-cm antenna is a 5-turn RHC helix supported by a frame. Its gain is 12.2 dBic and its 3-dB beamwidth is 49°. The 13-cm antenna is a 6-turn RHC helix providing 13 dBic gain and having a 3-dB beamwidth of 45°.

The satellite transmits a strong signal that can be heard well across a distance of as much as 40,000 km (25,000 miles). Phase 3C's effective radiated power referenced to an isotropic source (EIRP) is shown in Table 2.

Table 2

Phase 3C Effective Radiated Power, Isotropic (EIRP)

Mode	*Band*	*EIRP PEP*	*EIRP Average*	*Peak/Average*
B	2 m	23 dBW (200 W)	17 dBW (50 W)	6 dB
JL	70 cm	26.5 dBW (446 W)	20.5 dBW (111 W)	6 dB
S	13 cm	0.97 dBW (1.25 W)	(continuous)	0 dB

The Power Subsystem

The Phase 3C power subsystem consists of the solar-cell arrays, battery charge regulator and batteries. The solar arrays are made up of hundreds of silicon solar cells on six separate surfaces. Together, they generate 50 watts when first placed in orbit.

View of one arm of Phase 3C showing the sun sensor and earth sensor (left), sensor electronics unit (center) and propulsion flow assembly (right). (*photo by Robert J. Diersing, N5AHD*)

Table 3

Phase 3C Preliminary Telemetry Channel Allocations and Estimated Equations

Telemetry Channel	*Function*	*Typical Equation (Subject to final cal.)*	*Units*
00	Solar panel out and BCR input voltage	n × 150	mV
01	70-cm transmitter average power output	$(253 - n)^2 / 2000$	W
02	70-cm receiver temperature	(n – 127)/1.82	°C
03	(Reserved) 04 BCR output and main battery voltage	(n – 10) × 75	mV
05	(Special Purpose)	xxxxxxxxxxxx	—
06	2-m transmitter power amplifier temperature	(n – 127)/1.82	°C
07	+14-V rail current to transponder	(n – 15) × 20.64	mA
08	+10-V regulator voltage	(n – 12) × 50	mV
09	He tank high pressure	(TBD)	Bar
0A	IHU temperature	(n – 127)/1.82	°C
0B	+14-V rail current to magnetorquers		—
	and antenna relay	(n – 15) × 4.128	mA
0C	BCR oscillator #1 status	0 = Off; N < 10 = On	—
0D	He tank low-side pressure-control voltage	(TBD)	—
0E	BCR temperature	(n – 127)/1.82	°C
0F	+10-V regulator current	(n – 15) × 4.128	mA
10	BCR oscillator #2 status	0 = Off; N < 10 = On	—
11	N_2O_4 tank pressure	(TBD)	Bar
12	SEU temperature	(n – 127)/1.82	°C
13	Battery charge current	(n – 15) × 10.32	mA
14	Top (+Z) photocell sun sensor	(See note below)	—
15	Motor-valve status	(TBD)	—
16	Auxillary battery #1 temperature	(n – 127)/1.82	°C
17	Active BCR ouput current	(n – 15) × 20.64	mA
18	Bottom (– Z) photocell sensor	(See note below)	—
19	S-Band-transmitter power output	(TBD)	mW
1A	Auxiliary battery #2 temperature	(n – 127)/1.82	°C
1B	Active BCR input current on 28-V line	(n – 15) × 10.32	mA
1C	Spin rate {if n⁴139, r =	(139 – n) × 0.8 + 20	r/min
	or {if n < = 139	r = 508/ (n – 116)-2	r/min
1D	24-cm receiver	AGC {if n × 100 AGC = 0	dB
	or {if n < = 100	$AGC = (n - 100)^2 / 189$	dB
1E	Main battery temperature	(n – 127)/1.82	°C
1F	Solar panel #6 current	(n – 15) × 4.128	mA
20	2-m-transmitter average power output	$(200 - n)^2 / 2000$	W
21	He tank temperature	(n – 127)/1.82	°C
22	Solar panel #1 temperature	(n – 127)/1.82	°C
23	Solar panel #5 current	(n – 15) × 4.128	mA
24	70-cm receiver AGC	$(n - 83)^2 / 1000$	dB
25	70-cm transmitter PA temperature	(n – 127)/1.82	°C
26	Solar panel #3 temperature	(n – 127)/1.82	°C
27	Solar panel #4 current	(n – 15) × 4.128	mA
28	Special purpose	xxxxxxxxxxxx	—
29	24-cm receiver temperature	(n – 127)/1.82	°C
2A	Solar panel #5 temperature	(n – 127)/1.82	°C
2B	Solar panel #3 current	(n – 15) × 4.128	mA
2C	+14-V regulator voltage	(n – 10) × 61.5	mV
2D	RUDAK temperature	(n – 127)/1.82	°C
2E	Top (+Z) skin temperature of arm #1	(n – 127)/1.82	°C
2F	Solar panel #2 current	(n – 15) × 4.128	mA
30	Mode-B transponder +9-V supply voltage	(n – 10) × 50	mV
31	Wall temperature in arm #2	(n – 127)/1.82	°C
32	Bottom (–Z) skin temperature of arm #1	(n – 127)/1.82 C	
33	Solar panel #1 current	(n – 15) × 4.128	mA
34	Special purpose	xxxxxxxxxxx	—
35	Wall temperature in arm #1	(n – 127)/1.82	°C
36	N_2O_4 tank temperature	(n – 127)/1.82	°C
37	Reserved		—
38	Auxiliary battery voltage	(n – 10) × 75	mV
39	Mode-S transponder temperature	(n – 127)/1.82	°C
3A	+Z platform temperature (SERI experiment)	(n – 127)/1.82	°C
3B	Reserved		—
3C	Mode-L transponder +9 V supply voltage	(n – 10) × 50	mV
3D	AZ-50 tank temperature	(n – 127)/1.82	°C
3E	Nutation damper temperature	(n – 127)/1.82	°C
3F	Reserved		

Radiation damage incurred in orbit after the first three years is expected to reduce the total array power to about 35 watts. The battery charge regulator (BCR) ensures the two nickel-cadmium batteries on board are optimally charged. The primary battery has a capacity of 10 Ah; the auxiliary battery is rated at 6 Ah. Together, the elements of the power subsystem provide closely regulated power to the other subsystems. Thus, the battery ensures that the satellite is powered even when in Earth's shadow.

The Control Subsystem

The control subsystem is perhaps the most complex of all. It consists of a computer and its associated memory, software, command detectors, telemetry multiplexers, sensors and attitude-control devices. The heart of the control subsystem is the integrated housekeeping unit (IHU). The IHU consists of an RCA COSMAC CDP1802 microprocessor, its memory and various supporting elements. This CPU was chosen because a radiation-hardened silicon-on-sapphire version was available. Even though much more advanced CPUs are now available, the 1802's comparatively light task loading allows it to loaf along. The memory for the CPU consists of special Harris HS-6564RH radiation-hardened CMOS ICs donated by Harris' Custom Integrated Circuit Division, Melbourne, Florida. The total memory carried is 48 kbytes, of which the error-corrected available net memory is 32 kbytes. The software is written in *IPS*, a FORTH-like multi-tasking language developed by Karl Meinzer, DJ4ZC, and his colleagues about 10 years ago.

The IHU controls the satellite. Com-

Notes on Table 3

The equation values are preliminary estimates *only*.

- IHU = integrated housekeeping unit; the computer
- BCR = battery charge regulator
- He = Helium
- SEU = sensor electronics unit
- N_2O_4 = nitrogen tetroxide; the propellant oxidizer; AZ-50 is aerozine-50, the propellant fuel
- TBD = to be defined

Notes regarding channels 14 and 18:

These two sensors detect sunlight on the top (+Z) surface and the bottom (–Z) surface of the spacecraft. They provide only a rough indication of sun position and are used to resolve ambiguity in the readings from the sun sensors. When in full sunlight, a sensor count of 65 results. A count of about 10 is background noise only, and the sun is present when the count exceeds 20. The main spacecraft solar cell arrays receive maximum illumination when the sun is perpendicular to (normal to) the spin axis (Z axis). When this condition exists, both the +Z and –Z detectors will yield background readings (10) only. A count of 20 or greater on either indicates misalignment. The higher the count, the greater the misalignment of the spacecraft with respect to the sun angle (beta angle)—Source: Jan King, W3GEY, Apr 15 86; *ASR* No. 93, Dec 31 84; I. T. Ashley, ZL1AOX, Jan 27 88.

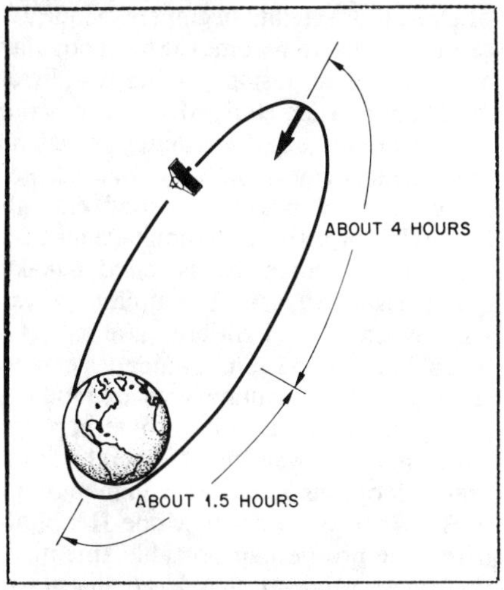

Phase 3C circles the earth in a semi-synchronous orbit called Molniya. The Molniya orbit is elliptical and has an orbital period of about 11 hours.

mands are uploaded from the ground to the IHU. The IHU then controls the satellite for weeks or months without intervention from ground controllers. The IHU turns the transponders on and off according to a prescribed schedule, carefully regulates the battery charge in conjunction with the BCR, and issues a continuous stream of telemetry via the communications subsystem to show sensor and status indicator readings in the satellite.

The IHU controls the attitude of the satellite in space to ensure it is aimed precisely at earth, so its antennas are properly illuminating the target area and so the solar panels are aligned toward the sun. To control the satellite's attitude, the IHU compares readings from its earth sensors and sun sensor with mathematical models contained in its memory. When it detects a deviation in attitude from the proper one, it applies carefully timed pulses to on-board electromagnets. The field from these magnets interacts with the earth's geomagnetic field, creating a torque that tends to reorient the spacecraft. When the spacecraft's attitude has been restored to the desired value, the magnetorquing ceases.

The IHU also maintains the proper spin rate for Phase 3C. Again using the magnetorquers, the IHU spins the satellite like the armature of a motor. The spinning stabilizes the satellite, just as spinning stabilizes a top. Spinning also ensures the satellite stays thermally manageable. Like the spit of a rotisserie, the satellite spins in the brilliant glare of the sun, absorbing heat when facing the sun, and radiating it to the blackness of space when facing elsewhere. Phase 3C will be spun at about 33 revolutions per minute for most of its operational life.

The IHU also schedules and transmits pre-stored bulletins on the various beacon frequencies. The bulletins usually consist of user-related information, such as the satellite operating schedules, orbital data, special advisories and so forth. The bulletins are sent in various modulation formats: (1) CW, (2) 45-baud FSK RTTY and (3) 400 bit/s PSK ASCII bulletins.

Temperature and pressure sensors, and various electrical sensors, feed a multiplexer that then feeds the IHU, which produces the 64-channel telemetry format. The telemetry suite (See Table 3) is comprehensive, allowing close monitoring of virtually all important aspects of satellite operation by command stations and suitably equipped ground observers. The earth sensors and sun sensor feed the sensor electronics unit (SEU) that the IHU uses to determine spacecraft attitude.

If it were not for the IHU, the satellite would be little more than a big hunk of dumb iron. *With* the IHU, the satellite is one of the most advanced Amateur Radio devices ever built. The fact that the satellite is totally under IHU software control ensures unprecedented satellite flexibility. The IHU can run the satellite for weeks without intervention from the ground command team.

The Propulsion Subsystem

The Ariane-4 rocket that carries Phase 3C to orbit is the largest launcher ever built by the European Space Agency. It will carry two large commercial geosynchronous satellites in addition to Phase 3C. But the Ariane-4 does not place any of the three payload satellites in their final orbits. Rather, each is deposited in its own geosynchronous transfer orbit (GTO—see Table 4). A GTO is the point of departure between the launcher and the payloads. The launcher orients itself, spins up the satellites and sets them off on their own. The GTO is a highly eccentric ellipse with a perigee around 220 km (137 miles) and an apogee of about 36,000 km (22,000 miles). Each satellite must get to a more usable orbit using its own rocket system called a *kick motor* (so named because it figuratively "kicks" the satellite from the GTO to a higher orbit).

For Phase 3C, the objective is to get from the GTO to a more stable orbit within a few days. There is some urgency in raising the perigee quickly, since satellites with 220-km perigees tend to fall from the sky regularly and, on occasion, in a great flurry of debris—literally as man-made meteorites. Since AMSAT folks fancy themselves builders of spacecraft and not ersatz meteorite makers, the designers have resolved to execute the first in-orbit burn as soon as the orbit parameters can be accurately determined. Using a special ranging technique and sophisticated mathematical models on powerful computers, AMSAT engineers will be able to develop GTO orbital data for Phase 3C within a few days of launch.

The perigee kick motor (PKM) on Phase 3C is a small rocket engine that uses two fluids stored in separate portions of a fuel tank. Under pressure from a helium system, the propellant and oxidizer combine in the combustion chamber and spontaneously ignite in a controlled explosion to produce a thrust of 400 Newtons (about 95 lbs). A 400-N thrust would not move your Buick up the highway that smartly, but on the business end of a 140-kg (309-lb) satellite, the result is moderately impressive.

In a series of kick-motor burns spread over a few weeks, the perigee is raised to about 1500 km and the inclination of the plane of the orbit is raised from the 10° GTO to about 57°. The total velocity change imparted by the little Messerschmitt-Boelkow-Blohm (MBB) engine amounts to an impressive 1480 m/s (4854 ft/s). To put that number in perspective, that's the equivalent of going from rest to 3310 mi/h (Mach 5). (Phase 3C could outrun an SR-71 Blackbird superspy jet!) Fortunately, the acceleration imposed on Phase 3C is not overwhelming: At just 3Gs, it amounts only

Table 4

Orbital Characteristics (at separation from launcher)

Geosynchronous transfer orbit (GTO)

Perigee altitude:	222.504 km
Apogee altitude:	36076.636 km
Inclination:	9.997 degrees
Argument of perigee:	178.148 degrees
Ascending node longitude:	−135.541 degrees/lift-off
True anomaly:	127.554 degrees
Epoch:	Instant of Separation (L +4797.1 s)
Spin rate at deployment:	29.47 degrees per second
Separation velocity:	0.59 meters per second

Objective Phase 3C orbit (final orbit after two or three burns)

Apogee: 36,000 km
Perigee: 1,500 km
Inclination: approx 57 degrees
Argument of perigee: 178 degrees (determined by launcher)
Anomalistic period: approx 662.4 minutes
Longitude increment: approx 184.5 degrees East per orbit

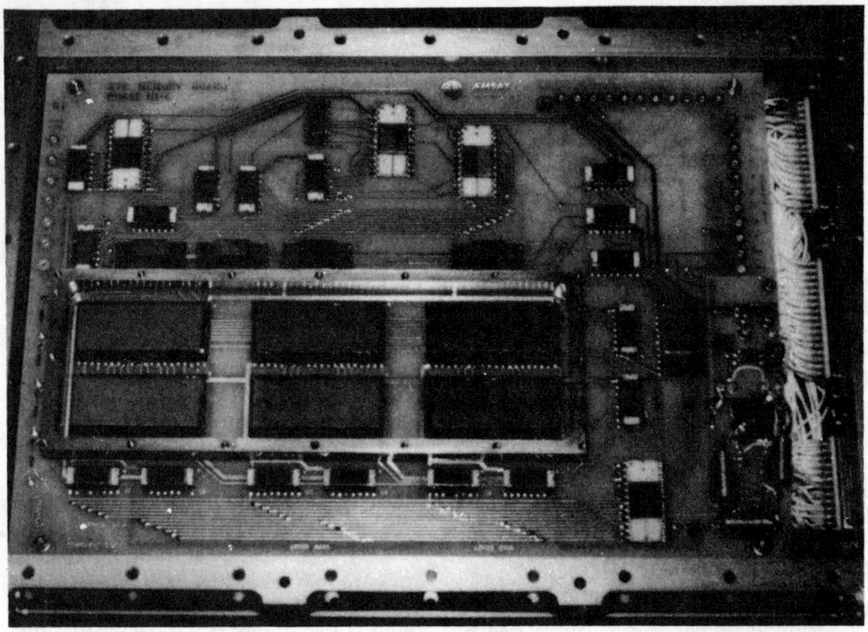

The Phase 3C integrated housekeeping unit, a sophisticated computer that controls the satellite, now contains radiation-hardened memory donated by Harris. The IHU was designed by Steve Robinson, W2FPY, and built by Gordon Hardman, KE3D. (*photo by Dick Daniels, W4PUJ*)

to a modest imposition for which the designers have taken adequate provision. The rocket engine can be restarted several times to refine the orbit until the desired result is obtained. All burns, however, should be completed within a month of launch.

What's To Do On Phase 3C

Since Phase 3C *is* primarily a spaceborne communications system, logic suggests communications is the main activity. Logic holds here. The Mode-B transponder provides a useful training ground for those learning the ropes. Its 150 kHz of available bandwidth is adequate for about 50 simultaneous QSOs under optimum conditions. Since most satellite contacts involve more than two participants, Mode B can actively serve more than 100 users at a time.

The equipment required to use Mode B is reasonably modest, and many individuals can get the feel of satellite operations on the new bird with borrowed equipment or that already on hand. Rag chews, DXing, nets and general socializing are popular. Round table discussions are a favorite of mine. Getting a half-dozen chums from across the globe together for an easygoing, relaxed rag chew is very enjoyable. Annoying QRM is virtually absent and QSOs are clearly audible. Conditions are comparable to those on the 20-meter band at its peak, as if you had a large swatch of it to yourself. With coverage times measured in hours, there's no need to rush QSOs as was necessary with low earth-orbiting satellites. And since Phase 3C moves slowly across the sky when near apogee, antennas needn't be moved much, if at all. Table 5A details ground station requirements for Mode B.

The Mode-JL Transponder

Although Mode B may become the mode of choice for satellite beginners, Mode JL seems destined to become the most popular and productive. Using combined uplinks on 24 cm and 2 meters, Mode JL has the right combination of attributes to delight the satellite veteran and newcomer alike. It combines a passband broad enough (290 kHz) for perhaps 90 simultaneous SSB QSOs with other attractions bound to make it a pleasure to use. The uplink power requirements on 24 cm are quite modest, as Table 5B shows. Since antennas can be small and power requirements are modest, I suspect Mode JL will become popular with amateurs wanting to operate from remote locations (campsites and mountaintops). Whereas the 24-cm Mode-JL uplink offers the prospect of portable antennas, the 2-meter Mode-JL uplink is designed for lesser-developed nations where 24-cm equipment is rare or nonexistent.

The Mode-S Transponder

Mode S will be a special delight to use if all goes according to plan. The Mode-S experiment is designed for a single FM channel. The actual use of this channel hasn't been determined, but some ideas have been suggested. Besides the obvious QSO activities between two or more individuals, the Mode-S transponder has been suggested for occasional use as a bulletin channel. The high-quality audio that can likely be received at well-equipped Mode-S stations could be easily patched into local terrestrial repeaters to furnish a

Table 5A
Minimum Mode B Station Requirements

Uplink
Frequency: 435.420-435.570 MHz
EIRP: 21.5 dBW (141 W) for 20 dB peak and 10 dB average SNR on downlink
Polarization: Right Hand Circular (RHC)
Suitable uplink components 10 watts to 12 dBic gain antenna

Downlink
Frequency: 145.975-145.825 MHz
Polarization: RHC
Minimum recommended antenna gain: 10 dBic
Maximum receive system effective noise temperature: 625 K (NF = 5.0 dB)
Minimum figure of merit: −18 dB/K

Table 5B
Minimum Mode JL Station Requirements

Uplink
Frequency: Mode L: 1269.620-1269.330 MHz
Mode J: 144.425-144.475 MHz
EIRP: Mode L: 25 dBW (316 W) for 20 dB peak and 10 dB average SNR on downlink
Mode J: 25 dBW (316 W) for 20 dB peak and 10 dB average SNR on downlink
Polarization: RHC
Suitable uplink components: Mode L: 10 watts to 15 dBic gain antenna
Mode J: 20 watts to 12 dBic gain antenna

Downlink
Frequency: 435.715-436.005 MHz
Polarization: RHC
Minimum recommended antenna gain: 13 dBic
Maximum receive system effective noise temperature: 290 K (NF = 3.0 dB)
Minimum figure of merit: −12 dB/K

Table 5C

Minimum Mode S Station Requirements

Uplink

Frequency: 435.601-435.637 MHz
EIRP: Approx 27 dBW (501 W) under average Mode B AGC conditions
Polarization: RHC
Suitable uplink components: 25 watts to 13 dBic antenna

Downlink

Frequency: 2400.711-2400.747 MHz + beacon @ 2400.325 MHz
Polarization: RHC
Minimum recommended antenna gain: 28 dBic
Typical antenna: 1.4 m dish (assuming 50% efficiency)
Maximum receive system effective noise temperature: 290 K (NF = 3.0 dB)
Minimum figure of merit: +3 dB/K

fine bulletin distribution system. This might be viewed as a prototype for operational planning for AMSAT's Phase 4 geosynchronous satellites planned for the early 1990s. Up to four SSB stations can use the Mode-S transponder, too. Ground station requirements for Mode S are detailed in Table 5C.

The Rudak Project

RUDAK is essentially a digipeater designed and built by AMSAT DL engineers in Munich. The architects of RUDAK envision it providing an interconnect between local area networks in addition to point-to-point contacts. An independent receiver in the Mode-L transponder is provided for the RUDAK uplink on 1269.710 MHz. The demodulator converts the 2400-bit/s biphase PSK signal into a clean digital signal for the RUDAK processor. Thanks to the sweep circuit in the demodulator, the uplink signals only have to be within ± 7.5 kHz of the center frequency.

On the downlink side, the output data modulates the RUDAK beacon transmitter in the Mode-L transponder on 435.677 MHz using BPSK at a data rate of 400 bit/s, the same as for the general beacon of Phase 3C. The rate can be increased to 1200 bit/s using NRZI (nonreturn to zero) modulation for experimental reasons. Details on interfacing to RUDAK are beyond the scope of this article and have been published elsewhere.[4]

Some basic RUDAK station requirements are provided in Table 5D.

QSOs, Competition and Techno-Sport

Satellite activities other than one-on-one QSOs, round tables or nets are organized by AMSAT and other groups. Emergency communications exercises have been carried out on earlier OSCARs and will continue on Phase 3C. On the other hand, linking terrestrial repeaters to the hemispheric coverage of Phase 3C should provide some excitement for many whose only radio is a 2-meter or 70-cm FM hand-held transceiver. Imagine talking to someone in Australia from the comfort of your easy chair while holding your hand-held transceiver! Gateways provide a means of consolidating resources so that many can enjoy the thrill of satellite communications without making a large investment in equipment. When users find out how much fun it can be, they may opt to establish their own satellite stations. Gateways are, in essence, a means of tasting the wine before buying the bottle.

Competition on OSCARs has always been approached with caution. There are good reasons for this. First, transponder operation is different from the HF bands. On HF, there is a degree of frequency sharing. If you turn your HF beam away from an interfering station, you can reduce the QRM and continue your QSO. Various propagation zones appear and disappear. Not so on the OSCAR satellites! On the transponder, everyone listening on a given frequency hears everyone else using that frequency equally well (more or less, assuming comparable equipment). There is no frequency sharing afforded by geography (space diversity). The satellite illuminates its footprint evenly. Consequently, the potentially disruptive effects of high-intensity contests are magnified within the bounds of the transponder passband.

Second, the competitive spirit of contesting on the HF bands leads some participants to use copious amounts of power. Increasing power on HF increases the coverage zone. The higher the power, the larger the zone covered, and the less are the possibilities of frequency sharing. (Some high-power Navy VLF signals are heard the world over, even by submerged submarines!) Barring untoward splattering, raising your power on 20 meters does not, however, affect a QSO 100 kHz away.

Unfortunately, the same cannot be said for satellite operation. A finite amount of power is available to the transponder. Since the transponders are linear, the manner in which the available downlink power is divided among passband users is in direct proportion to the strength of their uplink signals. If one very strong uplink signal appears in the passband, it uses an inordinate amount of the available downlink power and, consequently, reduces the power available to the other users. In contrast to HF operation, therefore, an overpowered station 100 kHz down the band *can* unduly affect your QSO. "Power hogging" is an abomination to the conscientious satellite operator and, since contests seem to promote power escalation scenarios, contests have been discouraged on all OSCARs.

But there is more to on-air competition than contests. DXing on satellites is a form of long-term competition that is reasonable insofar as it, too, stays under control. DXing and seeking awards for grid squares, countries or whatever is normally a lower-keyed form of competition and is encouraged and promoted with various satellite awards. Furthermore, a new type of competitive activity was begun on AO-10 and will soon be resumed and enhanced on Phase 3C. This new competitive activity is called *Techno-Sport*. It's a variation on the highly popular radio sport concepts of the USSR and other countries. In AMSAT's Techno-Sport activities, the idea is to harness the competitive drives of individuals in a way that promotes learning about technical matters and development of useful technical skills.

For example, AMSAT's *ZRO Test*[5] got started in 1985 on AO-10. The challenge of the ZRO Test is to develop and operate a superior Mode-B or Mode-L station that can "hear" exceedingly well. Through carefully calibrated and controlled conditions, an uplink signal is sent to the satel-

Table 5D

Minimum RUDAK Station Requirements

Uplink

Frequency: 1269.710 MHz
EIRP: 26 dBW (400 W)
Typical suitable uplink: 8 watts to 17 dBic antenna
Polarization: RHC

Downlink

Frequency: 435.677 MHz
Typical receive antenna gain: 10 dBic for 12 dB E_b/N_0 ratio†
Polarization: RHC

†Energy per bit to noise ratio

AMSAT PHASE III C

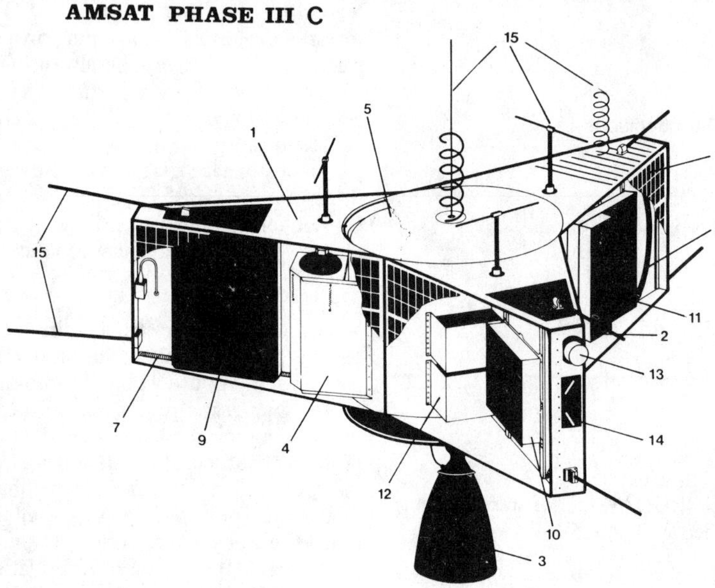

The AMSAT Phase 3C satellite. (*graphic by AMSAT-DL*)

1—Aluminum space frame
2—S-band transponder
3—Kick motor
4—Helium tank container
5—Fuel and oxidizer tank
6—Solar panel
7—Magnetorquer coil
8—Nutation dampener
9—Integrated housekeeping unit
10—Battery charge regulator
11—Modulator
12—Auxiliary battery
13—Earth sensor
14—Sun sensor
15—Antennas

lite. All listeners receive equal downlinks (within a fraction of a decibel) because of the position of the satellite. After a practice run, a series of CW numbers is sent at the baseline signal strength level. The baseline downlink level is set to equal the beacon. The power output of the beacon remains constant in both the short and long term. This ensures level correlation from month to month between test sessions and should reduce calibration errors because of variations in satellite attitude and ionospheric absorption.

ZRO Test participants carefully copy the numbers sent in slow CW. The uplink power is then reduced by half (3 dB). More CW numbers are sent and copied. Then power is reduced by another 3 dB and more numbers are sent and copied. The process continues in 3-dB increments until the CW on the downlink is so weak that virtually no one copies it (at 24 dB below the baseline level, the uplink is less than 1 watt!). Certificates are awarded to those who copy the baseline numbers. Endorsement stickers are awarded each time a competitor demonstrates that he or she has improved his or her receive sensitivity by 3 dB. Only one competitor (Jeffrey Bishop, W7ID) has ever garnered the long-sought Z-8 award—24 dB below the baseline.

New Techno-Sports are being planned for Phase 3C. There's *SatFox*. This is a derivative of the terrestrial radiolocation sport, Fox and Hound. In the satellite version, you and your computer try to figure out where the hidden transmitter is. Instead of traipsing through the swamps with your DF loops, however, you play hound from the comfort of your shack.

SatFox will use the movement of the satellite itself to obtain "fixes" on the hidden fox who could be 80 or 8000 miles away. If you're a clever hound, you should be able to narrow the fox's QTH down to a county-sized area. You send in your estimate by mail. If you do well, you earn a handsome award or an endorsement to a prior award.

The SatFox location technique will use Doppler-shift measurements to isolate a hidden RF source, rather than signal strength (used in some terrestrial Fox and Hound competitions). Doppler shift measurements are the basis of the search-and-rescue satellite system now being operated by more than a dozen nations using the SARSAT/COSPAS satellites of the US and USSR.[6] Project SatFox on Phase 3C will work in an analogous way. The fox will transmit a beacon, but since the motion of Phase 3C is low compared to SARSAT/COSPAS satellites, extra care will be required to make precise position determinations. That's where skill comes in. And that's what Techno-Sport is all about: combining the fun of competing with the satisfaction of learning and the occasional reward of prevailing and being recognized for superior performance.

Thus, there's plenty to do on Phase 3C. With all the activity that's on tap, contests are scarcely missed.

Operating Tips

Operating via any satellite is a snap once the basics are mastered. True, there are a few new things to learn to become proficient on the OSCAR satellites, but learning new techniques is part of the enjoyment of satellite operation. To successfully operate via the OSCAR satellites, you should have knowledge of five basic areas:

1) Where the satellite is
2) What mode it's in
3) What frequency to transmit on
4) What frequency to receive on
5) Basic operating practice[7]

Determining "where the satellite is" is called *tracking*. Since high-gain antennas are required, you need to aim them at the satellite properly. Tracking tells you where to aim. Manual tracking devices are convenient, inexpensive and sufficiently accurate for satisfactory results. Tracking with the aid of a computer is by far the easiest—just enter the data on the satellite's orbit.[8]

Item 2, mode of operation, is a matter of scheduling. The operating schedule of Phase 3C will be announced after launch. You can learn the operating schedule by listening to W1AW bulletins, by obtaining official AMSAT net bulletins via on-air nets, from packet-radio bulletin boards, or by land-line bulletin boards.[9]

Items 3 and 4, transmit and receive frequencies, are addressed in Table 1. More specific operating information comes in the form of band plans. The preliminary idea is to divide the satellite passbands into thirds, as was done for AO-10. The lowest third is for digital modes such as CW and packet, the upper third is for voice modes such as SSB, and the center third is for mixed modes.[10]

Item 5, basic operating practice, reduces to some very straightforward guidance. For example, always wear headphones when operating SSB. Why? Since you're operating full duplex, a feedback path will exist between your receiver's speaker and the transmitter microphone. The feedback path will round through the satellite back to you again. Howling feedback soon alerts you to the need to don the "cans." Next, never swish the transmitter across the passband to locate your downlink frequency. Estimate your downlink frequency by using Table 1. Then, send a short series of CW dots or briefly whistle into you microphone while listening carefully for your downlink signal and tuning your receiver slightly. To correct for Doppler shift on Mode B and Mode JL, adjust your transmitter frequency only. On Mode S, adjust your receiver frequency only. General operating guidelines appear in AMSAT's *Phase 3 Operating Handbook*. This Handbook is now being revised for Phase 3C and is due for completion soon. Experience is a good

The AMSAT-DL team members work on Phase 3C during integration in Golden, Colorado; (Left to right) Konrad Mueller; Hanspeter Kuhlen, DK1YQ; Karl Meinzer, DJ4ZC; Werner Haas, DJ5KQ. (*AMSAT-DL photo*)

teacher, and many helpful colleagues can be found on OSCARs, since they feel proud of having joined the space-age hobby. They are often glad to share their findings with you!

I hope you have gathered that becoming proficient on OSCAR, even Phase 3C, is no big deal. Sure, there is some esoteric information involved, but Amateur Radio in general probably appeared fairly mysterious to you until you got thoroughly involved. Identifying and using reliable information sources is the key.[11]

In this article, we've learned what Phase 3C is and what it can do. We've recognized that getting to know how to use it and have a great deal of fun in the process is simply a matter of getting interested and having access to the right information. Products and activities of the space age are all around us in our everyday lives. Getting your signal onboard OSCAR and being a part of the Amateur Radio space program is as natural for hams as can be. Phase 3C could be your entry into this vast, rewarding new realm of radio communications. See you there!

Acknowledgments

The propulsion section is based on Richard L. Daniels, W4PUJ, "The Propulsion Systems of the Phase-III Series Satellites," *Proceedings of the 1st Utah State University Conference on Small Satellites*, Oct 7, 1987. (This work is reprinted in the *AMSAT-NA Technical Journal*, Vol 1, No. 2, Winter 1987-88, published by AMSAT-NA).

The IHU section is based on Gordon Hardman, KE3D, "The Integrated Housekeeping Unit—A Method of Telemetry, Command and Control for Small Spacecraft," *Proceedings of the 1st Utah State University Conference on Small Satellites*, Oct 7, 1987. (This article is also reprinted in the *AMSAT-NA Technical Journal*, Vol 1, No. 2, Winter 1987-88, published by AMSAT-NA).

I am especially grateful to AMSAT's Vice President of Engineering, Jan King, W3GEY, for help in preparing this article and for his leadership in the amateur space program.

Notes

1 OSCAR stands for Orbiting Satellite Carrying Amateur Radio. OSCAR 1 was launched in 1961. President Gerald Ford's voice (tape delayed for the next orbital pass) was heard via AMSAT-OSCAR 7 on July 1, 1976. King Hussein of Jordan, JY1, has operated via AMSAT-OSCAR 10. Used as a generic term, OSCAR includes all the individual OSCARs and the Russian RS (Radio Sputnik) series as well. In a slightly more abstract sense, OSCAR connotes the notion that there's a place for direct public access to space and space-based activities, that is, the Amateur Radio space program.

2 The Russian RS10/11 and the Japanese FO-12 satellites carry on the Phase 2 satellite tradition.

3 Circular polarization is used extensively in space communication to offset the effects of polarization rotation in the geomagnetic field and to reduce the effects of the spinning spacecraft. Circular polarization is covered in the ARRL publication *The Satellite Experimenter's Handbook* and is recommended reading.

4 RUDAK description quoted from an article by Peter Guelzow, DB2OS, appearing in *Amateur Satellite Report* No. 126/127, June 24, 1986. Also, see the *QST* Amateur Satellite Communications column for July and August 1988.

5 The ZRO Test is the ZRO Memorial Satellite Station Engineering Award. It is a memorial to Kaz Deskur, K2ZRO, who, until his death in April 1984, was a strong AMSAT technical resource person.

6 SARSAT/COSPAS is the same system that was used to track the Russian and Canadian SKITREKers on their journey across the North Pole beginning in March. A small emergency locator transmitter (ELT) signal was picked up by the SARSAT/COSPAS satellites. On the ground, the Doppler shift of the resulting downlink was analyzed and the trekers' position closely determined by plotting various curves based on the Doppler shift measurements.

7 I've covered many of these topics in my Amateur Satellite Communications column appearing in *QST* over the last few years.

8 Orbital data originates with NASA. Two distributors of orbital elements are the ARRL and AMSAT. Tracking software is available from the AMSAT Software Exchange, PO Box 27, Washington, DC 20044. Send an SASE for a list of available programs.

9 Operating schedules in general were discussed in the Amateur Satellite Communications column in April 1988 *QST*.

10 An international band-planning committee is being considered to help develop a Phase 3C band plan.

11 AMSAT members receive regular newsletters and access to helpful publications, such as the *AMSAT-NA Technical Journal*.

Adventures In Satellite DXing

Part 1: Crowded HF bands and marginal propagation got you down? Use the high-flying DX machine to give your spirits a lift.

By Dick Jansson, WD4FAB
1130 Willowbrook Trail
Maitland, FL 32751

Is there such a thing as an impossible dream? Imagine relaxed ragchewing with exotic DX stations on SSB without the congestion found on 20 or 75 meters, all with only 15 watts of RF power. Not possible? Sure it is—just try your hand at OSCAR 10.

Oh sure, here we go again, another lecture on amateur satellites! Hold on there—don't turn the page yet! We are not going to talk strictly about satellites, but about how you can enjoy the fun of operating a super DX machine at a casual pace that won't push your stamina or heart! For example, one recent morning I talked with hams in Texas, Colorado, Antarctica, England, Massachusetts, Grenada and South Africa. All of this occurred when some operators were bemoaning that the satellite wasn't too active. Interested?

This is the first of a four-part series of articles that will show you what satellite operating is all about. This installment will explain what OSCAR 10 is and what it can do for you. In the coming months, we'll take a look at the equipment and antennas for satellite work and show how to assemble them into a station that really plays. Then we'll examine some of the finer points of communicating through OSCAR 10.

Not for Beginners Only

If you think that this discussion is aimed at beginners, you are very right. All of us, even old-timers, are "beginners" at the satellite game at one time or another. Part of the beauty of satellite operation is that there's always something new to learn. Just this year I've picked up some new tricks even though I've been operating amateur satellites regularly since 1977. This form of communication is very different from the HF bands.

As we proceed, I'll try to avoid some of the involved jargon of satellite talk. Where appropriate I'll explain what the terms mean so you'll be able to hold an intelligent conversation with others interested in OSCAR operation. I do highly recommend that every satellite user obtain and read a copy of *The Satellite Experimenter's Handbook* by Martin Davidoff, K2UBC.[1] This fine publication is packed with useful information that ranges far beyond the scope of this *QST* series.

One special term that needs to be explained up front is AMSAT.[2] This is the name given to the Radio Amateur Satellite Corporation, a nonprofit, scientific corporation founded for the creation and operation of satellites for Amateur Radio communications. Over the years, AMSAT has continued to make reliable communications satellites available to the amateur community. AMSAT's paid staff is very small. Hundreds of volunteers support the organization's efforts through donations of time, expertise and money, making possible the superb communications available from OSCAR 10 and other spacecraft.

Every amateur-satellite user should join AMSAT to show their support for the organization and to help with the construction of the satellites we use. AMSAT members receive *Satellite Journal,* a publication filled with useful information for everyone. New members also receive a copy of *A Beginner's Guide to OSCAR 10,* which is full of information helpful to the newcomers and old hands alike.[3]

Fig 1—OSCAR 10 is small enough that it can be carried by two or three people. Much of the outer surface is covered with solar panels that will power the satellite for years.

What Is OSCAR 10?

At the risk of boring the more knowledgeable readers, I'll give a short history of OSCAR 10. Some of you may want to skip to the next section.

OSCAR 10 (also called AO-10 for AMSAT-OSCAR 10) is the tenth in a series of amateur satellites. The name OSCAR, for *O*rbiting *S*atellite *C*arrying *A*mateur *R*adio pretty much tells the story. It is a communications satellite designed and built by radio amateurs for the sole purpose of supporting Amateur Radio communications and experimentation. It's very much like the satellites that allow you instant telephone access to relatives overseas and allow you to watch televised events occurring on the other side of the world as they happen. OSCAR 10 receives transmissions from earth stations and relays them back, allowing hams to communicate over great distances without worrying about the whims of ionospheric propagation.

Fig 1 shows OSCAR 10 pretty much as it looks today. Weighing about 200 pounds, this satellite was launched by a European Space Agency rocket in June 1983. Although it is an "amateur" satellite, there is nothing amateur about OSCAR 10's design and construction. It is built to the same high standards as other communications satellites and was subjected to strenuous testing before launch. Historically, amateur satellites have provided reliable service well beyond their design lifespans.

About Orbits

Some of you may have operated through OSCARs 6, 7 and 8. They were in circular orbits less than 1200 miles above the earth,

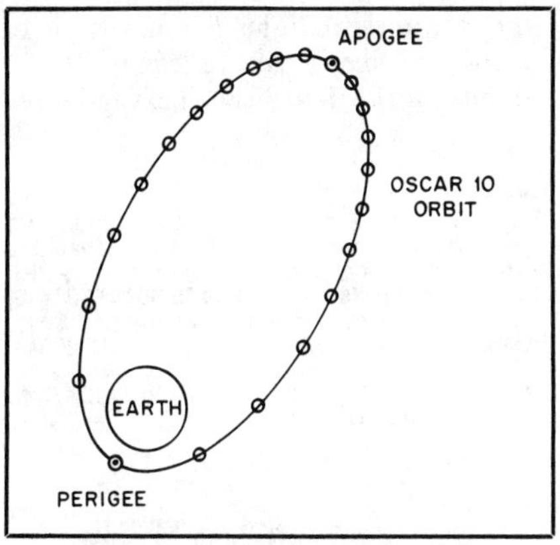

Fig 2—OSCAR 10 was designed for an elliptical orbit to allow it to be in view of much of the Northern Hemisphere for hours at a time. The circles on the ellipse represent the approximate position of OSCAR 10 during each half hour of its orbit. Note that the satellite "slows down" as it nears apogee. It passes through perigee (where it is out of sight of stations in the Northern Hemisphere) rather quickly.

Glossary

AMSAT—the Radio Amateur Satellite Corporation, a nonprofit organization located in Washington, DC has overseen the OSCAR program since the launch of OSCAR 5.

AO-10—AMSAT-OSCAR 10, the 10th amateur satellite in the OSCAR series.

apogee—the point in a satellite's orbit at which it is farthest from the earth.

downlink—the frequency on which signals are transmitted from the satellite to earth.

elliptical orbit—those orbits in which the satellite path traces an ellipse with the earth at one focus.

Mode A—transponders with a 2-meter uplink and a 10-meter downlink.

Mode B—transponders with a 70-cm uplink and a 2-meter downlink.

Mode L—transponders with a 24-cm uplink and a 70-cm downlink.

OSCAR—Orbiting Satellite Carrying Amateur Radio.

pass—that segment of a satellite orbit that brings it in range of your station.

passband—the range of frequencies handled by a transponder.

perigee—that point in a satellite's orbit at which it is closest to the earth.

Phase II—the name given to low-altitude-orbit (less than 1200 miles) OSCARs. Equipped with solar cells, these satellites have lasted for up to five years.

Phase III—the name given to extended-range, high-altitude OSCARs in elliptical orbit.

transponder—a device that receives radio signals in one segment of the spectrum, amplifies them, translates (shifts) their frequency to another segment of the spectrum and retransmits them.

uplink—the frequency on which signals are transmitted to the satellite from earth.

Known as Phase II satellites, these OSCARs provided communications over distances up to about 4500 miles. They were in range of a given point on earth for at most 20 minutes or so during each orbit. Phase II satellites moved quickly, so operators had to work hard to keep their antennas pointed at the "birds." One consequence of these 20-minute passes was that contacts tended to be short, contest-like exchanges of signal report, name and QTH.

Looking for something that would support communications for longer periods over longer distances, AMSAT designers developed a new generation of satellites, Phase III. As shown in Fig 2, these satellites have an elliptical orbit, rather than a circular one. At the apogee, the point in its orbit where it is farthest from earth, OSCAR 10 is about 22,000 miles away. At perigee, when it is closest, OSCAR 10 is about 2500 miles from earth.

In practice, this means that maximum communications distance via OSCAR 10 is more than 10,000 miles when the satellite is at apogee. It is accessible to nearly half the earth! Because the orbit is elliptical, OSCAR 10 is in view of stations in the northern hemisphere for up to eight hours at a time. Being able to work stations half a world away for up to eight hours at a time is my idea of relaxed DXing!

Links: Up and Down

OSCAR 10 carries two linear translators, or transponders. A transponder acts like a typical VHF FM repeater. The basic idea is the same: You transmit to it on one frequency, and it retransmits your transmission on another. There are some major differences, however. Unlike FM repeaters that are designed for nonlinear modes only, OSCAR 10's transponders are linear. They faithfully reproduce all modes, including SSB. The other big difference is that OSCAR 10's transponders cover not just a single frequency, but a whole range of frequencies. This range of frequencies is called a passband; the passband may cover 100 kHz or more. Amateur satellites retransmit every signal heard in the receiver passband, so many stations can use the transponder simultaneously.

The frequency on which you transmit to the satellite is called the uplink, while the frequency on which the satellite retransmits your signal to earth is called the downlink. Uplink and downlink frequencies are on different bands. Various band combinations are called modes. For example, Phase II satellites carried a Mode-A transponder that used 2 meters for the uplink and 10

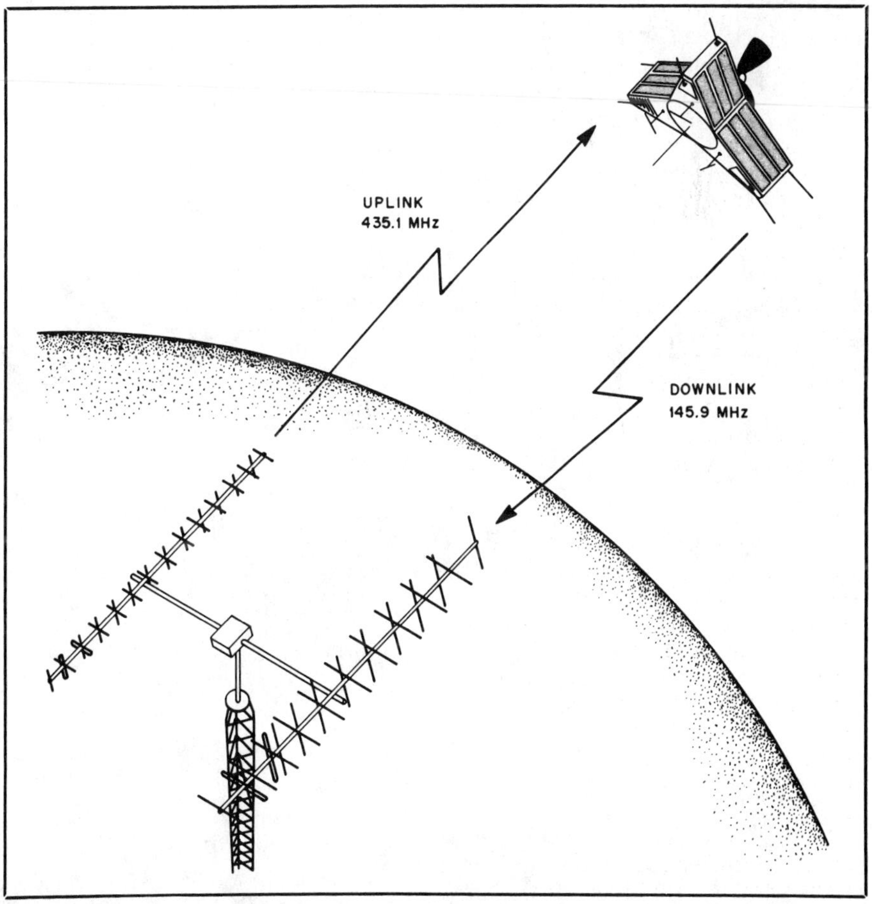

Fig 3—This series of articles will concentrate on Mode-B operation, whereby stations on earth transmit to the satellite on 435 MHz and listen on 145 MHz.

meters for the downlink.

OSCAR 10 carries a Mode-B transponder and a Mode-L transponder. The Mode-B uplink is at 435 MHz, while the downlink is at 145 MHz (see Fig 3). The passband is 152 kHz wide. Mode L uses a 1269-MHz uplink and a 436-MHz downlink. The passband is 800 kHz wide—more than twice as wide as the 20-meter ham band.

Most of the activity on OSCAR 10 is on Mode B, so I'll limit the scope of this article to that mode. Mode L presents a different set of equipment requirements. After you get some Mode-B experience, you may want to try your hand at Mode L. By that time, you'll know whom to contact for advice.

Some of the hard-core HF DXers will choke thinking that this VHF/UHF stuff is too complicated and want to return to 20 meters. Not so! The VHF and UHF parts actually make life much easier than you might think. There is a wealth of readily available commercial equipment for satellite work, as we'll see next month.

Notes

[1]M. Davidoff, *The Satellite Experimenter's Handbook* (Newington: ARRL, 1984). Available from your local radio store or from ARRL for $10 ($11 outside US). Add $2.50 ($3.50 UPS) per order for shipping and handling.

[2]AMSAT, PO Box 27, Washington, DC 20044. Dues are $24 per year.

[3]M. Crisler, *A Beginner's Guide to OSCAR 10* (Washington, DC: AMSAT, 1985).

Adventures in Satellite DXing

Part 2: In this installment, we'll take a look at some of the equipment you'll need to launch your OSCAR career.

By Dick Jansson, WD4FAB and Mark Wilson, AA2Z

1130 Willowbrook Trail
Maitland, FL 32751

Senior Assistant Technical Editor, ARRL

Last time we looked briefly at OSCAR 10's history and learned some basic terminology. Now it's time to get down to the specifics of the equipment you'll need to work stations through the bird. This month we will examine your options as you choose a receiver, transmitter and antenna system for OSCAR 10 operation.

The basic requirements for OSCAR 10 Mode-B operation are a sensitive 145-MHz receiver, a 435-MHz transmitter that can supply about 50 W of RF output and a high-gain antenna for each band. The antennas must be able to rotate in azimuth (side to side) and elevation (up and down).

In earlier times, the satellite communicator had to work hard to assemble a usable station. These days, however, amateur equipment manufacturers provide some nifty boxes that make the job easier.

Full-Duplex Operation

Perhaps the biggest difference from terrestrial work is that satellite work requires full-duplex operation. This means that you transmit and receive simultaneously. You can hear your own downlink signal while you're transmitting, as well as that of the station you're working. Full duplex provides the opportunity for a fully interactive conversation, as if the other station is in the very same room! Gone are the endless monologues, and in come new communications methods.

The ability to hear your own signal on the downlink offers several advantages. You are assured that you and the station you want to work will be able to get on the same frequency. If you're responding to a CQ, you'll hear your signal and know that you're tuned to the right part of the passband. In addition, if you can hear yourself, others can copy you as well. There is no question about whether or not your signals are getting through. Moreover, you will know if you're running too much power and being a "satellite hog." It's possible to have too strong an uplink signal, as we'll see in a later installment.

Successful satellite operation demands that you can locate and hear your own signal from the spacecraft. You should choose equipment with this goal in mind. Equipping your station for full duplex operation is easier than you might think because the transmitter is on a different band than the receiver. Fig 1 shows several different satellite ground-station equipment configurations. Each of these options is discussed in the following pages.

Table 1

Suppliers of Equipment of Interest to Satellite Operators

Multimode VHF and UHF Transceivers and Specialty Equipment

ICOM America, Inc, 2380-116th Ave NE, Bellevue, WA 98004.
Ten-Tec Inc, Sevierville, TN 37862.
Trio-Kenwood Communications, 1111 West Walnut St, Compton, CA 90220.
Yaesu Electronics Corp, 6851 Walthall Way, Paramount, CA 90723.

Converters, Transverters and Preamplifiers

Advanced Receiver Research, Box 1242, Burlington, CT 06013.
Angle Linear, PO Box 35, Lomita, CA 90717 (preamps only).
Hamtronics, Inc, 65-E Moul Rd, Hilton, NY 14468.
Henry Radio, 2050 S Bundy Dr, Los Angeles, CA 90025.
The PX Shack, 52 Stonewyck Dr, Belle Mead, NJ 08502.
Radio Kit, Box 411, Greenville, NH 03048.
Spectrum International, PO Box 1084, Concord, MA 01742.
Transverters Unlimited, Box 6286, Station A, Toronto, ON M5W 1P3.
The VHF Shop, 16 S Mountaintop Blvd, Rt 309, Mountaintop, PA 18707.

70-cm Power Amplifiers

Alinco Electronics, PO Box 20009, Reno, NV 89515.
Communications Concepts, Inc, 2648 North Aragon Ave, Dayton, OH 45420.
Encomm, 1506 Capitol Ave, Plano, TX 75074.
Falcon Communications, PO Box 8979, Newport Beach, CA 92658.
Mirage Communications, PO Box 1000, Morgan Hill, CA 95037.
TE Systems, PO Box 25845, Los Angeles, CA 90025.

Antennas

Cushcraft Corp, 48 Perimeter Rd, Manchester, NH 03108.
KLM Electronics, Inc, PO Box 816, Morgan Hill, CA 95037.
Telex/Hy-Gain, 9600 Aldrich Ave South, Minneapolis, MN 55420.

Note: This is a partial list. The ARRL and *QST* do not endorse specific products.

Receivers

Receiving requirements for OSCAR 10 are stiff, but you can achieve pleasurable results with the right kind of equipment. Do not expect to find 60-dB-over-S9 signals on the downlink. OSCAR operation is a weak-signal situation where contacts can be made with signals that are 4 dB stronger than the noise. Conversational quality can be assured with signals that are 6-9 dB or greater out of the noise.

The old adage "You can't work 'em if you can't hear 'em" especially applies to satellite work. The first step you should take toward gearing up for OSCAR 10 is to assemble the best receiving setup you can. There's no point in getting transmitting capability until you can hear signals, and hear them well.

There are a number of options open to you if you are starting from scratch. You may wish to try your hand at building receiving equipment, or you may wish to purchase everything. All of the necessary components for the 145-MHz downlink are readily available from *QST* advertisers.

If you're active on 2 meters with a multimode transceiver, you already have the basic building block of your receiving setup. If you don't have any equipment but think you would like to try terrestrial SSB operation on 2 meters, you should consider purchasing one of these all-mode radios. The basic requirements are that the rig includes SSB and CW modes and that it covers the entire 2-meter band. A

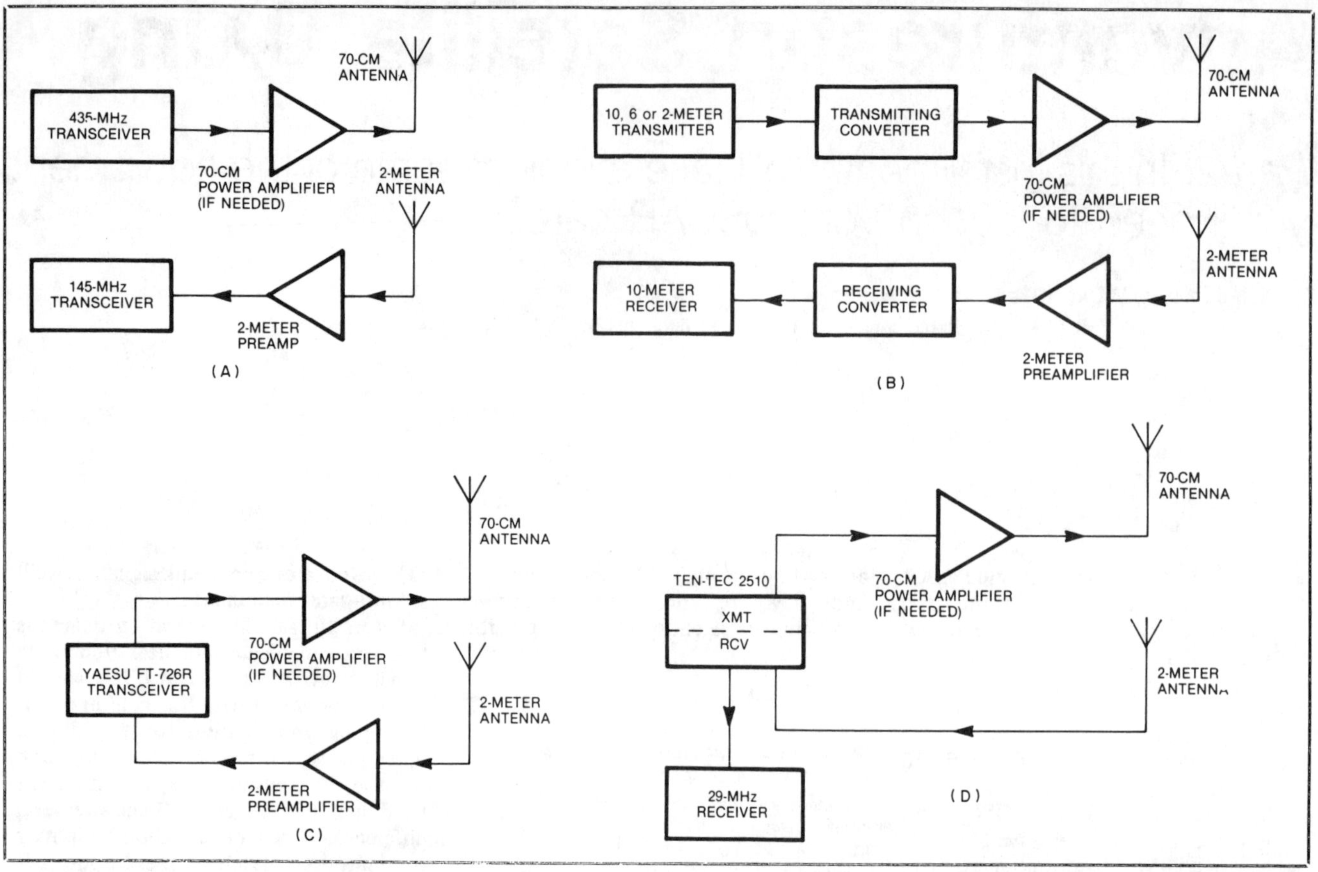

Fig 1—Several different satellite-station configurations are shown here and described in the text. At A, separate VHF/UHF multimode transceivers are used for transmitting and receiving. The configuration shown at B uses transmitting and receiving converters or transverters with HF equipment. At C, the Yaesu FT-726R can perform both transmitting and receiving functions, full duplex, in one package. The Ten-Tec 2510 shown at D contains a 435-MHz transmitter and a 2-meter to 10-meter receiving converter.

The ICOM IC-271A is typical of the 2-meter multimode transceivers on the market today. It can be used for reception on the OSCAR 10 downlink. The IC-471A, virtually identical in appearance, offers a matching 70-cm, 25-W signal for the uplink.

multimode transceiver also makes an excellent replacement for an FM-only 2-meter rig.

The major equipment manufacturers listed in Table 1 all make suitable transceivers. The current crop of base-station rigs includes the Kenwood TS-711A, ICOM IC-271A and Yaesu FT-726R. There are also several compact multimode radios intended for mobile use that will fill the bill. These include the Yaesu FT-480R, Kenwood TR-9130 and ICOM IC-290H. In addition, there are often good buys on the used market, if you're interested in an older radio. Gear such as the Kenwood TS-700 series, Yaesu FT-225RD and ICOM IC-251 are still popular. Many of these transceivers have been reviewed in *QST*.[1-5]

An excellent solution to receiving OSCAR 10 on 145.9 MHz can be found in the form of receiving converters used with your quality HF transceiver or receiver. The receiving converter consists of a 2-meter preamplifier, a mixer and a local oscillator. The local oscillator frequency is usually chosen so that 2-meter signals will be converted for reception by any receiver that covers the 10-meter band. In addition, a number of manufacturers offer transverters that include a receiving converter and transmitting converter in the same package.

Receiving converters are available commercially from several suppliers listed in Table 1. For those who enjoy building equipment, *The ARRL Handbook* presents several suitable construction projects in Chapter 31.[6]

There are several advantages to using a receiving converter. Your modern HF transceiver or receiver most likely has excellent frequency stability, a frequency readout in 1-kHz or smaller steps, good

Amateurs who own HF receivers or transceivers and who have no desire for transceive operation on 2 meters may find that a receiving converter such as this Advanced Receiver Research R144VDA will fit their needs. Shown with matching low-noise GaAsFET preamplifier, this unit converts 2-meter OSCAR 10 downlink signals for reception on any receiver that can tune to 29 MHz.

The Kenwood TS-811A is a 70-cm multimode transceiver that can be used to generate a 10-W, 435-MHz signal for the uplink. A similar unit, the TS-711A, may be used for the 2-meter downlink.

A low-noise GaAsFET preamplifier such as this Angle Linear GaAsFET model is essential if you want to maximize your downlink reception. The preamplifier can be mounted at the antenna for best results.

SSB and CW crystal filters, an effective noise blanker and high dynamic range. Chances are good that a multimode VHF transceiver will offer some, but not all, of these features. Cost is another factor. If you already own an HF rig and are not interested in terrestrial 2-meter SSB operation (that is, don't need a 2-meter transmitter), the cost of building or buying a receiving converter will be significantly less than that of even an older multimode transceiver.

The downlink receiver at WD4FAB had for years been a multimode transceiver. Daytime QRN often raised the practical receiver noise floor by 10 to 20 dB, thus eliminating OSCAR 10 daytime communications. Weak downlink signals were no match for the noise. In addition, local FM repeaters could be heard in the satellite passband because the VHF transceiver offered poor rejection of strong nearby signals. Use of a high-dynamic-range receiving converter with a good HF transceiver has, however, solved both of these problems. The lesson here is that many VHF transceiver noise blankers are inadequate for AO-10 operation, and that some VHF transceivers do not work well in areas with many strong, nearby signals. If you have QRN problems or live in an area with lots of 2-meter FM repeaters, you may have better luck with a receiving converter than with a VHF transceiver.

Preamplifiers

No discussion of satellite receiving systems would be complete without mentioning preamplifiers. A good, low-noise preamplifier is a great help for receiving those weak downlink signals. Multimode rigs and most transverters will hear much better with the addition of a GaAsFET preamplifier ahead of the receiver front end. While you can add a preamplifier right at the receiver in your station, it may not do you as much good as you think. You'll get much better results if the preamp is mounted at the antenna. Losses in the feed line will degrade the noise figure of even the best preamplifier mounted at the receiver.

Table 1 lists several sources of commercially-built preamplifiers. These are available in several configurations. Some models are designed to be mounted in a receive-only line, for use with a receiving converter or transverter. Others, designed with multimode transceivers in mind, have built-in relays and circuitry that automatically switch the preamplifier out of the antenna line during transmit. Still others are housed, with relays, in weatherproof enclosures that mount right at the antenna. If you like to roll your own, several suitable designs appear in Chapter 31 of *The ARRL Handbook* and in *The Satellite Experimenter's Handbook*, published by the ARRL.[7]

Transmitters

For transmitting to OSCAR 10, you'll need 5-25 W of 435.1-MHz RF at the antenna. This assumes a good antenna, which we'll discuss later. Feed-line losses at 435 MHz are much greater than at HF, so they must be taken into account here. Feed-line losses in a typical installation can easily run 3 dB, so you'll need anywhere between 10 and 50 W output from your transmitter.

Since the possible number of combinations of transmitter power and antenna gain needed to give a satisfactory signal through OSCAR 10 is infinite, satellite users generally talk about their uplink capability in terms of effective radiated power (ERP). ERP takes into account antenna gain, feed-line loss and RF output power. For example, if you run 10 W into a 3-dB-gain antenna, your ERP is 20 W (3 dB greater than, or twice as strong as, 10 W). This assumes no loss in the feed line; all 10 W from the transmitter reaches the antenna. If you use 10 W into a 10-dB-gain antenna, your ERP is 100 W. You could achieve the same 100-W ERP with a 50-W transmitter and a 3-dB-gain antenna.

Another means of generating a 435-MHz uplink signal is with an HF transceiver and a 10-meter to 70-cm transverter such as this SSB Electronics TV28-432.

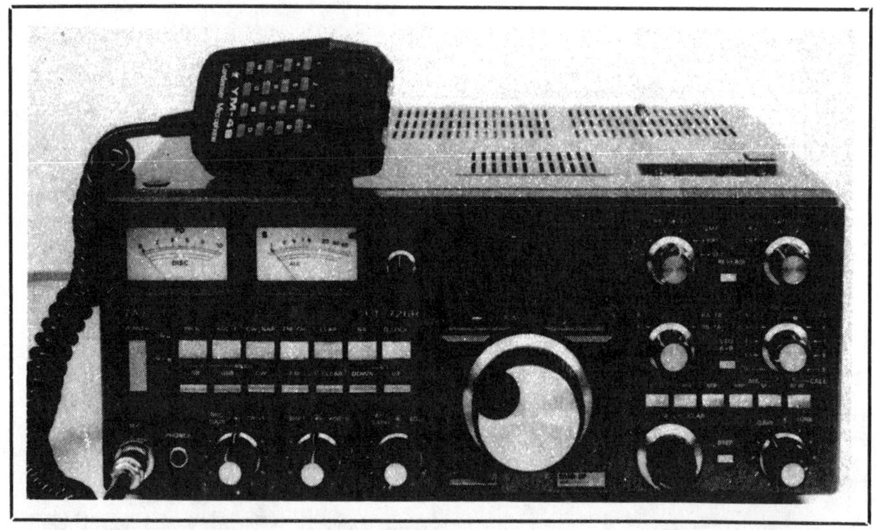

Yaesu's FT-726R is a favorite among satellite users because it can work on both 2 meters and 70 cm. With the optional satellite module that allows full-duplex operation, the effect is practically the same as having two separate transceivers in one box.

Stations with an uplink ERP as low as 10 W can be copied through OSCAR 10, but ERP levels of 100 to 400 W are the norm. No matter what your ERP, your signal on the downlink should never be stronger than the AO-10 general beacon at 145.81 MHz. You must have a way to adjust your uplink signal so that it is as strong or weaker than the beacon. We'll return to this point in detail in the operating installment of this series.

If you have a 10-W transmitter, a short run of low-loss feed line and good antenna gain, you're probably all set. Worry no more about added amplifiers. If losses and gains do not add up to enough ERP for you, a 30- to 40-W amplifier may be needed. Some operators have 100-W amplifiers, but with the antennas available today, use of that much power is guaranteed to create an uplink signal that far exceeds the beacon. This is considered by good operators to be an antisocial action. Considerate operators with the 100-W amplifiers quickly reduce drive power to lower the ERP to acceptable levels. Again, use only the RF power that will make your signal no stronger than the OSCAR 10 beacon.

Most satellite operators use UHF multimode transceivers to generate an uplink signal. The manufacturers listed in Table 1 all make 70-cm multimode transceivers that are similar to the 2-meter units described earlier. Although most of these transceivers provide 10-W output, some can deliver 25 W or more.[8]

Unless you are into 70-cm terrestrial communications (and that can be fun, too), there is no need for a complete transceiver. Transmitting converters for use with HF transceivers are available from suppliers listed in Table 1. In addition, some of those manufacturers make transverters that are suitable for satellite work. If you want to try to build your own equipment, *QST* recently presented a 70-cm transmitter construction project.[9]

If you find that you need more 435-MHz power, there are a number of solid-state amplifiers on the market. See Table 1. Choose carefully; you don't need a rock crusher.

Specialty Equipment

Separate transceivers or transmitting and receiving converters are no longer the only way to go. Modern equipment offerings by Yaesu and Ten-Tec, tailored for the satellite user, do it all in one package.

The Yaesu FT-726R starts out as a 2-meter multimode transceiver (see note 2). It is, however, expandable to work on other bands with the addition of optional modules. The Mode-B satellite operator would most likely be interested in an FT-726R with the stock 144-MHz and optional 430-MHz modules. To tie it all together, Yaesu offers an optional satellite module to allow you to transmit on the 435-MHz uplink while receiving on the 145-MHz downlink. This is full duplex operation; the effect is the same as having two separate radios in one box.

Ten-Tec's 2510 is tailored specifically for Mode-B satellite operation.[10,11] This unusual piece of equipment includes a hot receiving converter that converts 145-MHz signals to 10 meters for reception on any HF receiver or transceiver. A low-noise GaAsFET preamplifier is built in, so no external preamp is required. For the uplink, the 2510 has a complete 10-W, 435-MHz SSB and CW transmitter. The 2510 has only one frequency tuning control for the receiver and the transmitter. The receiver automatically tracks the transmitter, an exceptionally useful feature as we'll see when we discuss operating procedures in a later installment.

Antennas

This is probably one of the most controversial areas, as most amateurs are experts and the authors are no exception. The

Fig 2—These helical antennas were used for years at WD4FAD.

Glossary

circular polarization (CP)—describes an electromagnetic wave in which the electric and magnetic fields are rotating. If the electric field vector is rotating in a clockwise sense, as viewed along the path of radiation, then it is called right-hand circular polarization (RHCP). If the electric field vector is rotating in a counterclockwise sense, as viewed along the path of radiation, then it is called left-hand circular polarization (LHCP).

effective radiated power (ERP)—a measure of the power radiated from an antenna system. ERP takes into account transmitter output power, feed-line losses and other system losses, and antenna gain as compared to a dipole.

GaAsFET preamplifier—a low-noise receiving preamplifier that uses a gallium arsenide field-effect transistor as the active device.

The Ten-Tec 2510 Mode-B satellite station is designed specifically for Mode-B operation. The box contains a 435-MHz SSB and CW transmitter, as well as a 145- to 28-MHz receiving converter with a low-noise front end.

information presented here is based on years of experimentation at WD4FAB, but it should not be considered the final word.

The best antennas for OSCAR 10 have circular polarization (CP), rather than horizontal or vertical. For years, helical antennas like the one shown in Fig 2 were the way to go for satellite work.[12-14] An eight-turn helical for 70 cm and a huge six-turn helical for 2 meters provided excellent results for OSCAR 8 operation at WD4FAB.[15] For OSCAR 10, however, more gain was needed.

The present satellite array at WD4FAB uses a different method to achieve circular polarization. These antennas, shown in Fig 3, are essentially two complete Yagis mounted perpendicular to each other on the same boom. One set of elements is mounted ¼ wavelength ahead of the other, and the antennas are fed in phase. These particular antennas, manufactured by KLM, have proved to be excellent performers.[16] Cushcraft and Telex/Hy-Gain also manufacture crossed-Yagi satellite antennas.

Perhaps the most significant factor of the KLM "crossed Yagi" antennas is that they are switchable from right-hand circularly polarized (RHCP) to left-hand circularly polarized (LHCP). With AO-10, switchability is important. The side lobes of the AO-10 antenna patterns are LHCP, even though the main lobes are RHCP, and there are substantial side lobe operating periods for any OSCAR 10 orbit. Successful AO-10 operation requires not only antennas with circular polarization, but antennas that have switchable circularity as well.

Satellite antennas should be mounted as close to the station as possible. Height

Fig 3—The present satellite array at WD4FAB uses KLM Yagis for 2 meters and 70 cm. The large box on the mast contains a 2-meter preamplifier and a 70-cm power amplifier, as well as power-supply circuitry.

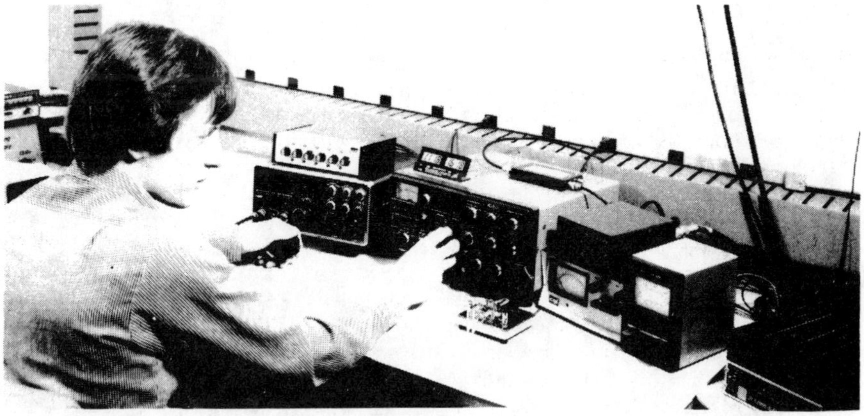

W1INF, the ARRL Laboratory station, has OSCAR 10 Mode-B capability. The uplink is a 2-meter multimode transceiver driving a 2-meter to 70-cm transverter, while the downlink is a receiving converter and 10-meter receiver. A GaAsFET preamplifier is mounted at the antenna.

Usually, a little more than 10-W uplink power is required for a good downlink signal. Solid-state "brick" amplifiers such as this Mirage D1010 provide the extra power needed. Care must be taken, however, to use only the minimum power necessary to maintain reliable communications.

above ground makes no difference for satellite work, except that the antennas must be mounted high enough that trees and other obstructions do not block the view of the satellite at low elevations. A low mount allows use of shorter feed lines (lower losses) and often reduces QRN pickup by the antennas. Many operators are able to set up their antennas on a 10- to 15-foot mast right next to the shack and have only 20 feet of feed line. The antennas at WD4FAB are mounted 63 feet above the ground to clear trees, and they require 80 feet of feed line. For feed lines, plan to use good-quality, low-loss coaxial cable from the start, such as Belden 9913. Even better is a run of Hardline with Belden 9913 for the flexible pieces at each end.

We've given you plenty to think about for now. If you need more information, see "A Survey of OSCAR 10 Station Equipment" in a past issue of AMSAT's *Orbit* magazine.[17] Next month, we'll look at useful accessories and antenna rotators, and show you how to assemble all of the pieces into a working OSCAR 10, Mode-B satellite station.

Notes

[1]M. Wilson, "ICOM IC-271A 2-Meter Multimode Transceiver," *QST*, May 1985, pp 40-41.
[2]M. Wilson, "Yaesu Electronics Corp. FT-726R VHF/UHF Transceiver," *QST*, May 1984, pp 40-42.
[3]M. Wilson, "Yaesu FT-480R 2-Meter Multimode Transceiver," *QST*, Oct 1981, pp 46-47.
[4]J. Kleinman, "ICOM IC-290H All-Modo 2-Meter Transceiver," *QST*, May 1983, pp 36-37.
[5]D. DeMaw, "Trio-Kenwood TS-700S 2-Meter Transceiver," *QST*, Feb 1978, pp 31-32.
[6]M. Wilson, ed., *The 1986 ARRL Handbook* (Newington: ARRL, 1985). Available from your local radio store or from ARRL for $18 ($19 outside US). Add $2.50 ($3.50 UPS) per order for shipping and handling.
[7]M. Davidoff, *The Satellite Experimenter's Handbook* (Newington: ARRL, 1985). Available from your local radio store or from ARRL for $10 ($11 outside US). Add $2.50 ($3.50 UPS) per order for shipping and handling.
[8]J. Lindholm, "ICOM IC-471A 70-cm Transceiver," *QST*, Aug 1985, pp 38-39.
[9]J. Reed, "A Simple 435-MHz Transmitter," *QST*, May 1985, pp 14-18.
[10]C. Hutchinson, "TEN-TEC 2510 Mode B Satellite Station," *QST*, Oct 1985, pp 41-43.
[11]D. Ingram, "The Ten-Tec 2510 OSCAR Satellite Station/Converter," *CQ* Magazine, Feb 1985, pp 44-46.
[12]R. Jansson, "70-Cm Satellite Antenna Techniques," *Orbit*, Mar 1980, pp 24-26.
[13]B. Glassmeyer, "Circular Polarization and OSCAR Communications," *QST*, May 1980, pp 11-15.
[14]C. Richards, "The Chopstick Helical," *Orbit*, Jan/Feb 1981, pp 8-9.
[15]R. Jansson, "Helical Antenna Construction for 146 MHz," *Orbit*, May/June 1981, pp 12-15.
[16]R. Jansson, "KLM 2M-22C and KLM 435-40CX Yagi Antennas," *QST*, Oct 1985, pp 43-44.
[17]H. Winard and R. Soderman, "A Survey of OSCAR Station Equipment," *Orbit*, Nov/Dec 1983, pp 13-16 and Mar/Apr 1984, pp 12-16.

Adventures in Satellite DXing

Part 3: Now that you've decided on some equipment for OSCAR work, it's time to assemble it into an effective station.

By Dick Jansson, WD4FAB
1130 Willowbrook Trail
Maitland, FL 32751

Last month, we talked about different ways of setting up your station for OSCAR 10, Mode-B operation. Now that you have a receiver, transmitter and a pair of antennas, you are probably wondering how to tie these parts together into a working system. In this part of the series on satellite DXing, you will discover those sometimes elusive techniques needed to make your radio equipment come alive with action.

Satellite work, like any other specialized facet of Amateur Radio, requires some specialized knowledge. Having the best equipment does not necessarily guarantee success. Presented here are a number of "hints-and-kinks" type ideas that have made OSCAR 10 operation more satisfying for me. Remember that this is my way of converting a basic receiver, transmitter and a pair of antennas into a fun operating position. My solutions are not the only ones—there are several ways to achieve the needed results.

Some of the items discussed here will provide capabilities beyond that of just operating AO-10, Mode B. They also apply to VHF and UHF terrestrial work. It's only natural: I enjoy terrestrial work as well, so I've equipped my VHF/UHF station with several uses in mind. Design your station to suit your own needs.

An often-heard cry is that there is nothing left to build in Amateur Radio these days. Hogwash! There are lots of useful items to construct, and this can be done without the investment of vast fortunes. Nearly everything you will see here has my own handmade (or modified) label attached. This arena also allows room for customizing a job *your* way. Of course, there are commercially available equivalents for nearly everything, if you prefer that route, but you'll miss a lot of fun.

Antenna Rotators

Unlike stations located on the surface of this good Earth, OSCAR 10 will be found

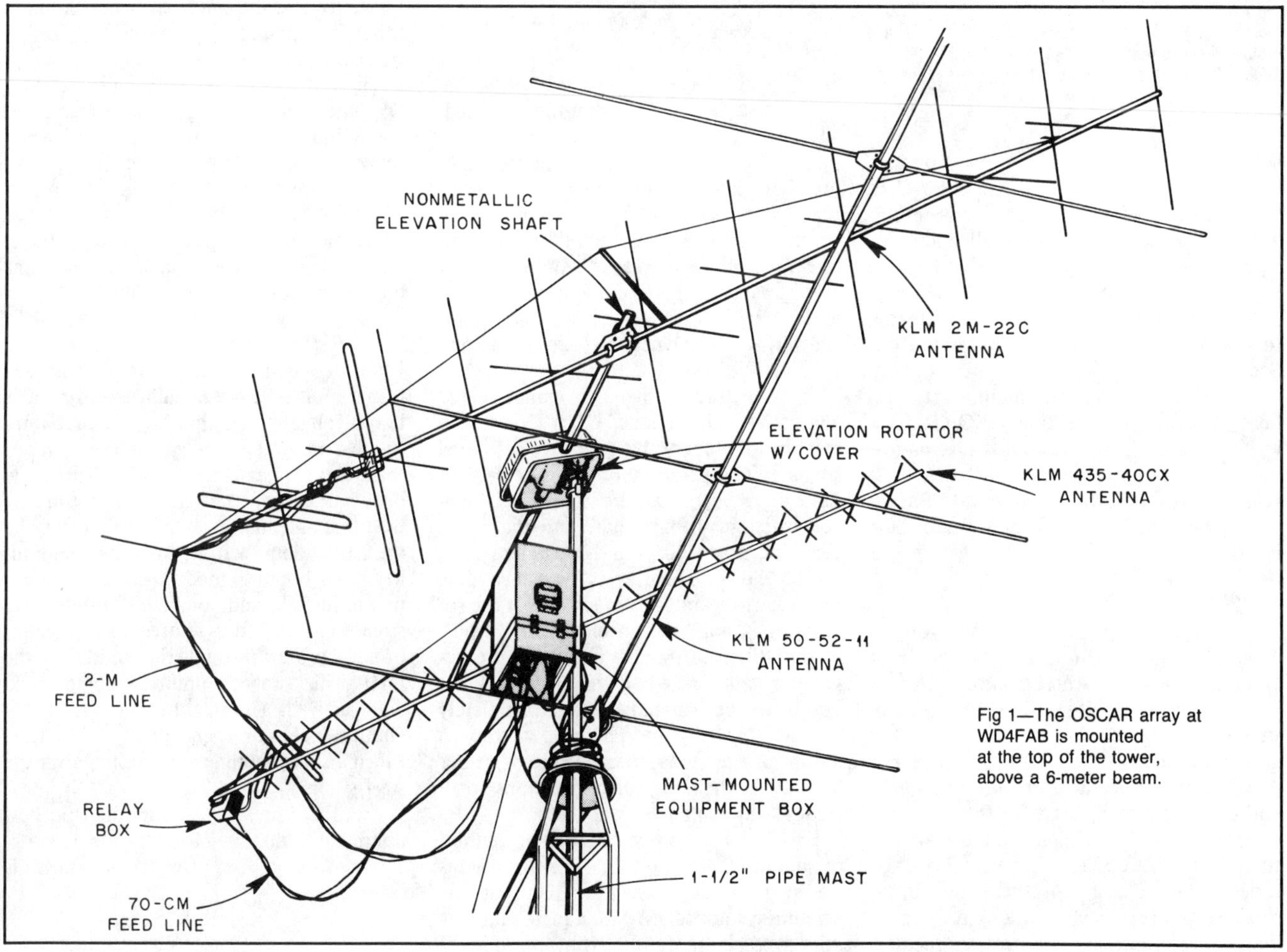

Fig 1—The OSCAR array at WD4FAB is mounted at the top of the tower, above a 6-meter beam.

Fig 2—The elevation rotator, an Alliance U110, is protected from the elements by plastic and aluminum covers. The large white box holds tower-mounted equipment.

Fig 3—Close-up of the U110 showing how it mounts to the mast. Note the PVC pipe that slides over the steel stub protruding from the rotator.

somewhere in the sky above us. You are used to pointing your antenna toward another station by changing the pointing angle, or azimuth (sometimes called az). To find OSCAR 10, you'll also need to be able to control antenna elevation (el). Your antenna must be able to rotate from side to side and up and down simultaneously. See Fig 1. While I will talk about the use of electrically controlled antenna rotators here, you might note that OSCAR 10's motions are slow enough that hand-operated, "armstrong" antenna control is feasible. At times, the antennas don't need to be repositioned for periods of up to four hours.

Azimuth Rotators

Azimuth rotators are common—you've probably got one turning your HF or VHF antenna right now. Antennas for OSCAR 8 and other low-orbit satellites were on the smaller and lighter side, so light-duty TV-antenna rotators such as those sold by Alliance, Channel Master, Radio Shack and others could be used for the azimuth rotator. Today's high-gain satellite array, such as the one described in Part 2 of this series, is a bit large for these light-duty rotators. You really should look for something more robust, such as a rotator recommended for turning a small HF beam or VHF array. Various models manufactured by Alliance, Daiwa, Kenpro, Telex and others are routinely advertised in *QST*.

Elevation Rotators

Elevation rotator selection is somewhat more limited, but there are some interesting things that can be done. Commercially manufactured models are available. The Kenpro KR500, designed specifically for elevating small- to medium-size VHF or UHF arrays, is quite popular among satellite operators. Recent additions to the marketplace include two combined az-el offerings: the Dynetic Systems DR10 and Kenpro KR5400.

A lower cost, commercially manufactured alternative is the Alliance U110 TV-antenna rotator. Rotators of this type have been used by satellite operators (including me) for quite a few years. Despite its relatively light construction, I have had antenna loads weighing up to 80 pounds mounted on a U110! The key to success is to achieve static balance of the antenna mass so that the rotator does not have to elevate a "dead" load. A highly attractive feature of the elevation rotators noted above is that the cross boom to be rotated passes completely through the rotator. This allows you to mount one antenna on each side of center and adjust their respective positions for a side- to-side balanced load.

Figs 2 and 3 show my particular method of mounting the U110. The rotator is clamped to the mast (the one that the azimuth rotator turns) with a plate that permits it to mount 90° from its normal orientation. With the rotator mounted in this position, it is not protected from rain or snow as well as it is in the normal position. I added a cover (an appropriately sized plastic dishpan or bucket is ideal) to afford protection from the elements. A problem with polyethylene plastics, commonly used in kitchenware, is that solar radiation quickly deteriorates their polymeric structure and causes the plastic to break apart. As shown, I have covered the plastic with an aluminum foil baking pan to provide some protection from the sun.

There are other ways to elevate your OSCAR array, although I have found the method just described to be inexpensive and reliable. An ingenious "tilt rather than twist" concept was described in *Orbit* magazine by Al Zoller, W6OTE.[1] This method uses a modified Alliance HD73 azimuth rotator and appears to be viable, despite some limitations for long-boom antennas.

Cross Boom Construction

One requirement not commonly discussed is that of using a nonmetallic elevation axis boom for antennas that have their boom-to-mast mounting hardware in the center of the boom. A metal cross boom will seriously distort the beam pattern of a circularly-polarized antenna, so it's important to make the cross boom from nonmetallic material. My cross boom is made from a combination of metallic and nonmetallic tubing. For strength and stiffness, I used a short length of steel tubing through the middle of the U110. Thick-walled aluminum tubing would work as well. The steel tubing extends for about 6 inches on each side of the rotator. I then installed nonmetallic masting over the steel stubs.

From a structural standpoint, the best nonmetallic material for this job is glass-epoxy tubing, because its stiffness is

Fig 4—Details of the position potentiometer mounting and weighted arm.

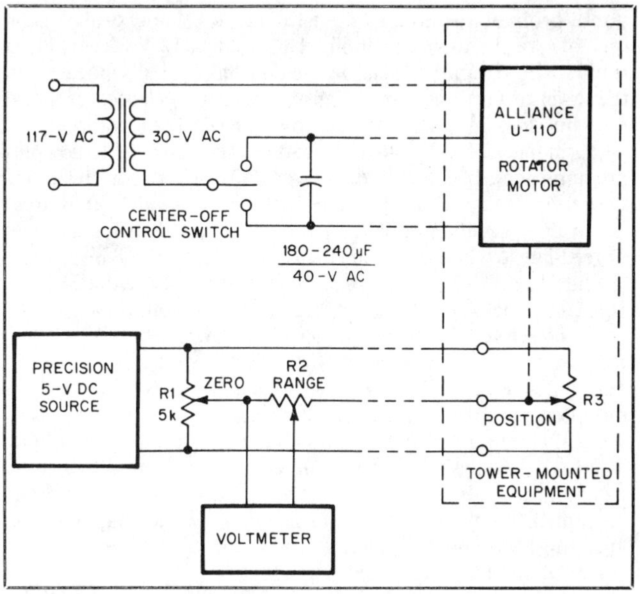

Fig 5—Block diagram of the elevation rotator direction control and position readout.

Fig 6—The circuitry in Fig 5, taken to extremes, provides control and position readout for three rotators.

excellent. You may be able to find this material at an industrial supply house that specializes in plastics. Also, KLM sells lengths of 1½-inch-OD fiberglass masting for this purpose. If you have a rotator that will accept a 1½-inch elevation boom, then your best bet is to use a single section of this tubing.

An alternative nonmetallic material, one that I use, is PVC pipe. Unlike glass-epoxy tubing, however, PVC pipe is not very stiff; it needs help. Based on a suggestion from Nick Laub, WØCA, I built the elevation boom pictured in Figs 1-3. The center piece that fits through the U110 is a 2-foot section of 1.33-inch-OD steel tubing that originally was part of the top support rail of a chain-link fence. Attached to the steel stub on each side of the rotator is a 3- or 4-foot length of 1¼-inch, schedule-40 PVC pipe. PVC pipe is specified by the nominal ID, here 1¼ inches. There are several varieties of 1¼-inch PVC pipe—schedule 40 indicates a thick-wall, heavy-duty version. I was able to slip the PVC pipe over the center stub. The fit is perfect—no machining needed!

Now comes the secret to making PVC pipe capable of supporting satellite Yagis. Insert a wooden dowel into the PVC pipe, along its entire length. The finished dimension of 1-3/8-inch wooden clothes rod dowel (the kind you might hang inside a closet) is just perfect for a slide fit into the pipe. This material is available from most lumber yards. Add a few ¼-inch bolts to each side to secure the pieces, and you've got a sturdy, inexpensive, nonmetallic elevation boom.

Position Indicators

You've probably noticed additional hardware around my elevation rotator. With the use of high-directivity antennas, the accuracy of the U110 control box is questionable. Adding a single-turn, 1-kΩ precision potentiometer provides the ability to closely control and position the elevation boom. See Fig 4. The potentiometer (a large surplus instrumentation model) is attached to the elevation boom with a U bolt and angle bracket. A metal arm with lead weights at the end is attached to the potentiometer shaft. The weighted arm and gravity hold the shaft still while the potentiometer body turns with the elevation boom.

A simple circuit, shown in Fig 5, is all that is needed to control the U110 and to use signals from the precision potentiometer (R3) for an accurate position indicator. R1 is used to zero the scale, while R2 calibrates the range of the indicator. The value of R2 will depend on the value of the voltmeter you use. For example, you might use a 0- to 100-mV meter and adjust it so that 10 mV equals 10° elevation, 30 mV equals 30° elevation, and so on. Just to show that simple circuits can easily be corrupted by some of us, Fig 6 shows a controller for up to three rotators. One *useful* feature of this box is that the voltmeters are OEM digital panel meters. The calibration is set up so that 1 mV equals 1 angular degree.

Tower-Mounted Preamplifiers

Last month we briefly discussed low-noise receiving preamplifiers and said that you'll probably need one to get the most out of your satellite station. For best results, the preamp should be located on the tower or mast, near the antenna so that feed-line losses do not degrade low-noise performance. Feed-line losses ahead of the preamplifier add directly to receiver noise figure. A preamp with a 0.5-dB noise figure won't do you much good if there is 3 dB of feed-line loss between it and the antenna.

Mast mounting of sensitive electronic equipment has been a fact of life for the serious VHF/UHFer for years, although it may seem to be strange or difficult technology for many HF operators. A mast-mounted preamp is not difficult to construct if you prefer to build things yourself. There is a growing number of commercially available models as well. See the list of equipment suppliers in Part 2 of this series. Just to show you that simple ideas can really be made complicated, let's take a look at what I've done with mast mounting of radio equipment.

Take another look at Fig 2. You can't miss the large white box located below the elevation rotator on my antenna stack. Fig 7 shows the interior of this box: It contains a lot of items besides a simple preamp! The box holds two racks of equipment. On the right are two dc voltage regulators with their pass-transistor heat sinks. These regulators provide on-site-regulated 28-V dc and 12-V dc from an unregulated 50-V dc supply located in the shack. Below the regulators is a 24-cm transmitting converter for Mode-L operation (1269-MHz uplink, 436-MHz downlink). Opposite the regulators on the other rack panel is a 70-cm solid-state power amplifier, a 70-cm preamplifier and relays.

Fig 8 is another view that details the area below the 24-cm transmitting converter. If you look closely, you'll see a 2-meter preamplifier and relays to switch it in and out of the line to the antenna. Before you close the magazine in dismay, remember that this is my particular way of doing things. I'm a fanatic about feed-line loss. There are plenty of successful OSCAR 10 stations that mount only the preamp at the antenna, and that will most likely work for you, too.

Control Circuitry

Fig 9 is a schematic diagram of the control circuitry for the tower-mounted rack. You'll find parts of this diagram helpful, even if you mount just a preamp at the antenna. You should note that I designed this circuit around the surplus coaxial relays that were available at the time. Your version will probably be different and will depend on the relays available to you. Switching requirements for coaxial relays were the subject of a comprehensive discussion by Joe Reisert, W1JR.[2] Fig 9 is my version of his concepts.

This circuitry performs several functions. For starters, it places the preamp in the line only during receiving periods and takes it out of the line during transmitting periods and at those times when the station is not in use. This is necessary because I use my satellite array for terrestrial transceive operations as well. The circuitry isolates the preamplifier when it is not used for receiving, protecting it from stray electromagnetic pulses (EMP), such as lightning strokes. EMP protection is desirable even if you use the antenna and preamp only for receiving AO-10 signals.

Fig 9 is a bit more complicated than the average mast-mounted preamp setup because I also use 2-meter RF to drive the 24-cm transmitting converter. I have an extra relay (K3) to switch between 2-meter and 24-cm operation. K1, a DPDT transfer relay, switches the input of the preamp between the antenna and a 50-ohm termination. K2, another DPDT relay, switches the preamp output between a 50-ohm termination and the feed line to the shack. The coaxial cable used for connections between the relays is cut to 0.1 to 0.2 electrical wavelength as recommended by W1JR to

Fig 7—Interior of the tower-mounted equipment rack with the cover removed. The 70-cm equipment is on the left, while power-supply regulators, a 24-cm transmit converter and a 2-meter preamp are mounted on the right.

Fig 8—Close-up of the 2-meter preamplifier and relays.

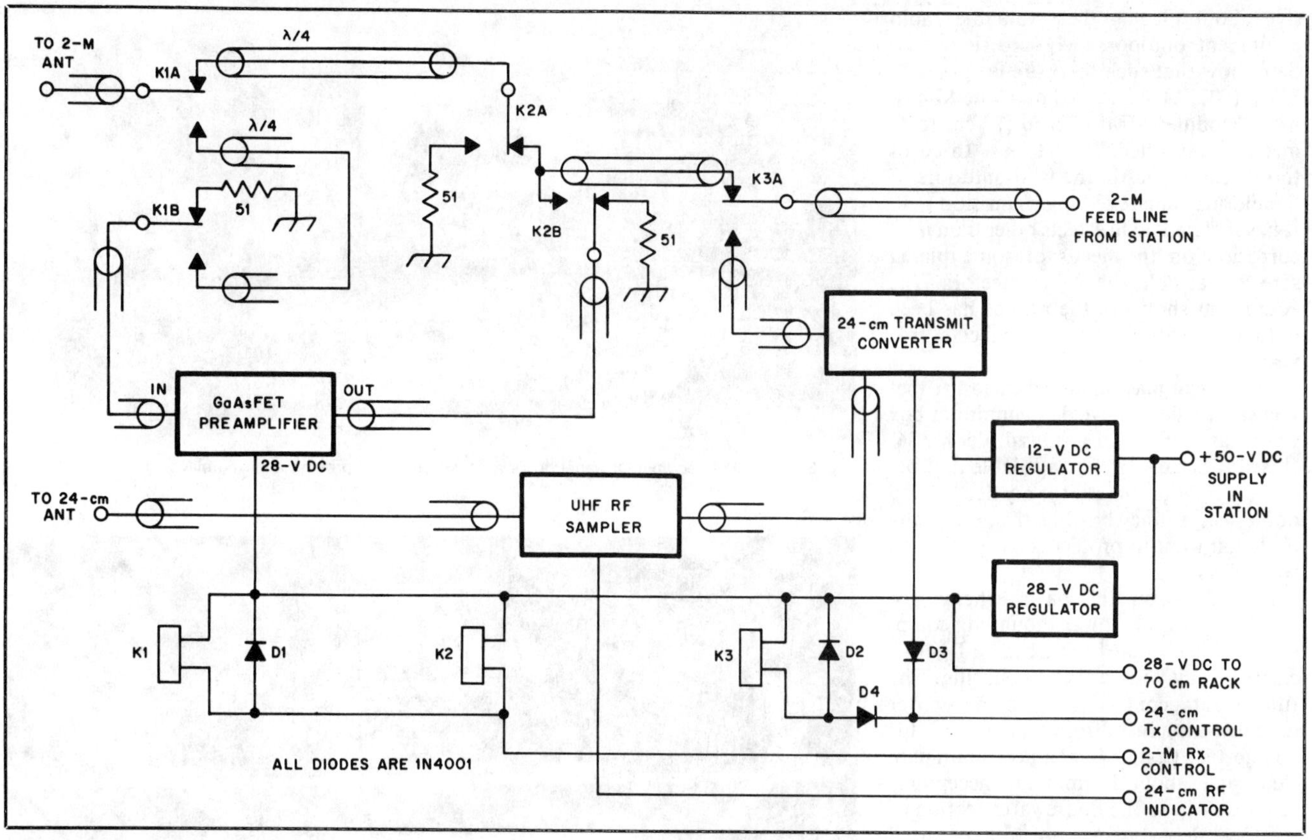

Fig 9—Control circuitry for the mast-mounted 2-meter preamplifier. K1-K3 are surplus coaxial relays.

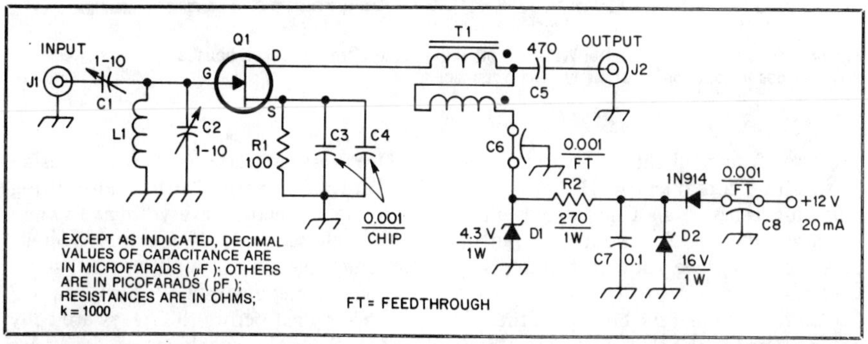

Fig 10—Schematic diagram of the 2-meter, W6PO-type GaAsFET preamplifier. Construction hints may be found in Chapter 31 of *The 1986 ARRL Handbook.*

C1, C2—1-10-pF ceramic or piston trimmer capacitor.
C3, C4—0.001-μF ceramic chip capacitor.
C5—470-pF silver-mica capacitor.
C6, C8—0.001-μF feedthrough capacitor.
C7—0.01-μF disc-ceramic capacitor.
D1—4.3-V, 1-W Zener diode.
D2—16-V, 1-W Zener diode.
J1, J2—Female chassis-mount BNC connector.
L1—6t no. 14 wire, ¼-inch ID, ½ inch long.
Q1—GaAsFET: Suitable parts include MGF1202, MGF1402, NE72089.
R1—100-Ω, 1/4- or 1/8-W carbon-composition resistor installed with leads 1/8 inch or less.
R2—270-Ω, 1-W resistor.
T1—12t of a twisted pair of no. 24 enam wire on T37-0 toroid core.

Fig 11—The completed preamplifier is housed in a small aluminum enclosure.

achieve maximum isolation between the transmitted RF and the preamp input. The relays are connected so that they must be energized to place the preamp in line. This setup has worked well for me. I have not lost any GaAsFETs because of EMP or routine RF transmissions, and central Florida is probably the champion lightning-storm area of the country, if not the world.

As you can see, this is all homemade or modified surplus equipment—I enjoy doing things myself. Construction of preamps has been rewarding and relatively easy. I found the basics for the W6PO design (Fig 10) in a newsletter.[3] Similar designs have been documented in *QEX*.[4] There is also a wealth of ideas in Chapter 31 of *The 1986 ARRL Handbook*.[5] The construction process is not terribly complicated, as shown by my 2-meter preamp (Fig 11).

Tower-Mounted Equipment Shelters

A great many amateurs seem apprehen-

Fig 13—The 70-cm equipment panel holds a power amplifier, preamp and TR relays.

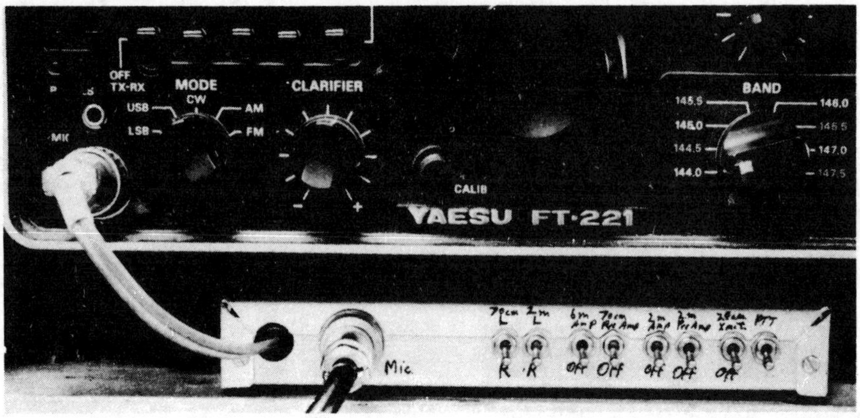

Fig 14—The station control unit at WD4FAB fits underneath a transceiver. It houses the TR sequencer and provides instant control of many station functions.

sive about placing their valuable radio equipment outdoors. My experiences to date show that such fears are unfounded. Since 1977, I have owned only one Microwave Modules MMt 432/50 (70-cm to 6-meter) transverter. For at least three of those years it was in the wild outdoors of the Florida climate serving its mission well. It has suffered no ill effects other than mild corrosion on the heads of some plated screws that hold the RF connectors. The equipment shown in the photos has been outdoors, without adverse effects, for years.

My present mast-mounted enclosure that you saw earlier is a welded aluminum box I purchased at a local surplus dealer for $6. I used it because it was available and because it is large enough for my needs. You don't need a fancy box like this, especially if all you want to protect is a preamp and two relays.

Fig 12 shows the basic scheme for weatherproofing tower-mounted equipment. This is what I used before I got so carried away with remote mounting. The fundamental concept is to provide a cover to shelter equipment from rain (or snow for you northerners). A 2-inch-deep aluminum cake pan is about the minimum acceptable cover. A trip to the housewares section of the local department store will reveal all manner of plastic and aluminum trays and pans that make great rain covers. As mentioned before, polyethylene plastic must be protected from sunlight. Clear polystyrene refrigerator containers work better, and aluminum is best of all. Choose a cover that is large enough for your equipment; remember to leave room for connecting cables.

You'll notice that the bottom of the rain cover is open to the elements. This is done on purpose and will not cause any problems. Do *not* try to hermetically seal the enclosure. By leaving the bottom open, you provide adequate ventilation, and there will be no accumulation of water condensation. Just make sure that water cannot run into the enclosure by way of cables coming from above. Bend the cables as shown in Fig 12 to provide drip loops.

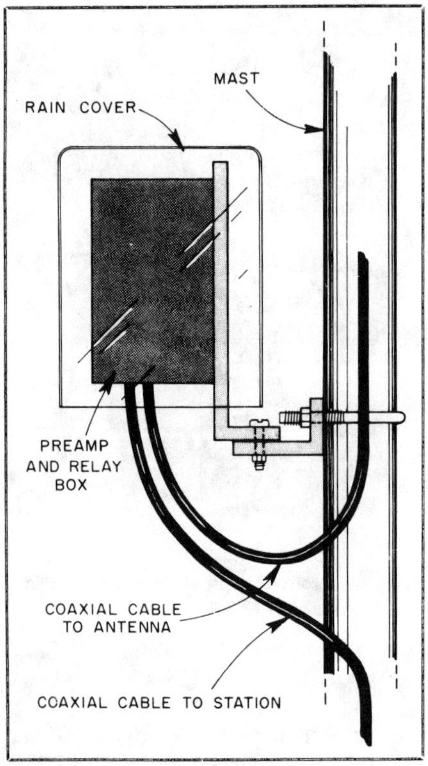

Fig 12—Protection for tower-mounted equipment need not be elaborate. Be sure to dress the cables as shown so that water drips off the cable jacket before it reaches the enclosure.

Transmitting

Fig 13 shows the 70-cm rack from the mast-mounted equipment box. I mounted my 70-cm power amplifier (built on the heat sink at the left of the photo) near the antenna to avoid feed-line losses, but this isn't necessary. I probably wouldn't do it again. Attached to the amplifier output is a coaxial RF sampler for remote power monitoring. To the right of the power amplifier is a 70-cm preamp and coaxial relays I use for OSCAR Mode-L reception and terrestrial operation.

One very important aspect of using GaAsFET preamps with transmitting equipment is getting everything to switch in the right sequence. If you apply voltage to your transmitter, amplifier and antenna relays simultaneously, it's likely that RF will be applied before the relays are fully closed. Such hot switching can easily arc the contacts on your expensive coaxial relays. In addition, if the TR relay is not fully closed, RF may be applied to your preamplifier. Such bursts of RF energy will, in less than the wink of an eye, cleanse your treasured preamplifier of its expensive active device, *guaranteed.* Many pieces of transmitting equipment (especially multimode transceivers) emit a short burst of RF power when switched on or off, so you run the risk of transmitting into your preamp even if you are careful to wait a second to speak or press your CW key.

Ideally, you would set your sequencing up something like this: When you switch into transmit, the coaxial relays change state to remove the preamplifier from the line. Next, the power amplifier is keyed on. The last thing that happens is that the transmitter is enabled. When you switch back to receive, the sequence is just the opposite. First, the transmitter is switched off, then the power amplifier is disabled, and then the TR relays change state.

Proper TR sequencing is easy to implement with simple circuitry described in *The 1986 ARRL Handbook*.[6] If you wish to purchase a sequencer, check with the equipment suppliers listed in Part 2 of this series. I've found out the hard way that some form of automatic TR sequencing is necessary with remotely controlled equipment to protect the unwary preamp from cockpit error. Most of us are more fallible than the GaAsFET can stand.

Receiving

The only additional equipment I have found useful applies to those of you who use a receiving converter and an HF receiver for downlink reception. I built an in-line switchable attenuator to use between the converter output and the antenna jack of my 10-meter receiver. I use the attenuator to lower the AGC level and improve the perceived signal-to-noise ratio. In addition, by adjusting the attenuator so the S meter on my HF rig rests at zero, I can give more-accurate signal reports. The attenuator circuit is shown in Chapter 25 of *The 1986 ARRL Handbook*, but I modified it so that there are only three steps: 5, 10 and 20 dB. These three settings allow attenuation in 5-dB steps from 0 to 35 dB.

Station Control

Depending on how complicated you make your satellite setup, you might want to combine most of the switching and control circuitry into a single box so that you have ready access to all controls. Fig 14 shows the system I use. A Minibox cut to a low profile (small enough to fit underneath a transceiver) contains all of the switches I need to control my station, as well as the TR sequencer circuit board. With these switches, I can change polarization on both antennas from RHCP to LHCP; activate, at will, the 2-m and 70-cm preamplifiers; and switch the power amplifier in or out of the line for QRP/QRO operation. I also have the option of manual PTT. The microphone PTT line activates the sequencer.

I hope that this discussion has provided some food for thought for your station. The setup is really not complex; by no means do you need all of the gadgets described here. Perhaps it is all in the mind of the beholder—I happen to enjoy building and modifying equipment. In any event, the last installment of this series will discuss finding and operating through OSCAR 10.

Notes

[1]A. Zoller, "Tilt Rather Than Twist," *Orbit*, Sep/Oct 1983, pp 7-8.
[2]J. Reisert, "VHF/UHF World—Protecting Equipment," *Ham Radio*, Jun 1985, pp 83-87.
[3]C. Osborne, ed, *Southeastern VHF Society Newsletter*, May 1983.
[4]G. Krauss, "VHF and UHF Low Noise Preamplifiers," *QEX*, Dec 1981, pp 3-6.
[5]M. Wilson, ed, *The 1986 ARRL Handbook* (Newington: ARRL, 1985). Available from your local radio store or from ARRL for $18 ($19 outside US). Add $2.50 ($3.50 UPS) per order for shipping and handling.
[6]Sequencing ideas are shown on pp 31-6 to 31-12, 32-37 and 32-38.

Adventures in Satellite DXing

Part 4: At last! You've assembled your station and are eager to work DX. Now it's time to find OSCAR 10 and operate through it.

By Dick Jansson, WD4FAB and Mark Wilson, AA2Z
1130 Willowbrook Trail
Maitland, FL 32751
Senior Assistant Technical Editor, ARRL

In this concluding part of the series on DXing by way of OSCAR 10, we'll examine the subject of locating AO-10 and aiming your antennas toward the satellite. We'll also take a look at those aspects that make OSCAR operation different from routine HF work.

Satellite Tracking

Expert HF DXers know where and when to point their beams, based on years of experience. Tracking satellites is similar in some ways, yet strikingly different in others. It does take experience to become a proficient satellite tracker and to really understand what is going on. In this way, satellite trackers and HF DXers are similar. HF DXers, however, sometimes have to shrug their shoulders at the vagaries of ionospheric propagation, which at times is simply unpredictable. Predicting OSCAR access is much more precise. There is an enormous satisfaction in positioning a simple graphical tracker or dumping a bunch of numbers into a computer and being presented with the information that an object traveling at greater than 18,000 miles per hour is going to pop over your horizon in precisely 38 minutes and 22 seconds. And then it does.

There are two fundamental reasons that you need to keep track of OSCARs. First of all, they move—some fast, others not so fast. You need to keep track of when the satellite is "in view" of your QTH. Second, since most satellite communications require some sort of directional antennas, you need to know where to point the array. Thus, the two primary functions of OSCAR-tracking efforts are position determination and scheduling. There are other functions that might be determined, but these two are the most basic.

Tracking OSCAR satellites requires information in four areas:

1) You need information about the OSCAR to be tracked—its precise location and rates of movement at a precisely defined instant.

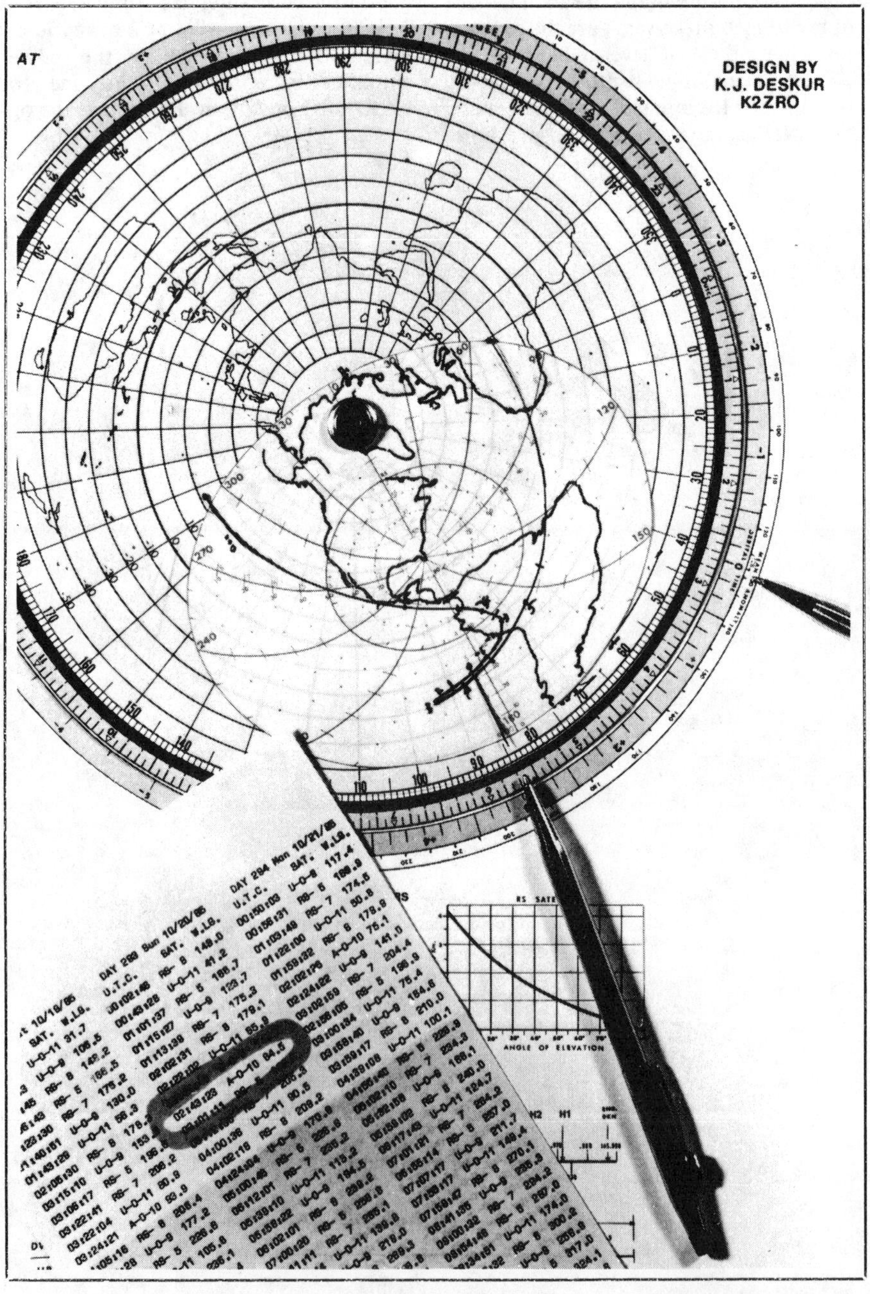

Fig 1—The *Satellipse* from ZRO Technical Products is an easy, inexpensive way to track OSCAR 10. The table at the lower left is part of the monthly orbital information available from ARRL for an SASE.

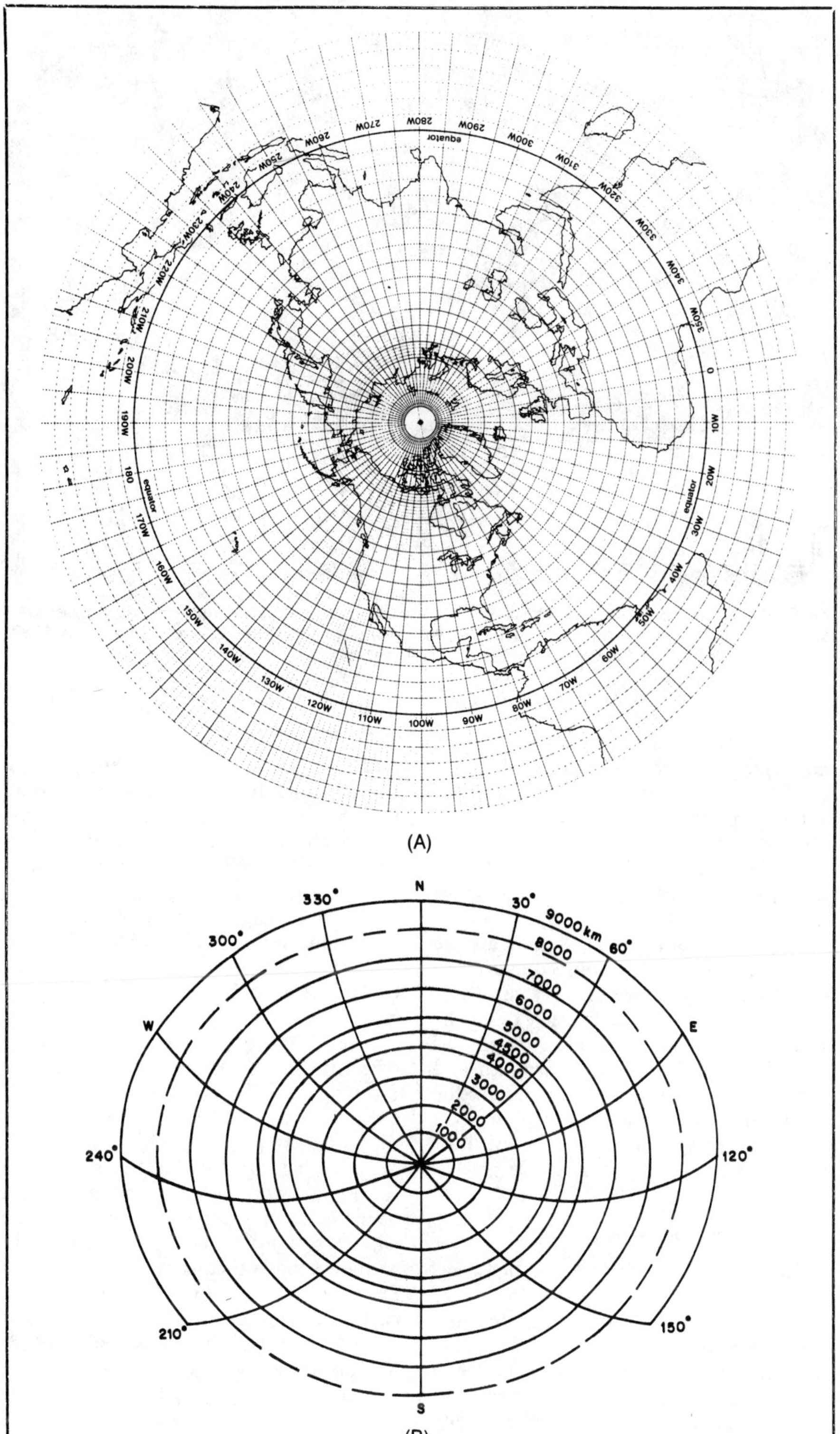

Fig 2—The *OSCARLOCATOR* from ARRL contains all of the tools needed to find OSCAR 10. The polar projection map at A is used for tracking all amateur satellites. The clear acetate QTH range circle (B) is centered over your QTH. The AO-10 ground track, shown at C, shows the path the satellite will take. The ground track changes periodically, and updates are published as necessary in *QST*.

2) You must know your own location to a reasonable degree of accuracy.

3) You must know the time of day reasonably accurately.

4) Most importantly, you need a device to coordinate the first three items. This can be a graphical tracker or a computer program. Both will be discussed here.

Graphical Tracking

Graphical (or manual) tracking methods generally employ a map, typically an azimuthal equidistant projection centered on the North Pole, and one or more clear overlays that allow you to use the map for changing satellite orbits and for different locations on Earth. The overlays allow you to determine which satellite orbits will bring the bird within range of your QTH. They also give beam headings for azimuth and elevation. We'll get to the details shortly.

Most amateur operators who are new to the OSCAR 10 scene are caught up with the idea that they *must* use computer tracking methods to generate the numerical data needed to aim their antennas at the satellite. To those of us who used graphical tracking methods for years to follow the Phase II satellites, such as OSCAR 8, the computer methods were such a revelation that we quickly became married to them. The notion that computers were the only hope was reinforced by the graphical tracking presentations for Phase III satellites given to us at the time of the Phase IIIA demise in 1980. Those manual tracking methods seemed unduly complicated, so we put on our blinders and charged ahead with our computers.

While a great many amateurs do have computers that can be used for tracking (and if you have one, that is the way to go), there are a large number of new satellite operators who are not so equipped. It's easy to be misled into thinking that you must purchase and master a computer before making even a single OSCAR contact. That's enough to make some potential satellite operators lose interest at the onset. Don't be intimidated! Today there are at least two very good, low-cost graphical tracking packages available to you. They give excellent results—finding OSCAR 10 is a snap. Best of all, the investment is downright trivial compared to the cost of even the least-expensive computer.

We highly recommend that you try one of the graphical tracking methods, even if you already have a computer to use for satellite tracking. The introduction to, and use of, the graphical methods will expand your knowledge and understanding of the nature of the OSCAR 10 orbit and make you a wiser communicator.

The two graphical tracking packages are the *OSCARLOCATOR* from ARRL and the *Satellipse* from ZRO Technical Products.[1,2] See Fig 1. While you are at it, obtain a copy of *The Satellite Experimenter's Handbook* by Martin Davidoff, K2UBC.[3] This publication presents an excellent discussion of graphical tracking. As an added bonus, these publications treat Phase II spacecraft tracking as well as Phase III.

All satellite tracking methods, computer and graphical, need periodic updating of orbital parameters and other reference information. Each satellite has different characteristics, so you'll need data for each satellite of interest. Amateurs can obtain this information from the following sources:

- AMSAT publications, including *Amateur Satellite Report,* a biweekly newsletter.[4]
- *QST*
- Daily W1AW Bulletins[5]
- *Project OSCAR Orbital Calendar,* a yearly publication of daily satellite reference predictions[6]
- Various AMSAT nets, especially the Tuesday evening net on 3857 kHz at 9 PM Eastern, Central and Mountain times, and 8 PM Pacific time.
- Tabulated satellite reference information, covering all current amateur satellites and good for about six weeks at a time, is available from ARRL HQ. Include a legal-size SASE with two units of First Class postage with your request. Keep a number of SASEs on file, and you will receive the routine updates.

As mentioned before, most graphical tracking methods are based on an azimuthal equidistant projection map of the Earth, centered on the North Pole. A series of clear-plastic overlays is supplied. See Fig 2. Different satellites usually have different orbits, which means that separate overlays are needed for each bird. Both of the graphical tracking packages mentioned here provide overlays for current satellites.

You'll need two overlays for each satellite. The ground-track overlay, which pivots around a rivet positioned at the North Pole, relates the path of the satellite to the map of the Earth. It shows the various locations that the satellite track can take.

The other overlay provides satellite *visibility circles* for your QTH. This overlay tells you which part of an orbit will bring the satellite in view of your QTH. It also shows the azimuth and elevation headings so you can point your antennas at the satellite.

Each of the graphical tracking packages mentioned here comes with complete instructions for use. While it might seem like a lot of work to set one up, graphical trackers really don't require that much effort. They become a lot of fun and a self-satisfying achievement, once the method is learned.

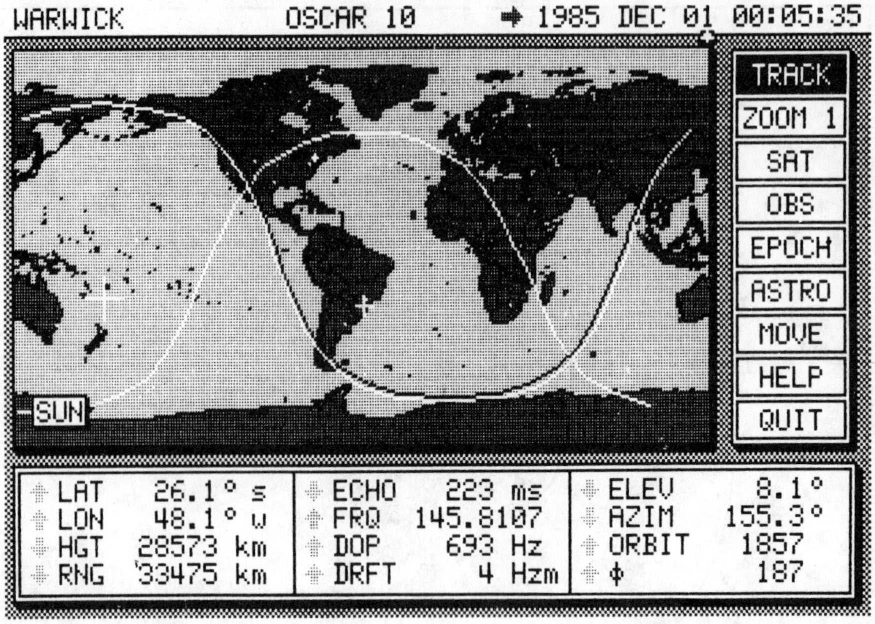

Fig 3—GRAFTRAK II from Silicon Solutions provides an elaborate map display as well as all important satellite parameters. This software runs on the IBM PC and requires an 8087 math coprocessor to help with its intensive calculations.

A valid question is, "How good are the graphical tracking methods compared to computer-based systems?" We ran some test cases to find out. In each case, the *Satellipse* results were within 3 degrees of the computer data in both azimuth and elevation. These differences are well inside the half-power beamwidth of highly directive crossed Yagi antennas. Even the most proficient operator would not be able to detect them.

Computer-Based Tracking

For those of you with personal computers, there is a wealth of software available. Most operators are quite satisfied to use the computer to provide numerical data to locate OSCAR 10. They then take this information and aim their antennas accordingly. For AO-10 this is usually sufficient. Changes in antenna positions are infrequent—anywhere from every half hour up to three hours before significant repointing is needed.

Another class of software allows the computer to automatically control antenna position. This approach has some inherent technical problems that are very far afield from computer byte bashing. Unless you are extremely well versed in the software, electronics and mechanics of digitally controlled, closed-loop servo systems, you should forget automatic-antenna tracking. Once you get into tracking AO-10 you will find that you need to adjust the position of your antennas only once or twice an hour by fairly small increments. It is just not worth the effort to control the antenna position automatically! In the days of OSCARs 6, 7 and 8, when the satellite was workable for 16 to 22 minutes each pass, operations in the shack were a bit like the proverbial one-armed paperhanger in a stiff breeze. AO-10 is literally a world of difference.

Satellite-tracking software for a number of computers is available from AMSAT, through the AMSAT Software Exchange (ASE). Most of this software is based on the original work by Dr Tom Clark, W3IWI, that was published in *Orbit.*[7] Since the original work, software specialists have found many innovative ways to express Dr Clark's computational methods. A listing of the various versions as of early 1986 is given in Table 1. For a current program catalog and ordering information, write to AMSAT Software Exchange, PO Box 27, Washington, DC 20044, tel 301-589-6062.

Some commercial software vendors advertise satellite-tracking programs in the ham magazines. An elegant package that is advertised in *QST* is Graftrak II from Silicon Solutions. This program, which operates on the IBM® PC, provides a sophisticated, colorful map display showing the satellite path over your QTH. See Fig 3. Also from Silicon Solutions is Silicon Ephemeris, a satellite-tracking program that has a tabular output. Both packages are available from Silicon Solutions Inc, PO Box 742546, Houston, TX 77274-2546, tel 713-661-8727.

Spectrum West offers Autotrak: Computer Rotor Control for several popular

Table 1
AMSAT Software Exchange Satellite-Tracking Programs

1) Radio Shack TRS-80® Model I, Level II BASIC, 32-kbytes RAM needed. No instructions included; software manual (see item 20) recommended.
2) Radio Shack TRS-80 Model III, 32-kbytes RAM needed.
3) North Star BASIC under North Star DOS for 5¼-inch, hard sector, single- or double-density drives.
4) Microsoft BASIC, version 5.21 under CP/M®, single-density, single-sided 8-inch disk. No instructions included; software manual (see item 20) recommended.
5) Apple® II, APPLESOFT BASIC, on 13- or 16-sectored diskettes or cassette. Menu driven, output to screen or printer.
6) IBM PC, PC-XT or PC-AT version, by WØSL. Menu driven for tabulated output for up to eight satellites in real time. Graphics display of world map. Requires 128-kbytes RAM, DOS 2.0 or later, and BASICA.
7) IBM PCjr version by WØSL. Tracking with graphics. Requires 128 kbytes RAM, DOS 2.0 or later and BASICA as above, but modified to run on PCjr.
8) IBM PC and compatibles version by N4HY. Called QUIKTRAK, it is menu driven for tracking and scheduling and features a new "Window Track" mode for DX.
9) Texas Instruments TI 99/4A, cassette only.
10) Apple II antenna positioning and controlling software by KØRZ.
11) Radio Shack TRS-80 Model 4, for TRSDOS Version 6.0.
12) Radio Shack TRS-80 Color Computer. Requires 32-kbytes RAM and extended BASIC (cassette only).
13) Commodore 64™, AMSAT VR85. Datapoint map of 2000, 20 satellites.
14) QUIKTRAK-2064, enhanced version of AMS-2064, including machine-language file, cassette or disk.
15) Atari® —disk only.
16) Timex-2068, cassette only of W3IWI program.
17) HP-41C programmable calculator, version ORBIT I of the W3IWI program (approximates real-time operation).
18) HP-41C programmable calculator, version ORBIT II of the W3IWI program, converted to run with time module (real-time tracking).
19) Heathkit H89 version of W3IWI program. CP/M version configured for H89, CP/M & MBASIC. Requires 5¼-inch H-17 single-sided, single-density, hard-sector disk.
20) *Using Microcomputer Programs for Radio Amateur Satellite Orbital Prediction* by N5AHD. This manual tells how to use the W3IWI program on Radio Shack, CP/M and S-100 bus computers.
21) UoSAT telemetry capture and decoding software for the IBM PC.

computers. This software and hardware package allows the computer to control azimuth and elevation rotators, so the antenna positions are updated as the computer recalculates the satellite position. For more information, contact Spectrum West, 5717 NE 56th, Seattle, WA 98105, tel 206-523-6167.

Another package, using a different computational algorithm than W3IWI employed, is available from Manfred, KG6EF, and Gordon Mueller, KB6BPL. The Muellers provide a Sharp PC-1246 pocket computer and a BASIC routine that was conceived by Dr Karl Meinzer, DJ4ZC. While this computation is somewhat simpler than the W3IWI Keplerian method, it has yet to achieve a great following in the US. For more information, contact the Muellers at 4914 Commonwealth Ave, La Canada, CA 91011, tel 818-790-6695.

Operating Schedule

The last bit of information you need to know before you turn on your gear and start working exotic DX is the OSCAR 10 operating schedule. The satellite does not operate Mode B and Mode L simultaneously all the time. Rather, the transponders are turned on and off according to a fixed operating schedule defined by control stations on Earth. This is done to make sure that the spacecraft's batteries are charged (from solar cells) and discharged (through transponder use) at a rate that will assure the longest possible battery life. The OSCAR 10 schedule needs to be adjusted several times each year because of the satellite's position relative to the sun and earth. The current operating schedule will include the on and off periods for both the Mode B and Mode L translators.

You can obtain the current OSCAR 10 operating schedule from several sources. If you're active on HF, you can hear the schedule on the weekly 75-meter AMSAT net mentioned before. Or, if you've located OSCAR 10, you can get this information on the AO-10 General Beacon frequency of 145.810 MHz. Most of the time, this beacon is sending information about important spacecraft parameters (called *telemetry*) back to Earth by means of a phase-shift-keyed (PSK) signal. PSK telemetry has a raspy buzzing sound. Every 30 minutes, though, the PSK telemetry is interrupted by a five-minute CW bulletin that includes the operating schedule and other bits of important news. These bulletins start on the hour and at 30 minutes past each hour. At 15 and 45 minutes after each hour, another five minutes of information is sent by means of 170-Hz shift, 50-baud RTTY. These RTTY bulletins also contain telemetry samplings, for those interested in that aspect of satellites.

How Well Can You Hear?

This is the point where we put all of your efforts to use. You have high-quality 2-meter receiving capability, modest transmitting power on 435 MHz, good antennas with azimuth and elevation rotators, and a knowledge of where to find OSCAR 10. You *are* ready, aren't you?

It's a good idea to tune to the beacon frequency of 145.81 MHz each time you begin satellite operation. Among other things, the beacon provides a constant signal for peaking your antenna on the satellite. Determine the beacon strength. If you have the receiving capability recommended earlier in this series, you will have useful readings on your S-meter (normally, less than S9 values). It may be helpful to use a signal source and a switchable attenuator to calibrate your S-meter in terms of decibels. This way you can note signal strengths in decibels above the noise, which has more meaning in weak-signal work than normal S-meter readings.

Table 2
AMSAT-OSCAR 10 Frequency Conversion Chart

Mode B ± Doppler Shift

Uplink	*Downlink*	
	145.987	EB
435.0323	145.9720	SSC H1
435.0423	145.9620	SSC H2
435.0477	145.9600	GCB UL
435.0477	145.9570	ACNF
435.050	145.955	
.055	.950	
.060	.945	
.065	.940	
.070	.935	
.075	.930	
.080	.925	
.085	.920	
.090	.915	
.095	.910	
.100	.905	
435.1037	145.901	
.105	.900	
.110	.895	
.115	.890	
.120	.885	
.125	.880	
.130	.875	
.135	.870	
.140	.865	
.145	.860	
.150	.855	
.155	.850	
.160	.845	GCB LL
435.1647	145.840	SSC 12
435.1747	145.830	SSC L1
	145.810	GB

SSC—Special Service Channel
GCB—General Communications Band
ACNF—AMSAT Calling and Net Frequency
EB—Engineering Beacon
GB—General Beacon
LL—Lower Limit
UL—Upper Limit

Once you've found the beacon and know that you're hearing OSCAR 10, tune up through the passband (145.830 to 145.970 MHz). Note that the satellite passband is divided according to a voluntary frequency plan, shown in Fig 4. Nearly all of the CW activity is below 145.900 MHz; nearly all of the SSB activity is above that frequency. You will be able to hear packet activity on Special Service Channel (SSC) L2, near 145.840 MHz.

It will take a while to get oriented to Mode B operation because the spacecraft translator is *inverting,* as shown in Fig 5. This means that a signal transmitted at the high end of the 435-MHz uplink passband will come out on the low end of the 145-MHz receiving passband. SSB signals are inverted as well: If you transmit LSB on the uplink, it will come out as USB on the downlink. Common practice is to transmit up to AO-10 on LSB, providing a USB downlink signal.

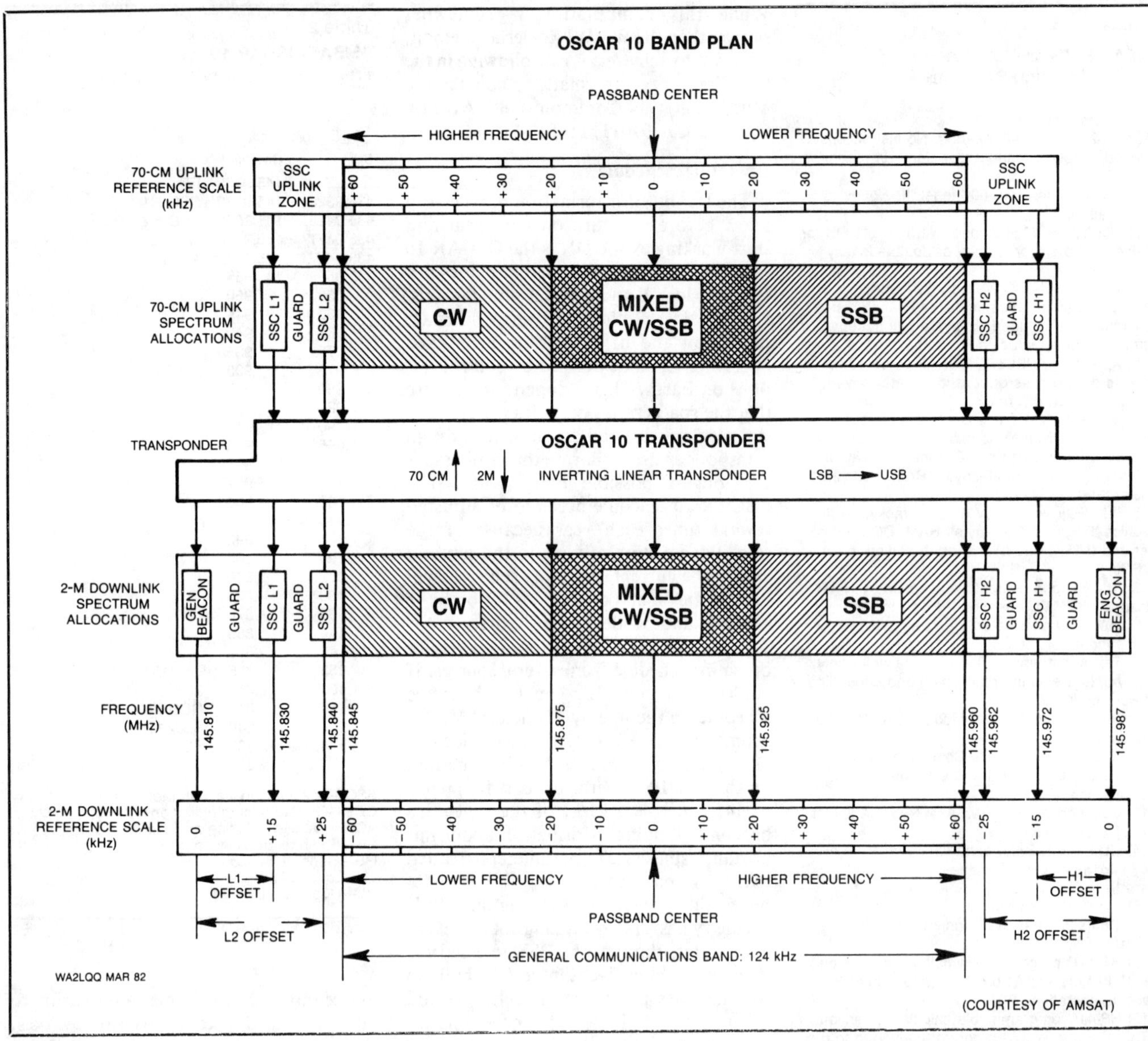

Fig 4—The OSCAR 10 band plan allows for CW only, mixed CW/SSB and SSB only operation. Courteous operators observe this voluntary band plan at all times.

If everything is working right, conversational QSOs can be held with signals ranging from 6 to 15 dB above the noise floor of your receiver. Typically, the beacon is 12 to 15 dB above the noise. Confirmable QSOs have been made with signals as low as 2 to 4 dB above the noise. It is amazingly different from the type of communications that you may have been doing on the HF bands. Note that there is *no* excuse for QRM. Anyone able to receive the satellite should also be able to hear *everyone else* and allow sufficient elbow room for rational QSOs without crowding.

Locating Your Signal

Find some vacant territory on the receiving passband of the satellite for testing your own signal, for example, about 145.960 MHz. There's no need to hurry—AO-10 will be around for awhile. The frequency chart shown in Table 2 will help you to find the right 435-MHz transmitting frequency to correspond with your chosen 145-MHz downlink frequency. If you wish, you can purchase a handy circular slide rule for the uplink-downlink frequency relationships.[8] Assuming you've tuned your receiver to 145.960 MHz, the nominal transmitting frequency is 435.045 MHz. Send a few dits and listen for them on the receiver. Headphones are very helpful here. Tune your *transmitter* frequency a bit on either side of nominal and find your own signal coming back. Note the offset from the nominal frequency; you'll need to know this number any time you want to bring your transmitter to a frequency you're listening on.

The offset is a combination of equipment calibration and *Doppler shift*. Doppler shift is caused by the relative motion between you and the satellite. As the satellite moves toward you, the frequency of the downlink signals will increase slightly. As the satellite passes overhead and moves away from you, the frequency of the downlink signals will be slightly lower than nominal. Doppler shift through a transponder becomes the sum of the Doppler shifts of both the uplink and downlink signals. Since the AO-10 Mode B transponder is inverting, an increase in uplink frequency causes a decrease in downlink frequency, so the Doppler shifts tend to cancel.

If you are using the Ten-Tec 2510 Mode B Satellite Station, tuning the frequency offset is even easier. Set your HF receiver, used as a tunable IF, to 29.0 MHz, and set the 2510 to the desired receiving frequency. Tune the HF receiver a few kilohertz on either side of 29.0 MHz, and you will find your signal. Once set, keep your hands off the HF receiver tuning knob! Adjust the HF rig only for very small Doppler shift corrections and do all of your QSYing with

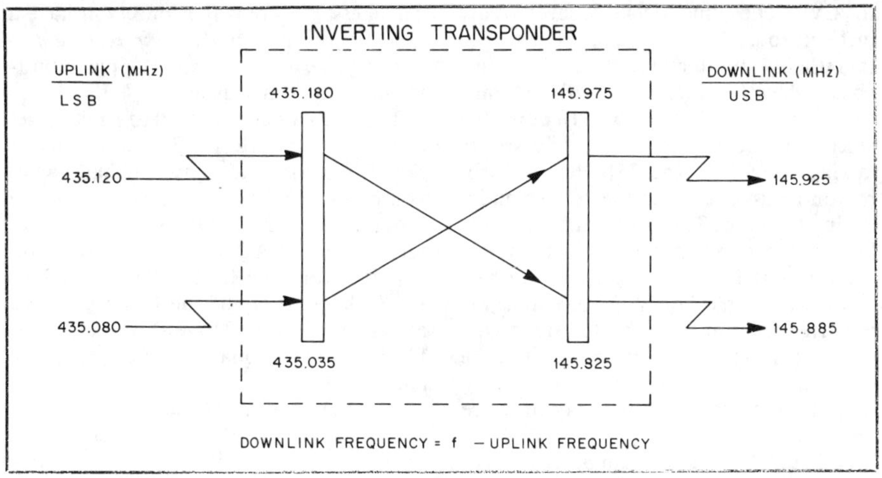

Fig 5—The OSCAR 10, Mode B transponder is inverting. Signals transmitted to the satellite at the high end of the 435-MHz uplink come out at the low end of the 145-MHz downlink. Signals transmitted to the satellite on LSB return to Earth as USB signals. The translation frequency, f, is 581.005 MHz.

the 2510 tuning knob. Your transmit signal will always follow your receiver; it's that easy.

Now that you've found your signal, compare its strength with that of the 145.810-MHz general beacon. Your signal strength on the downlink should *never* exceed that of the beacon. If it does, decrease your transmitter power output accordingly. The transponder must share its power among all users. If your signal is louder than the beacon, you'll activate the transponder AGC and degrade performance. It takes only one hog to make communications difficult for everyone.

At Last: Operating Through OSCAR 10

Let's try a CW QSO first. There are two ways of finding someone to work on the satellite, just like on any other band or mode: You can call CQ and hope someone answers, or you can answer a CQ. If you've got a good signal through the satellite, you may want to try calling CQ at first. This way, you won't have to worry about bringing your transmitter to someone else's frequency. You'll be able to get the frequency controls set in advance, allowing you to concentrate on making the QSO. After a QSO or two, venture down the band and try to find another station to call.

Find a clear spot in the CW portion of the passband and bring your transmitter to the frequency. Do this the intelligent way: Look up the frequencies in Table 2, set your transmitter to the right frequency (remember the offset) and send a couple of dots if necessary to zero in on your signal. Resist the temptation to put a brick on the dot lever and crank the transmitter control

Fig 6—These are but some of the DX QSL cards gathered from Mode B OSCAR contacts at WD4FAB.

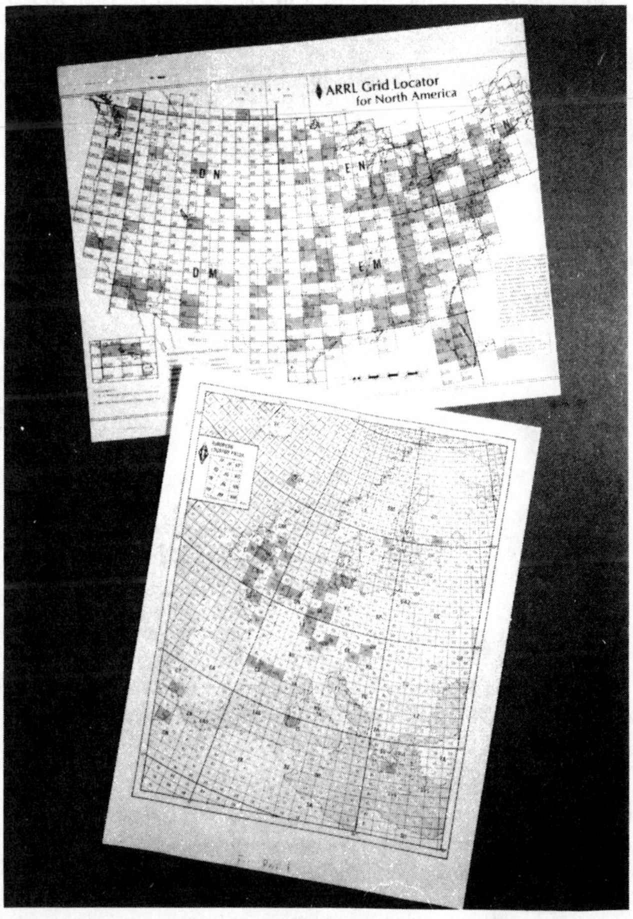

Fig 7—If you're into grid-square chasing, quite a number can be worked via the satellite.

until you find your signal. Such "swishing the passband" causes QRM to everyone else and is considered extremely bad manners.

Now call CQ. Although you can hear your signal on the downlink, you'll probably want to use a sidetone oscillator for monitoring your sending. OSCAR 10 is quite a distance away, so it takes a little time for your signal to make the round trip. When AO-10 is in the highest part of its orbit, the delay is about ¼ second. It can be disorienting to listen to a delayed downlink signal while you're sending. It's a good idea to adjust the sidetone level so that it's loud enough to use as a monitor, yet weak enough to let you hear downlink signals between characters or words.

Since satellite operation is full duplex, don't be surprised if someone answers your CQ before you've finished. There's really no reason to wait—it's not like routine single-frequency communications where the receiver is disabled until the end of a transmission. This won't be difficult to get used to, especially if you've used a QSK CW rig before. Should Doppler change during the course of your QSO, tune your *transmitter* to keep your transmitter and receiver on the same frequency. This way, you won't "walk" down the band as things change. That's all there is to it: Now OSCAR 10 operation is just like what you're used to on HF, only the band's always open when the satellite's in view.

Now Try SSB

SSB operation via OSCAR 10 is similar to CW. The time delay is even more difficult to get over, though. New operators usually stumble over their own return voices when they first try AO-10. You may find it more comfortable to turn down the receiver audio gain control while you're talking. The Ten Tec 2510 has a pushbutton control to mute the receive audio during transmit. These approaches, while helpful, force the operator back to monolog transmission without the full-duplex features available from AO-10. With some practice, you should be able to listen to the *pitch* of your return voice and not be bothered by the *content* of what is being said, thus achieving full break-in voice operation.

Although headphones can be used to enhance any weak-signal work, they are mandatory for AO-10 SSB operation. If you don't use headphones, you'll have problems with the receiver audio getting into the transmitter. The result can be anything from lousy, booming transmitted audio to a screeching, full-feedback oscillation through the satellite. Please use your headphones.

An added bonus of lightweight headphones that do not block off all external sounds is that you can hear your own acoustic voice, as well as your voice as transmitted through the satellite. You can readily tune your *transmitter* for the same voice pitch from both sources, thus ensuring that you are on "your frequency" and that any other station that hears you will be able to make contact without chasing you up and down the passband. The message here is that once you have a QSO established, *hold your receive frequency fixed* and make any Doppler adjustments with your transmitter VFO.

That's about all you need to know to get started on OSCAR 10. There are lots of rare DX stations to chase, if that's what you enjoy. And there is always someone around for a ragchew. You'll find the relaxed pace of AO-10, Mode B operation a relief from the hectic doings on HF. Fig 6 shows some of the QSLs gathered at WD4FAB from Mode B contacts, and Fig 7 shows grid squares worked (both here and abroad).

Good DXing on AO-10.

Notes

[1]The *OSCARLOCATOR* is available from your local radio store or from ARRL for $8.50. Add $2.50 ($3.50 UPS) per order for shipping and handling.

[2]The *Satellipse* is available from ZRO Technical Products, Box 11, Endicott, NY 13760 for $10.

[3]M. Davidoff, *The Satellite Experimenter's Handbook* (Newington: ARRL, 1984). Available from your local radio store or from ARRL for $10 ($11 outside US). Add $2.50 ($3.50 UPS) per order for shipping and handling.

[4]AMSAT, PO Box 27, Washington, DC 20044. Dues are $24 per year. *Amateur Satellite Report* is published biweekly and is included with AMSAT membership.

[5]See the W1AW Schedule in Jun 1986 *QST* for more information.

[6]Available annually for a $10 donation from Project OSCAR, PO Box 1136, Los Altos, CA 98510.

[7]T. Clark, "Basic Orbits," *Orbit,* Mar/Apr 1981, pp 6-11 and 19-20.

[8]The OSCAR 10 "No Ditter" is available from Dave Guimont, Jr, WB6LLO, 5030 July St, San Diego, CA 92110, for $3, postage paid.

A Mode-L Parabolic Antenna and Feedhorn for OSCAR 10

Get away from the crowded HF bands. Open new doors with this easily built Mode-L dish.

By Eugene F. Ruperto, W3KH
RD 1 Box 366
West Alexander, PA 15376

OSCAR 10 is the space-age answer to poor or crowded conditions encountered on the lower amateur bands. Sitting here at or near the bottom of the sunspot cycle has really put a crimp in my DXing habits lately, so I decided to put some effort into my OSCAR station. It seems like only yesterday that I listened to the weak CW "HI-HI" from one of the earlier OSCARs and marveled at the technology behind the effort. Later I taped and compared the analog audio telemetry from another OSCAR and wondered where it would end. Throughout the years, I have worked through all of the amateur satellites and mourned the death of AO-7 where I cut my teeth on Mode B.

Now I can sit at the OSCAR station for hours and work at my leisure. No more hurry-up, 10-minute passes. No more frantic antenna positioning. OSCAR 10, with its high elliptical orbit, is "a set it and forget it" type of satellite, for all practical purposes. Being a chronic AO-10 user, I have a tendency to become complacent and take AO-10 for granted. I have access to it nearly every day of the week, and have my choice of ragchewing, working DX, slow- or high-speed CW, certificate chasing, RTTY or just some old-fashioned antenna experimenting. This "bird" gets my vote for being the best so far. In mid-1986, another Phase III satellite with Mode-B and Mode-L transponders will be placed in orbit.

Each satellite poses a new challenge for users and contributes something new to the amateur space program as we know it today. Satellite experiments involving preamplifiers, antenna configurations, polarity or power changes provide instantaneous feedback for analysis. In this respect, AO-10 represents a test bed for the amateur. Now is the time to get the bugs out of your present satellite system and, if possible, explore the world of Mode L. For future launches, the trend is toward UHF, and the amateur with only Mode-A or -B equipment will not be able to take advantage of all that is available.

Since discovering the Mode-L beacon, I've been interested in getting something going. I monitored the frequency when the bird switched from Mode B and found stations on Mode L that are using modest power levels and simple antennas on the downlink. This gave me the incentive to design an uplink antenna for Mode L. Despite the fact that the Mode-L transponder was not performing as planned, what I heard and read confirmed that with a modest addition to the Mode-B station, Mode L could be used. With a 2-m/23-cm transverter at hand, only a small amplifier and a suitable antenna were needed to use Mode L.

Design Strategy

I decided that because of the small antenna sizes required at this frequency (1269.5 MHz) a parabolic dish antenna would be best. Some of the stations on Mode L are using commercially built TV dishes. But, considering the work needed to put them together, cover them with screen, build a feed antenna and supports, add a mount, and live with a deep f/D (usually 0.375), the buyer basically gets only a preformed wire grid for his money. I decided to build my own dish from readily available materials. This custom-design approach offers the builder some measure of control over the finished product. By using this method, one can design and construct parabolic reflectors of any reasonable size for any phase of amateur endeavor.

I used a three-step approach to the design. First, the dish should be effective, which means that a study of size vs power must be considered. My calculations indicated that a gain between 21 dBi and 27 dBi would be sufficient to hear my signal through the 436-MHz downlink, provided

Table 1

Design Considerations for Parabolic Dish Antennas

Dish Size			
Beamwidth	4†	5†	6†
(Deg)	13.2	10.5	8.7
Gain (dBi)	21.8	23.7	25.3
Output Power (W)	*EIRP*	*EIRP*	*EIRP*
100 W	16.2 kW	25.4 kW	36 kW
50 W	8 kW	12.75 kW	18.3 kW
30 W	4.8 kW	7.65 kW	11 kW
15 W	2.4 kW	3.75 kW	5.4 kW
10 W	1.6 kW	2.5 kW	3.6 kW
5 W	800 W	1.25 kW	1.8 kW
2.5 W	400 W	625 W	900 W

†Based upon 50% reflection efficiency and 10-dB taper feedhorn for 0.4 f/D dish

Table 2

Detail Design for Three Parabolic Dish Antenna Sizes

Dish Size (Feet)	*Y, X Coord (In)*	*Focal Length (In)*	*Depth of Dish (In)*	*Gain (dBi)*	*Beamwidth (Degrees)*
	0, 0				
	3 0.117				
	6 0.468				
	9 1.054				
4	12 1.875	19.2	7.5	21.8	13.8
	15 2.929				
	18 4.218				
	21 5.742				
	24 7.5				
	0, 0				
	3 0.093				
	6 0.375				
	9 0.843				
	12 1.5				
5	15 2.343	24	9.375	23.76	10.54
	18 3.375				
	21 4.594				
	24 6.0				
	27 7.60				
	30 9.375				
	0, 0				
	3 0.078				
	6 0.312				
	9 0.703				
	12 1.25				
	15 1.953				
6	18 2.812				
	21 3.828	28.8	11.25	25.35	8.78
	24 5.0				
	27 6.328				
	30 7.812				
	33 9.453				
	36 11.250				

†Cartesian coordinates derived from $y^2 = 4FX$.
y = radius of dish, x = axis of focus, 0, 0 = dish center.

that the combination of RF output power and dish gain would allow me to reach the target value of 3 kW of EIRP (see Table 1). Second, the dish should be light so that it can be mounted at the mast with my other satellite antennas. This prevents an aiming discrepancy later on (such as my downlink antenna pointing at the bird and my uplink antenna pointing toward some meaningless position in space). This becomes more apparent as dish size increases, which brings up the third requirement—beamwidth. A wide-beamwidth dish is nice to have for a moving satellite, but it means a sacrifice in gain. On the other hand, too large a dish will narrow the beamwidth sufficiently to make tracking a chore. Although the Phase III satellites don't require much beam pointing near apogee, the Mode-L operating period is sometimes changed to a lower mean anomaly for operational reasons, and the ground track can cover a considerable angle in terms of antenna movement. It's a nice feeling to not have to aim the antenna more than once every 10 or 15 minutes during the Mode-L period. I decided that a 5-foot dish, with 12 watts of power at the feedhorn, should do the job for me.

Materials

I used ¼-inch-diameter steel pencil rod (a mild steel) for the rib construction. With a weight of 0.167 pounds per foot, it would allow the antenna to be light enough to rotate with the other antennas. This pencil stock is usually sold in 20-foot lengths, called "joints," and at this length they are extremely flexible. To get them home, plan to cut them in half with a hacksaw or carry them, as I did, on an extension ladder on top of the pickup. Keeping the original length will minimize waste when making your cuts. At this writing, the cost of a 20-foot joint was $1.30. Roughly figured, five joints will be needed for a 5-foot dish. Excluding the price of a piece of pipe and three hose clamps, the steel needed for the 5-foot dish will set you back about $6.50, which is a lot less than the cost of your average catalog TV dish. Previous experience using ¼-inch hardware cloth and wire ties for dish coverings led me to abandon that approach in favor of a suggestion by Richard Dolenc, WB3CRF, to use common aluminum screen-door material instead. An added bonus is the lack of bandages required for the inevitable cuts that result from using hardware cloth. The door screen material mesh size is much smaller than the one-tenth wavelength required to be a perfect reflector at this frequency, but it also presents greater wind loading, with the probability of ice and snow accumulation. The fact that the dish can be pointed to a "stored" position when not in use, however, minimizes these effects. A 16-foot-long by 3-foot-wide piece of aluminum screen, obtained at the local hardware store for $6, was more than ample for the 5-foot dish.

A very neat, taut covering can be accomplished by using Liquid Nail™ or similar material to glue the screen to the ribs. Use a caulking tube (price less than $2) to apply the glue. Make sure the glue is waterproof since it will be exposed to the weather. A question arises concerning possible galvanic action between the steel rod and the aluminum screen. The glue matrix acts as a buffer between the metals and, for the most part, as an insulator between the two. As a consequence, only very small areas will occasionally make contact. Though these could disintegrate over a period of time, the glued surface area will be much larger and still retain the original strength. The entire screen surface may be removed with a pair of scissors or a sharp knife; after grinding the rib surfaces free of glue, a new screen surface can be applied.

Dish Construction

A ¼-inch-thick piece of scrap steel plate, 2 feet wide by 4 feet long, is used as a jig to build the ribs. The parabolic X and Y coordinates (see Table 2) are transferred to the plate, spaced roughly every three inches, by tracing the figure on the plate. Short pieces of ¼-inch steel strap are tack welded along the curve to hold the pencil rod along the front of the curve; then similar pieces are tack welded along the back to hold the pencil rod at the desired shape (see Figs 1 and 2). The process is repeated for the back rib member as well as the piece of pencil rod that forms the hub portion of the rib. The hub pieces extend about 2 inches beyond the rib dimensions so that when completed, a hose clamp can be fitted on both front and back of the rib to clamp around a slightly longer piece of ½-inch pipe, threaded at both ends, that forms the central hub.

Once the jig is completed, and the first rib welded and checked, the remaining five ribs can be constructed in a short time. The

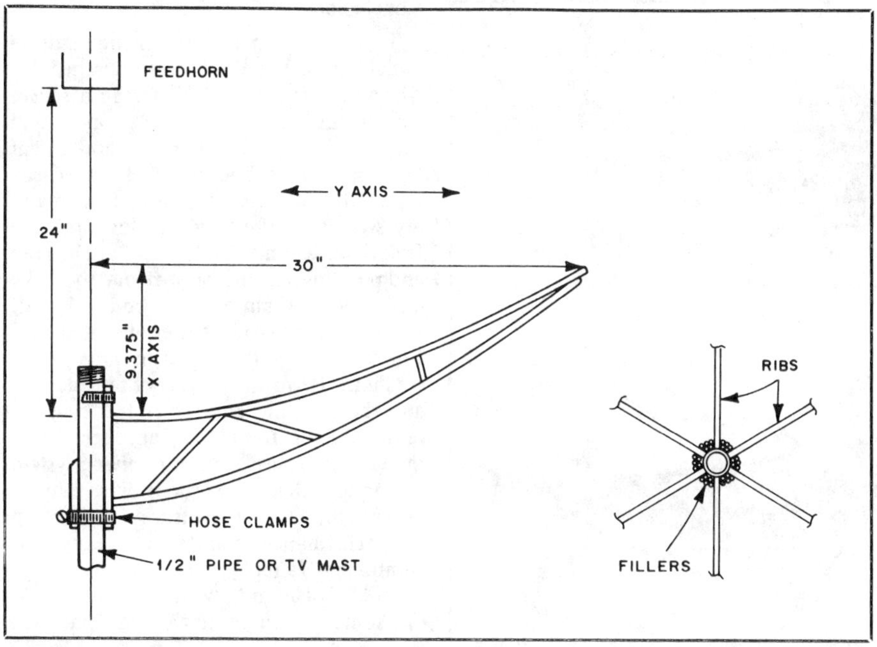

Fig 1—Rib construction details. Dimensions are as specified in Table 2.

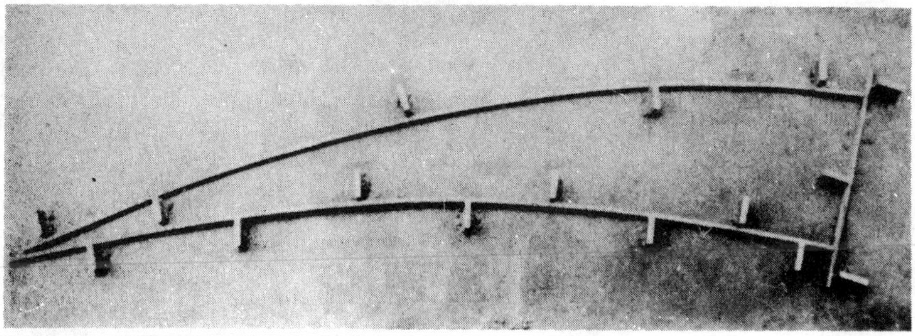

Fig 2—Rib assembly jig.

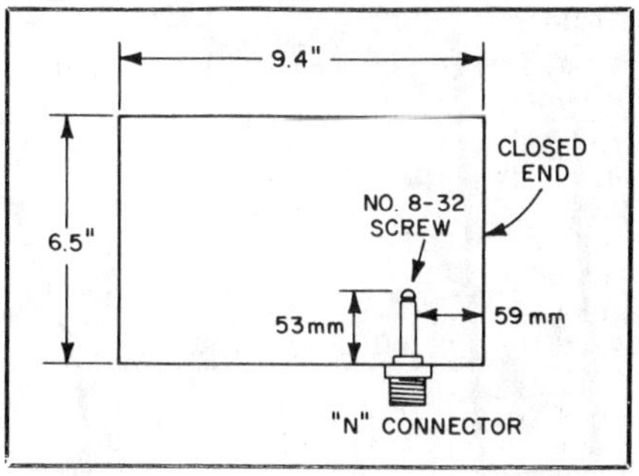

Fig 3—Feedhorn construction dimensions. See text for details.

rib accuracy is checked using a plywood curve gauge cut out on a bandsaw. Because of the 6-rib design, a sloppy fit results when the ribs are clamped to the hub piece. Insert additional 9-inch pieces of pencil rod as fillers to make a tighter fit when attaching the ribs to the ½-inch pipe hub. Place the ribs and pipe "face down" to space the ribs evenly. I used a joint of pencil rod, bent to a diameter of 5 feet around a tractor tire, and welded it to the outer tip of each rib before tightening the hose clamps. Alternatively, single pieces of rod may be cut to fit between the ribs at the edge of the dish to form the rim. The completed dish, with center pipe hub, weighs approximately 12 pounds. More ribs could be added, at the expense of additional weight.

Cut sectors of aluminum screen that are slightly larger than the rib spacing so that the sectors will overlap. Run a bead of Liquid Nail, or other glue, on the front side of two ribs and the included part of the external ring and press the screen sector in place. The glue dries fairly rapidly at room temperature. Run a strip of thin wood over the screen surface to tighten it and allow the glue to penetrate and hold the screen surface. By the time this operation is complete, the next sector can be applied in the same manner.

Feedhorn Construction

There is a plethora of tin-can feedhorn designs described in other articles. I prefer to steer away from using motor oil and coffee cans. They seem to work well enough, but require some modification, usually in the length, to perform optimally at the design frequency. In addition, they also have a tendency to disintegrate after a short stay in the elements, even when painted. The feedhorn used here was constructed to my specifications by Dick Dolenc, WB3CRF, using approximately 26-gauge galvanized steel capped and soldered at one end. It has only one seam running longitudinally along the feed axis. A piece of copper tubing, threaded to accommodate a no. 8-32 bolt for tuning, is soldered to an "N" connector (see Fig 3). The "N" connector is then soldered with a propane torch into a 5/8-inch hole, located as shown in Fig 3. Apply two coats of paint to the outside of the horn for protection.

I use a linear-polarized feed for several reasons. Most of the stations heard on Mode L are using linear polarization, and the downlink signals sound okay. Circular polarization complicates construction, especially when you're in a hurry. Feedhorns can be easily replaced, so we can try a switchable left- or right-hand circularly polarized feed at a later date. It might be worthwhile to mention that most feedhorn designs use a full guide wavelength in their construction. At the risk of drawing flack from the experts, I believe that the feed acts better if designed at half the guide wavelength, and it reduces the amount of tin in the construction and the weight by half. H. J. Griem, DJ1SL, reported experiments on a tubular horn for the 13-cm band.[1] He discovered that by using a full guide wavelength for the horn, a resonance lower in frequency exists outside the amateur band that corresponds to one-half of the guide length, which is, of course, one full guide wavelength at 13 cm. This effectively narrows the bandwidth of the 13-cm horn, making probe tuning more critical. By using half of the calculated guide length, the bandwidth is increased and probe tuning is less critical. Using this method, several successful feeds have been constructed for a variety of microwave frequencies. The design described here has an SWR of 1.15:1 at 1269.5 MHz, measured at the feedhorn.

The feedhorn is mounted on a small plywood saddle attached to a length of ¼-inch pipe by two small U clamps. The ¼-inch pipe is offset at the center of the dish with a ¾-inch, 90° elbow, a short nipple, another 90° elbow, another short nipple, and a reducer from ¾ to ½ inch (see Fig 4). I prefer a tripod method of mounting to this method because the ¼-inch pipe passes close to the mouth of the horn.

[1]H. J. Griem, DJ1SL, "Tubular Radiator for Parabolic Antennas on the 13-cm Band," *VHF Communications*, Apr 1976.

Fig 4—Completed dish assembly. Note the feedhorn mounting scheme.

Conclusion

The rib design is very strong. During initial testing, the dish took an unscheduled trip across the backyard during a severe windstorm. It suffered only one small deformation on the outer ring and a bent feedhorn mount, both of which were easily repaired. I surprised myself by listening to my signals on the Mode-L downlink the first time. Running only 12 W at the feed and pointing the dish approximately at the bird, I worked almost everybody I heard.

The antenna is now tower mounted, and I have increased the power to 40 W at the feedhorn. Performance is very satisfactory, and the pointing angles for tracking are reasonable. I found out another thing, though—you need a better receiving system on Mode L than on Mode B. This may be because the Mode-L transponder is not up to performance standards because of component failure.

Build a dish and try Mode L. It sure is lonesome up there now, but that will change! QST

A Profile of the UoSat-OSCAR 11 Satellite

By Jon Bloom, KE3Z
ARRL Senior Laboratory Engineer

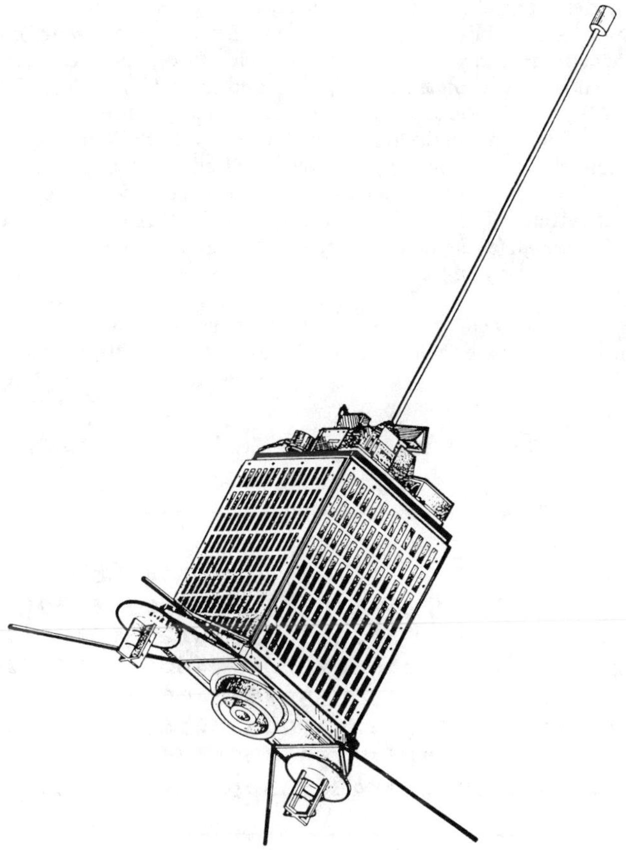

The spacecraft named "UoSat" were built by the UoSat Spacecraft Engineering Research Unit of the Department of Electronic and Electrical Engineering of the University of Surrey, England. At this writing, there are two active satellites in the UoSat series: UoSat-OSCAR 9 (UoSat 1) and UoSat-OSCAR 11 (UoSat 2). Each of these satellites was built in order to support scientific experimentation and space education and to engender a low-cost-satellite design and construction capability at Surrey. UoSat 1 is described in the ARRL publication, *The Satellite Experimenter's Handbook*.

UoSat 2: A Second-Generation Experiment

UoSat 2 was launched aboard a Delta rocket on March 1, 1984, from Vandenberg Air Force base in California. The polar, sun-synchronous orbit is nearly circular at an altitude of approximately 680 km (423 miles). UoSat 2 circles the earth approximately once every 99 minutes.

In addition to the spacecraft "housekeeping," such as the telemetry and attitude control systems, UoSat 2 contains a number of *experiments*. The Digital Communication Experiment (DCE) provides a mechanism for sending and receiving digital data. An NSC-800-based microcomputer aboard the satellite controls this experiment and includes 128 kbytes of memory. The DCE is configured as a "flying mailbox," allowing messages to be stored and retrieved by authorized ground stations.

The Space Dust Experiment, built by students at the University of Kent, England, detects impacts of dust particles on the experiment sensors and measures the momentum of the particles.

The Charge-Coupled-Device (CCD) Camera Experiment is a redesigned version of an experiment flown on UoSat 1. It produces a picture of 384 by 256 pixels, each of which can take on any of 128 brightness levels. The camera points toward the earth.

The Digital Store and Readout (DSR) Experiment stores the information from the CCD and space dust experiments along with data from the on-board computer and formats the data for transmission.

The UoSat 2 Ground Station

Like UoSat 1, UoSat 2 uses Amateur Radio primarily as a means to an end, rather than an end in itself. That is, the transmissions from UoSat-2 are performed within the amateur bands in keeping with the experimental nature of the satellite. The frequencies on which UoSat transmissions may be received are 145.825, 435.025 and 2401.5 MHz. The signals carry digital data transmitted using audio frequency-shift keying (AFSK) on a standard FM signal. (Note: the 435.025- and 2401.5-MHz signals can be phase-shift keyed as well.) When the satellite signals are strongest (on orbits when the satellite passes nearly overhead at the receiving station), the signals can be heard on a minimal receiver—a hand-held transceiver with a "rubber duck" antenna. For serious users, a circular polarized (left-hand circular polarization) directional antenna is recommended.

To make use of the signals from UoSat 2, two special-purpose devices are needed: a *demodulator* and a computer or terminal. The demodulator changes the AFSK tones from the receiver audio output into the signal needed by the computer or terminal. The UoSat 2 signals are sent using 1200- and 2400-Hz tones, with a 1200-Hz tone representing a binary 0 (space) and a 2400-Hz tone representing a 1 (mark). Each 7-bit character of the data is sent in a serial frame with one start bit, one parity bit and two stop bits, at 1200 bauds. This format is compatible with most terminals and computers. Suitable demodulators for UoSat 2 have been described in several publications (and earlier in this anthology).[1,2] (Note: UoSat 1 uses the same transmission format except the tones are reversed. Demodulators designed for UoSat 1 must have their outputs inverted for use with UoSat 2.)

UoSat 2 Data Formats

A typical UoSat 2 telemetry data *frame* is shown in Fig 1. The data is preceded by an ASCII RS ($1E_{16}$) character. The first line of the frame identifies the source as UoSat 2 and gives the date and time. The following lines give numeric values for each *channel* of the telemetry (typically, a channel is the readout value from a single sensor on the spacecraft). The first 60 channels (channels 0 through 59) are representations of analog measurements. These values may be converted to standard units by use of the conversion formulas given in Table 1. The final 10 channels (60 through 69) are in hexadecimal and are decoded bit by bit (see Table 2).

As an example of telemetry conversion, channel 00 in Fig 1 has a received telemetry value of 504. Substituting this value into the telemetry equation for channel 00 from Table 1 gives:

$$I = 1.9\ (516 - 504) = 22.8\ \text{mA}$$

UoSat 2 can also send data in other formats. *Whole Orbit Data* (WOD) are telemetry readings stored in the spacecraft during the orbit, when the spacecraft is out of view of a ground control station. Upon command from the ground station, the WOD can be sent in a specialized telemetry transmission. Computer status messages and data from the CCD experiment can also be transmitted.

The UoSat 2 DCE software, developed by Harold Price, NK6K, Jeff Ward, K8KA, and Larry Kayser, WA3ZIA/VE3, provide a message store-and-forward system. The intent of the system is that a few authorized stations act as *gateways* between terrestrial packet-radio networks and the satellite. This makes UoSat 2 an effective means of interconnecting distant packet networks for message traffic.

Periodically, the downlink transmission switches to the DCE, at which time frames are transmitted that tell a receiving station what messages are in the satellite, by addressee. A ground station can then establish communication with the satellite and read any messages that it can gateway to the local packet network.

UoSat 2 can also send computer-generated voice messages on the downlink via the Digitalker experiment. As this is being written, the Digitalker is being used to periodically send voice messages giving the progress of the Skitrek team across the Arctic.

For a detailed description of the UoSats, the *UoSat Spacecraft Data Booklet* can be obtained from:

UoSat Spacecraft Engineering Research Unit
Department of Electronic & Electrical Engineering
University of Surrey
Guilford, Surrey, GU2 5XH
ENGLAND

for GBP3.50 or $7.00, plus airmail postage (no US checks accepted).

Notes

[1]J. Miller, *Wireless World*, May 1983.

[2]R. Diersing, "Microcomputer Processing of UoSat-OSCAR 9 Telemetry, Aug 1984 *QST*, p 23.

```
UOSAT-2              8510270104138
00504101482F02672103349D04052305039F0602510705200804 7B09037D
```

Fig 1—A UoSat 2 Telemetry Data Frame. Each telemetry channel is sent as 5 characters followed by a checksum character. The first two characters are the channel number; the next three characters are the telemetry channel. For analog channels (00 through 59) these are decimal digits. For digital channels (60 through 69) the digits are hexadecimal. For example, the data for channels 00 and 61 appear above as: 005041 and 615BE7

Tuning OSCAR with Separate Radios

Tired of tuning your satellite uplink and downlink radios separately? This simple circuit—the OSCAR Tuner—can make operating through the birds easier and more fun for you.

By Paul Summers, KB3ML
122 E Bell Ave
Altoona, PA 16602

Satellite operation can be great fun! If you use separate VHF and UHF radios for Mode B satellite operation on OSCARs 10 and 13, you've probably wished for a way to tune both radios via a single tuning knob, not having to worry about maintaining the proper frequency offset. The simple interface circuit described here, dubbed the OSCAR Tuner, answers this problem. As a bonus, contesters can use this circuit to control two radios for VHF/UHF, or even MF/HF, to tune almost any two modern rigs together and cover two bands at once, suitably separating or mixing the audio outputs of the two rigs.

The Mode B transponders on AO-10 and AO-13 are *inverting,* meaning that an increase in downlink frequency corresponds to a decrease in uplink frequency.[1] The OSCAR Tuner tunes the uplink and downlink radios while maintaining the proper frequency relationship.

I don't like to modify my radios, so this circuit uses microphone up and down tuning inputs; no radio modifications are required. A block diagram (Fig 1) gives an overview of how the OSCAR Tuner fits into your satellite station and the sidebar describes circuit operation. You can use unmatched radios with this circuit: I use a TR-751A for the 145-MHz downlink and an older TR-9500 for the 435-MHz uplink. These rigs have different tuning-step sizes; the TR-751A tunes in 50-Hz steps and the TR-9500 tunes in 100-Hz steps. You can easily configure the OSCAR Tuner for such conditions, as I'll show. As shown in Fig 2, the circuit is set up for use with my Kenwood radios.

Construction

I chose CMOS logic for the OSCAR Tuner because CMOS consumes little power and is easy to work with. The circuit's total current requirement is less than 20 mA, and practically all of that is used by the rotary encoder. Because the circuit consumes so little power, the **POWER** switch shown in Fig 2 is optional. A fuse in an in-line holder (available from Radio Shack) protects the circuit.

Use any construction technique you feel comfortable with. I built this circuit using wire-wrap techniques to keep the board layout simple and easy to construct. I used a Radio Shack 276-168 PC board, which has two busses that can be used for +5 V and ground. I soldered wire-wrap sockets into the board to position their pins on either side of the supply busses.

I enclosed the circuit in a small plastic box from Radio Shack. Such a box is small enough that you can attach it to your operating table or a radio with a piece of Velcro or double-sided tape. Because this circuit's output uses the microphone inputs of the radios, you'll need plugs to match them and a jack that matches your microphone. Connect microphone-audio and PTT lines to the uplink radio via shielded cable.

Options

As stated earlier, I developed this circuit for my Kenwood radios. You can easily implement derivations of this circuit for other radios. If you'd like to do this, determine the synthesizer resolutions of the radios you're using. For example, if your radios tune in identical synthesizer increments (as do VHF and UHF radios of the same series from the major manufacturers), drive their tuning inputs from pins 11 of U3 and U4. Exception: If you use a Yaesu FT-290R II/ FT-790R II pair, drive them from pins 9 of U3 and U4 because of the relatively slow input recognition of those radios (discussed under "Operation"). (Pin 9 is the divide-by-eight output, which is half the rate of the divide-by-four output at pin 11 of U3/U4.) You can implement other tuning rates by using other outputs of U3 and U4. Division rates of 2, 4, 8, 16, 32, 64 and 128 are available.

You can use a rotary encoder other than the one specified in Fig 2, but the Clarostat

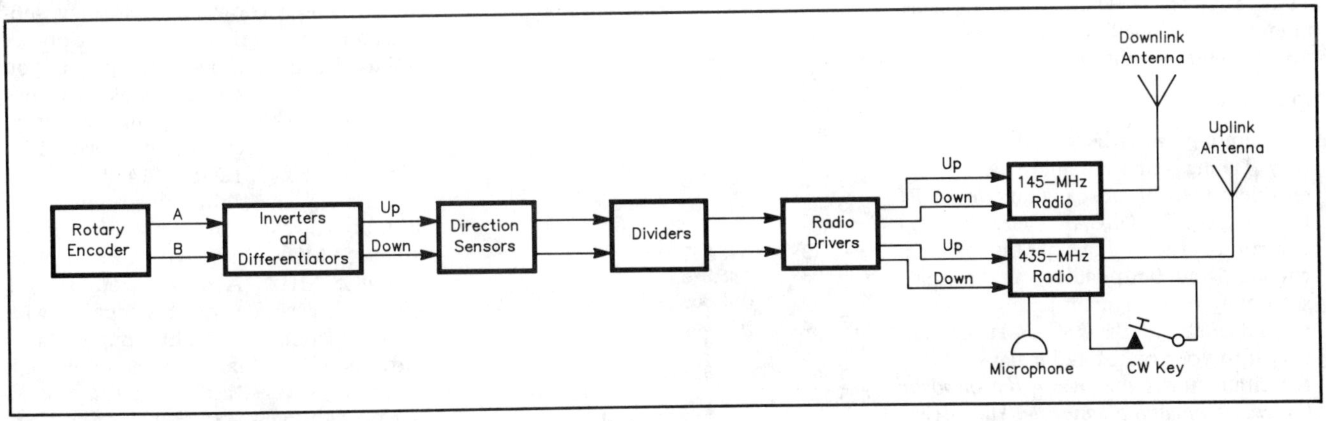

Fig 1—Block diagram of the OSCAR Tuner.

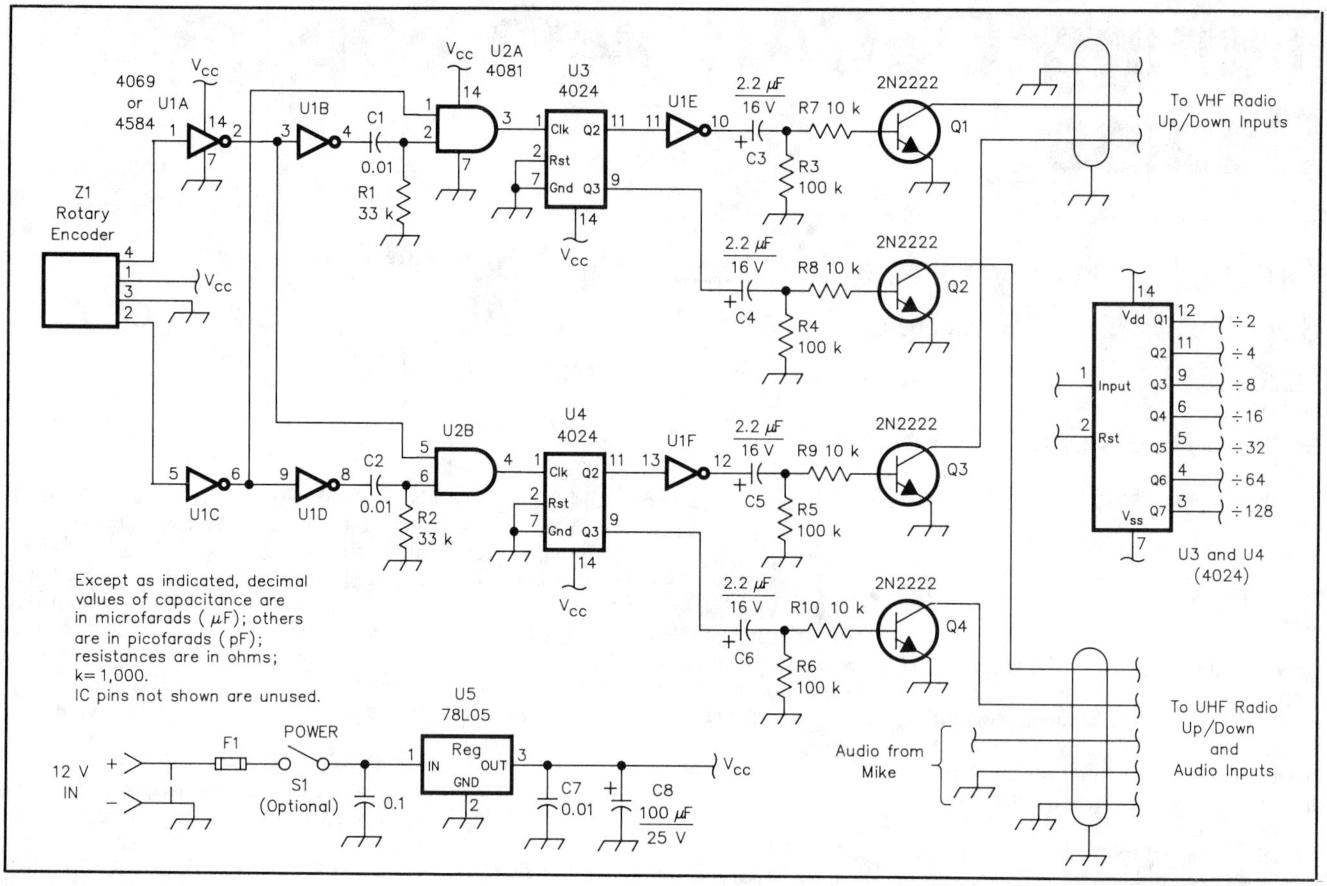

Fig 2—Most OSCAR Tuner parts can be purchased from Digi-Key Corp, including the Clarostat rotary encoder. Other parts, such as the PC board, IC sockets and connectors can be obtained from Radio Shack. (Radio Shack part numbers are given where appropriate in the parts list.)

Parts list

Z1—Rotary Encoder—Available from Digi-Key Corp, 701 Brooks Ave S, PO Box 677, Thief River Falls, MN 56701-0677, tel 800-344-4539. The PC-board version is Clarostat part no. 601-128-C24, Digi-Key part no. 601CVS-ND ($23.77). A cable-mount version is also available (Clarostat no. 600-128-CBL; Digi-Key no. 600CS-ND [$25.07]).

U1—4069 CMOS hex inverter or 4584 hex Schmitt trigger (see text).
U2—4081 CMOS quad AND gate.
U3, U4—4024 CMOS divider.
U5—7805 5-V regulator.
Q1-Q4—2N2222.
C1, C2, C7—0.001 µF, 35 V, disc ceramic.
C3-C6—2.2 µF, 35 V, tantalum electrolytic.
C8—100 µF, 35 V, aluminum electrolytic.
R1-R2—33 kΩ, ¼ W.
R3-R6—100 kΩ, ¼ W.
R7-R10—10 kΩ, ¼ W.
F1—0.5-A fuse (RS 270-1271).

Miscellaneous

Fuse holder (RS 270-1211).
Enclosure (RS 270-223).
Circuit board (RS 276-168).
Microphone connector.
Wire-wrap IC sockets.

model I use has clean output and appropriate rise time for this application. If you use an encoder that doesn't have a conditioned output, I recommend substituting a 4584 hex Schmitt trigger for the OSCAR Tuner's 4069 (U1); The 4584 has the same pinout as the 4069, but provides some needed signal conditioning.

Operation

Operating with the OSCAR Tuner is easy. Tuning is smooth, unlike the detented encoders used in most multimode VHF/UHF radios. The OSCAR Tuner gives you control of the radios via the external encoder, and both radios can be tuned separately by their main tuning knobs.

To operate with the OSCAR Tuner, connect it to your radios and make sure that the circuit tunes the rigs *in the opposite directions and at the same rate.* Then, select the correct uplink frequency by (1) reading frequencies from a published chart (such as Table 1); or (2) developing your own reference by adding the uplink and downlink frequencies used during operation, or from lists such as Table 1. Then, when you've chosen a downlink frequency, subtract it from the reference to get the proper uplink frequency.[2] For example, if you want your OSCAR 13 downlink frequency to be 145.915 MHz, the uplink frequency, as determined from Table 1, would be 435.483 MHz (581.398 − 145.915).

Table 1
OSCAR 13 Mode B Uplink and Downlink Frequencies

Uplink (MHz)	*Downlink (MHz)*
	145.985 (Engineering beacon)
435.423	145.975 (Upper passband limit)
435.433	145.965
435.443	145.955
435.453	145.945
435.463	145.935
435.473	145.925
435.483	145.915
435.493	145.905
435.503	145.895
435.513	145.885
435.523	145.875
435.533	145.865
435.543	145.855
435.553	145.845
435.563	145.835
435.573	145.825 (Lower passband limit)
	145.812 (General beacon)

Let's say that, after fine-tuning your uplink so that the downlink is at 145.915 MHz, the UHF radio shows 435.4838 MHz. (Assuming your radio's display is accurate, this discrepancy with the calculation is caused by Doppler shift.) Now, add the actual uplink and downlink frequencies to get a more accurate reference: 145.915 + 435.3988 = 581.3988. Any downlink frequency subtracted from

Circuit Description

A Clarostat optical rotary encoder serves as the heart of the OSCAR Tuner.† The encoder outputs two quadrature (90 degrees out of phase) square waves at a rate of 128 pulses per shaft revolution (see Fig A). Which signal leads the other in phase depends on which direction the shaft is rotated.

The encoder outputs are fed to U1, which inverts and differentiates the pulses to detect the leading edges of the square waves derived from turning the rotary-encoder shaft. The AND gates in U2 determine rotation direction. For clockwise rotation, C1 and R1 produce short pulses at the leading edge of the positive-going square-wave input at U1, pin 1. This pulse, fed to U2, pin 2, is phase-compared with the signal at U1, pin 6 (which, during clockwise rotation, is high when each pulse arrives at U2, pin 2). During counterclockwise rotation, U1, pin 6, is low when each pulse arrives at U2, pin 2. This output pulses at U2, pin 3, during clockwise shaft rotation. The same is true with U2, pin 4, during counterclockwise rotation. Inverters U1E and F provide proper output phase with my radios; they're not required with radios that use the same synthesizer resolutions.

†See the caption for Fig 2.

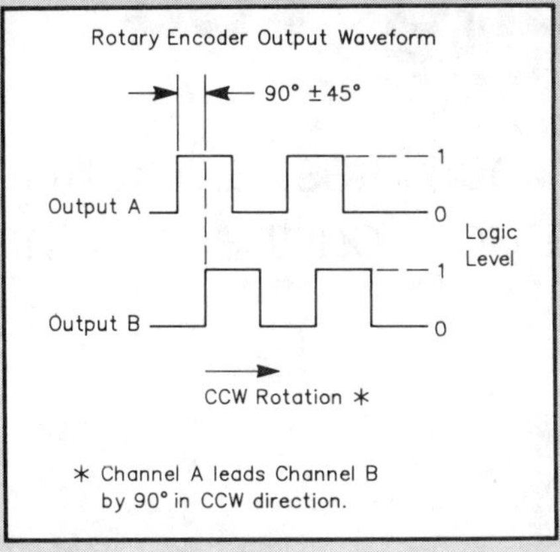

Fig A

The encoder provides 128 pulses per revolution, which is too fast for normal tuning. Dividing this signal (by four for the TR-751A and by eight for the TR-9500) gives a more comfortable tuning rate and provides the correct 2:1 drive ratio for my radios. The radios are kept together by taking the divide-by-4 output (U3 or U4, pin 11) or the divide-by-8 output (U3 or U4, pin 9) from the appropriate divider and directing these outputs to inverters U1E and U1F, and then to the radios.

Driver transistors Q1 through Q4 pull the up/down lines for each radio low at the appropriate times. The divider outputs are capacitively coupled to the driver transistors. Without the capacitors, the divider outputs would remain in the high state and the transistors would hold the output lines low. This would cause the radio(s) to start scanning as if you had held the up or down button.

In my OSCAR Tuner, Q1's output is directed to the VHF radio's up input, and that from Q2 goes to the UHF radio's down input during clockwise rotation. Q3's output is fed to the VHF radio's down input and Q4's output drives the UHF rig's up input during counterclockwise rotation. Connecting the radios in this manner causes the VHF radio to tune up with clockwise encoder rotation and down with counterclockwise rotation. Because the tuning connections to the UHF radio are reversed with respect to those to the VHF rig, the radios tune in opposite directions. To use the OSCAR Tuner with a noninverting transponder, add a toggle switch to swap the outputs of Q1 and Q3 *or* Q2 and Q4.—*KB3ML*

this reference gives the correct uplink frequency for the conditions at that time. If you now want your downlink to be 145.950 MHz, simply subtract 145.950 from 581.3988, which gives an uplink frequency of 435.4488 MHz. This method is more accurate and convenient than referring to a frequency chart, and you can keep a record of the reference for future use. Once you've reached the desired frequency by adjusting the radios, don't tune them manually except to correct for Doppler shift; tune with the OSCAR Tuner.

This circuit's only inherent limitation results from the speed at which the radios check their tuning inputs for activity. This limits maximum tuning speed. If you turn the OSCAR Tuner's knob too fast, creating pulses at the microphone input at a rate too high for the radio to follow, pulses can be lost. The logical low applied to the microphone input must be long enough for the CPU to recognize the request, but not so long that it causes the radio to start scanning (as some radios do if you press and hold the up or down button on the microphone). For example, my TR-751A scans its tuning inputs much faster than the TR-9500 does, so the TR-9500 limits the system's maximum tuning speed. This isn't much of a problem for me, as the TR-751A has to step twice as fast as the TR-9500 for the same tuning rate (the TR-751A's 50-Hz synthesizer steps are half those of the TR-9500, as mentioned earlier). As long as you don't get carried away and try to zip from one end of the passband to the other, the OSCAR Tuner should have no trouble keeping uplink and downlink frequencies together as you tune the rigs. Even if the rigs get out of sync, you can retune one of the radios to bring them back together.

I have also used the Yaesu FT-290R II and its twin, the FT-790R II, with the OSCAR Tuner. I found that the Yaesu microphone-jack tuning inputs respond more slowly than those of the Kenwood radios, as mentioned earlier. The Yaesu synthesizers have selectable tuning rates of 25, 100, and 2500 Hz. I recommend using their 100-Hz steps. With their slower input recognition, these radios tune at a reasonable rate when set for 100-Hz tuning steps.

I have not used other radios with this circuit, so I can't make specific recommendations regarding such applications. The small synthesizer resolutions of some radios may require too many input steps to give a reasonable tuning speed from the microphone-jack tuning inputs. If you want to use such a rig with the OSCAR Tuner, you may have to modify it.

For simplicity and smoothness, there's no better way to increase your OSCAR-operating pleasure than to build and use the OSCAR Tuner. With it, I spend less time tuning and more time *talking!* See you on the air?

Notes

[1]For more information on satellite operation, see M. Davidoff, *The Satellite Experimenter's Handbook*, second edition (Newington: ARRL, 1990).

[2]See note 1.

Paul Summers is a Senior Communications Technician at the Pennsylvania Electric Company. He has been a ham since 1980 and holds an Extra Class license and a General radiotelephone license. His primary operating interests are HF CW, SSB and CW satellite operation, and packet radio.

Microsats and You

Got the urge to try out our latest amateur satellites? Here's a look at what it takes to get "on the air" through the new Microsats.

By Doug Loughmiller, KO5I
President, AMSAT-NA
PO Box 27
Washington, DC 20044

Amazing, simply amazing! These were my initial thoughts as I copied signals from the Microsats for the very first time, shortly after their launch in January of this year. As the satellites filed past my Texas QTH, I admired the strong downlink signals of all of the new birds and marveled at how easy they were to copy. Being an old hand at the OSCAR game, you'd think that I would be past the stage of experiencing the thrill and excitement of tracking an OSCAR—but it wasn't so!

What's the big deal, you ask? You might point out (and rightly so) that amateurs have been tracking their own satellites for nearly three decades now, and hearing an amateur satellite signal from space is hardly an unusual event. Besides, these new birds are running a whopping 4 watts—they're supposed to be loud. Well, all of that may be true, but the source of my excitement stemmed not only from the performance of the spacecraft orbiting 800 kilometers overhead, but more from the simplistic ground station I was using to track them. My station consisted of an omnidirectional antenna on the balcony of my second-story apartment (surrounded by trees in all directions), feeding an old 70-cm (437 MHz) multimode transceiver into a PSK modem, a TNC and a computer, which was used to process the data on the downlink signal. That's hardly a textbook ground station, but it worked quite well. A diagram of my simple Microsat station appears in Fig 1.

After years of paying painstaking attention to detail while tracking OSCARs with gain arrays and low-noise, high-gain receiving setups, it was almost mesmerizing to watch the telemetry flow across the screen using this simple arrangement. Carlos Huertas, LU4ANQ, President of AMSAT Argentina, phoned me after the first few orbits to tell me that he was copying the LUSAT CW beacon on 437.125 MHz with a hand-held from his hotel room in Atlanta, where he was staying while in the US on business. And as countless radio amateurs can now attest, the strong 2-meter downlink of the DOVE spacecraft is "easy copy" with the simplest of 2-meter FM equipment.

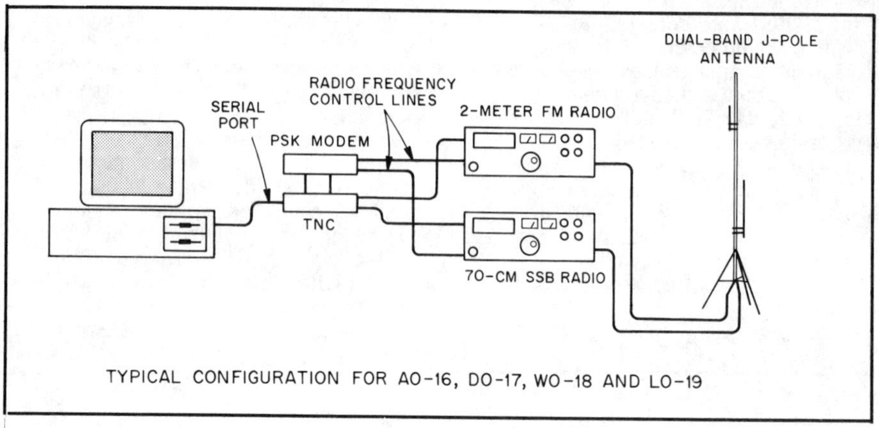

Fig 1—A typical Microsat ground station.

Even after having been active since the days of OSCAR 6 and seeing the advances made in this facet of our hobby, I never grew immune to the excitement of making amateur satellite communications easier and more enjoyable for everyone. As you are about to see, it's easy to join in the excitement! In this month's installment of our on-going series of articles about amateur radio's newest "flock of birds," we'll depart from our review of the individual Microsats[1,2,3] and turn our attention to information of use to those who want to assemble a Microsat ground station.

Background

The Microsats are the first OSCARs dedicated exclusively to digital store-and-forward communications by radio amateurs[4,5]—a relatively new concept. Although joining the packet radio revolution and OSCAR technology had been discussed since the early '80s, full-blown PACSATs took some time to reach fruition.[6,7]

The first "proof-of-concept" experiment was flown aboard UoSAT-OSCAR-11 and is known as the DCE (Digital Communication Experiment). This DCE was designed to show the feasibility of such a system while supporting only a small user base scattered around the globe. UOSAT-11 was launched in March of 1984, and since then, the DCE has supported limited operations from stations on virtually every continent and remains active. The results of this experiment have shown the effectiveness of satellite-based store-and-forward communications systems in low Earth orbit in providing global communications and has served as the basis for further experimentation.[8]

The first system intended for a broad-based user group was incorporated into the first Japanese amateur satellite known as FUJI-OSCAR-12. This satellite housed two separate systems, the first being a linear transponder similar to the those used in Phase II OSCARs. This transponder was configured for a 2-meter uplink and a 70-cm downlink (Mode J) and became known as Mode JA (analog).

The second system, known as Mode JD (digital), used four 2-meter FM uplink channels and one 70-cm SSB downlink channel. It used Manchestered FSK at 1200 bit/s on the uplink and PSK at 1200 bit/s on the downlink.[9,10,11]

Unfortunately, this satellite never

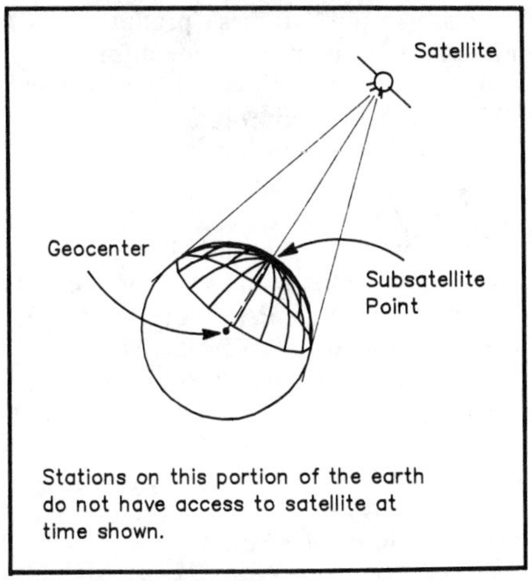

Fig 2—Stations working through conventional "transponder" satellites must be able to "see" the satellite simultaneously. The diagram shows the satellite's "footprint" or "window."

achieved its fullest potential because it suffered from a negative power budget. At best, its operations were sporadic. Its limited operation did, however, serve as a proving ground for the communications standard it employed.

The design of FO-12's digital circuitry was quite sound, so when data standards for the Microsats were being selected by the AMSAT design team, the FO-12 standard was adopted. By using the same standard, countless radio amateurs around the world would already be equipped to communicate through the new satellites.

About Digital Store and Forward

The use of a digital store-and-forward satellite is somewhat different than that of a satellite using a communications medium such as a linear transponder.

As shown in Fig 2, for two ground stations to be able to communicate with each other using a satellite that employs a linear transponder, they must both have access to the satellite at the same time (in other words, share a common window). As you might expect, the communications capability of the given satellite is limited by its footprint, which is determined by the height of the satellite above the surface of the Earth.[12]

Fig 3 shows the concept of digital store-and-forward communications. When the satellite passes within view of a particular ground station, that station can place data (a message) into the memory of the on-board computer destined for a station at any point on the globe, regardless of whether the two stations share a common window of visibility. As the satellite passes within view of the "destination" station, that station can simply connect to the satellite and retrieve the message. In this way, global communications can be supported with the use of satellites in low Earth orbit.

Putting a Station Together

Now that we've got some basic concepts out of the way, let's take a look at the specific requirements of a Microsat ground station.

In the simplest terms, as with any Amateur Radio operation, for satellite communications to take place, two processes must occur: reception and transmission. In this case, the reception and transmission will be between a ground station and a given satellite and will involve digital information.

The first issue to be dealt with is satellite tracking. Because the Microsats are in low Earth orbit (LEO), circling the globe roughly 14 times a day, we must have a means of determining when the spacecraft will be in view at our location. The simplest way to track the Microsats is with a personal computer and satellite-tracking software. AMSAT has developed a number of tracking programs for a wide variety of personal computers. For more information, write to AMSAT Headquarters and ask for the current software catalog.[13]

Once we've found a way to track the satellites, let's turn our attention to the individual components of our Microsat ground station.

As we can see in Fig 1, the basic Microsat ground station comprises six items: an omnidirectional dual-band antenna, a 2-meter FM transceiver, a 70-cm SSB receiver, a standard TNC, a PSK modem and a personal computer with the appropriate communications software. For those who already possess an OSCAR-13 satellite station, the only needed additions are the TNC, PSK modem and PC. The need

Table 1

Microsat Frequency Guide

ID	*Name*	*Primary Downlink*	*Secondary Downlinks*	*Uplinks[A]*
AO-16	PACSAT	437.025 PSK	437.050 PSK	145.900, .920, .940, .960
DO-17	DOVE	145.825 AFSK	------------------	NONE
WO-18	WEBERSAT	437.075 PSK	437.100 PSK	145.900
LO-19	LUSAT	437.150 PSK	437.125 PSK	145.900, .880, .860, .840

Notes:
(A) All uplinks require 1200-Hz Manchester-encoded binary modulation of an FM transmitter. This results in a 1200 bit/s Manchester-encoded FSK signal.
(B) All downlinks except DO-17 require an SSB receiver; DO-17 requires an FM receiver.
(C) DO-17 can transmit voice or AFSK data.

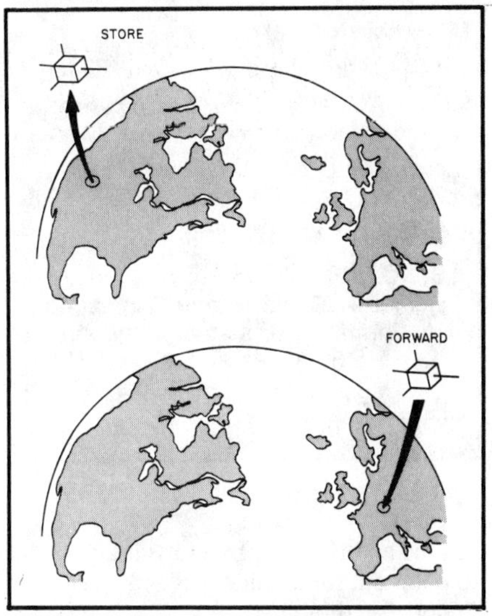

Fig 3—With store-and-forward satellites, stations do not have to have a "mutual window"—they must simply be able to see the satellite on successive orbits.

for precision tracking will be greater with this arrangement, however, as you must point your OSCAR 13 gain array at the satellite.

Each of the Microsats makes unique use of its digital store-and-forward capabilities. Because of this, the exact ground station requirements for each differ slightly. The chart in Table 1 outlines the operation of each Microsat.

Referring to Fig 1, we find that the basic Microsat ground station shown can be used for each of the individual applications involved.

For instance, in the case of DOVE, the Digital Orbiting Voice Encoder, the omnidirectional antenna, 2-meter FM receiver and TNC would be used to collect packet data from this satellite, while only the omnidirectional antenna and the 2-meter receiver would be needed when the satellite is transmitting digitized voice.

For WEBERSAT, to extract data from the on-board experiments, the ground station requires only the omnidirectional antenna, the 70-cm SSB receiver, the TNC, the PSK modem and the computer. To receive CCD images from WEBERSAT, additional software known as *Weberware* is needed.

To send messages using the store-and-forward capability of AO-16 or LO-19, the complete station—the omnidirectional dual-band antenna, 2-meter FM transmitter, 70-cm SSB receiver, the TNC, the PSK modem and the computer—is needed.

Power and Antenna Choices

An in-depth discussion of the power needed to connect to the PACSATs is intentionally avoided here. A discussion of this type is always fraught with variables that must be considered on a case-by-case basis. Rather than try to offer link calcu-

Glossary of Terms

AFSK—Audio Frequency-Shift Keying.

Bit/s—Abbreviation for *bits per second*, a measure of the speed at which information is transferred. A *bit* is a binary digit.

Low Earth Orbit—A satellite's path that remains at a relatively low altitude, typically less than a couple of thousand kilometers. Abbreviated *LEO*.

Manchestered FSK—Biphase-L Frequency-Shift Keying.

PSK—Phase-shift keying.

Telemetry—Radio signals originating at a satellite that convey information on the performance or status of onboard subsystems. Also refers to the information itself. Sometimes abbreviated *TLM*.

TNC—Terminal Node Controller, a device that assembles and disassembles packets (frames).

lations and the like, I feel it's much better to point out some guidelines and offer some "food for thought."

In an ideal setting (if you were the only one trying to use the satellite), you would find that relatively low power could be used to connect with the satellite. One of the command stations has reported getting packets into the system with 25 watts of output power and a modest antenna setup. As we all know, however, you (or I) won't be the only ones trying to access the satellite at any given time, so competition with other stations will have to be considered.

Keep in mind that uplink signals are being transmitted on FM. Because of FM's capture effect, the strongest signal at the receiver will override all of the competition. Thankfully, there are four uplink channels for the traffic to spread out across.

Another hotly debated topic in the Microsat operations arena is efficient omnidirectional antennas. The debate is centered around two very basic designs: the turnstile and the J-pole.[14]

The turnstile has long been thought to be the antenna of choice for use by satellite operators who want to work through LEO satellites using simple omnidirectional antennas. Recent evaluation of the subject has, however, led many to believe that a better choice might be the J-pole antenna, because of its lobes at 30° or less—the part of the sky that a LEO bird occupies most of the time it's above the horizon.[15] Although the jury is still out, both antennas are being used successfully and I don't hesitate to encourage the use of either one.

Why PSK?

The downlink signals of all of the Microsats (with the exception of DOVE) use PSK modulation. With the countless number of AFSK TNCs, you might question the decision to use PSK, necessitating the addition of a dedicated modem in the satellite ground station. (The use of PSK signals for store-and-forward communications dates back to the design of FO-12.[16])

One of the fundamental reasons for PSK is that it offers at least a 16-dB performance increase over AFSK. The net result is that data can be successfully extracted from a PSK signal that is 16 dB further down in the noise than an AFSK signal—an attractive feature when you're experiencing fading on a downlink signal.

Another fundamental reason for using PSK is that it requires less power to generate a PSK signal than it does to generate a comparable AFSK signal aboard the spacecraft. The efficient use of power is always of paramount concern to satellite builders. Because of these reasons—and AMSAT's desire to work with an already-existing user base—the decision was made to adhere to the Japanese Mode-JD standard. FO-20, a follow up mission to FO-12, which uses an identical PSK modulation scheme, was launched in early February of this year. It rounds out the complement of digital store-and-forward packet satellites available for use today by the world's radio amateurs.

Sources for Specialized Modems

While most of the equipment needed to set up a Microsat ground station is readily available, one item that is essential but not as easily found is a PSK modem. There are three sources for this item as of this writing, with additional sources sure to follow. The first two sources provide the modems in kit or partial-kit forms. They are: TAPR, The Tucson Packet Radio Corporation[17,18] and AMSAT-UK.[19] The third source, PacComm,[20] produces a wired and tested PSK modem known as the PSK-1. This modem, while primarily designed for use with the Microsats and Fuji satellites, incorporates a 400 bit/s demodulator for decoding AO-13 telemetry as well.

The author and *QST* in no way warrant or endorse any of these products. This material is being offered for information only, as an aid to those who are having difficulty finding appropriate components to assemble their ground stations.

Next Time

The next article in our Microsat series takes a look at the final two "stars" of the Microsat cast, the PACSATs: AMSAT-OSCAR-16 and LUSAT-OSCAR-19.

Well, there you have it! Putting together a Microsat ground station is an easy and rewarding experience. I hope to be exchanging packet messages with you via AO-16, LO-19 or FO-20 soon. Good luck and see you on the birds!

Notes

1 Doug Loughmiller, KO5I, "Successful OSCAR Launch Ushers in the '90s," *QST*, Apr 1990, p 52.

2 Doug Loughmiller, KO5I, "DOVE: The Digital Orbiting Voice Encoder," *QST*, May 1990, p 40.

3 Doug Loughmiller, KO5I, "WEBERSAT-OSCAR-18: Amateur Radio's Newest Eye in the Sky," *QST*, Jun 1990, p 50.

4 Doug Loughmiller, KO5I, and Bob McGwier, N4HY, "Microsat: The Next Generation of OSCAR Satellites—*Part 1*," *QST*, May 1989, p 37.

5 Doug Loughmiller, KO5I, and Bob McGwier, N4HY, "Microsat: The Next Generation of OSCAR Satellites—*Part 2*," *QST*, Jun 1989, p 53.

6 Tom Clark, W3IWI, "AMSAT's Microsat/Pacsat Program," *Proceedings of the AMSAT-NA 6th Space Symposium* and Annual Meeting, Nov 1988, p 4.

7 Tom Clark, W3IWI, Courtney Duncan, N5BF, Bob McGwier, N4HY, Jan King, W3GEY, "The First Flock of Microsats," *AMSAT Journal*, May 1989, p 3.

8 University of Surrey, *UOSAT Spacecraft Data Booklet*, Jun 1987.

9 JARL, *JAS-1 Satellite Handbook*.

10 Fujio Yamashita, JS1UKR, "A PSK Demodulator for the JAS-1 Satellite," *QEX*, Aug 1986, p 3.

11 Tom Clark, W3IWI, "FO-12 Modems," *Proceedings of the 4th Annual AMSAT Space Symposium*, Nov 1986, p 8.

12 Marty Davidoff, K2UBC, *Satellite Experimenters Handbook*, Chapter 9, (ARRL: Newington, 1985).

13 AMSAT Software, PO Box 27, Washington, DC 20044

14 Dick Jansson, WD4FAB, "Antennas for Microsat Ground Stations," *AMSAT Journal*, Mar 1990, p 11.

15 Courtney Duncan, N5BF, "A Method of Evaluating Antennas For a Low Earth Orbit Mission," *AMSAT-NA Technical Journal*, Winter 1987-88, p 36.

16 Courtney Duncan, N5BF, "Toward the Future in the Amateur Satellite Program," "Next Steps in the Ground" segment, *Proceedings of the AMSAT-NA 6th Space Symposium* and *Annual Meeting*, Nov 1988, p 15.

17 Lyle Johnson, WA7GXD, "TAPR PSK Modem," *QEX*, Sep 1987, p 3.

18 TAPR PSK Modem, TAPR, The Tucson Amateur Packet Radio Corporation, PO Box 12925, Tucson, AZ, 85732.

19 G3RUH PSK Modems, AMSAT-UK, 94 Herongate Road, Wanstead Park, London, E12 5EQ, England.

20 PSK-1, PacComm, 3652 West Cypress St, Tampa, Florida 33607.

Microsat: The Next Generation of OSCAR Satellites—*Part 1*

Did you know that it is not only possible, but probable that OSCAR satellite enthusiasts will be tracking OSCAR 20 by the end of this year?

By Doug Loughmiller, KO5I, and Bob McGwier, N4HY

President, AMSAT-NA
620 Fairway Drive
Paris, TX 75460

Assistant VP Engineering, AMSAT-NA
15 Cherrybrook Lane
East Windsor, NJ 08520

There are currently no fewer than seven different OSCAR satellites under development worldwide for launch during 1989. Among these satellites are four payloads that AMSAT-NA[1] plans to launch into low-earth orbit (LEO) on a single launch vehicle. These super-small satellites represent the first in a series of a new generation of OSCARs. Dubbed Microsats because of their small size (yet powerful capabilities), these spacecraft are 10-kg cubes, approximately 230 mm on a side. An exploded view of a Microsat is shown in Fig 1. Microsats are the most technologically advanced OSCARs to date. While these satellites will serve a number of purposes, the primary goal of the project is to implement a digital store-and-forward message handling packet-radio satellite system available worldwide. This article will provide you with various mission profiles, technical details of the individual satellites and information you will need to operate through the new Microsats.

Mission Background

This year, 1989, marks AMSAT's 20th anniversary. Since its inception in 1969, AMSAT has led the international amateur satellite community into the future with the development of small, low-cost and innovative amateur satellites. The evolution of these spacecraft has been dependent upon a number of factors:

- the advancing technology of small, efficient electronic components;
- the application of that technology within the realm of Amateur Radio;
- and the ability of our volunteer engineering staff to successfully envision future uses of leading-edge satellite technology, and to complement the Amateur Radio service as a whole, particularly in the areas of public service and educational activities.

The Microsat project is an example of how all these factors work together in defining the objectives of an OSCAR satellite mission.

Since the early days of TAPR,[2] while the TNC 1 was still on the drawing board, and before TAPR fomented the "packet revolution," some AMSAT and TAPR members were dreaming of building a satellite dedicated to packet radio.[3] Tom

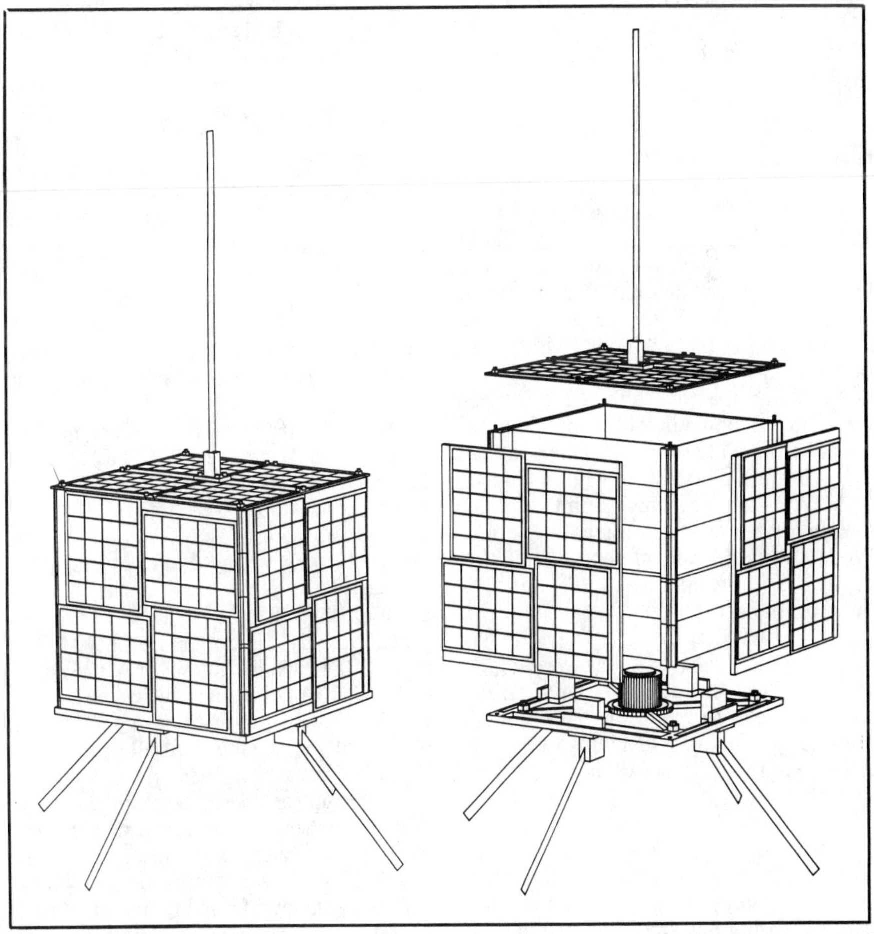

Fig 1—Two views of a Microsat. The drawing at A shows the satellite with the covers on; B is an exploded view. Note the exterior solar panels and the five "trays" or internal modules that contain the satellite's circuitry and make it structurally sound. *(drawings courtesy WD4FAB)*

Clark, W3IWI, and Den Connors, KD2S, former president of AMSAT and the first president of TAPR, respectively, started a project to build such a satellite. Volunteers in Technical Assistance (VITA), under the direction of Gary Garriott WA9FMQ, formed a working relationship with AMSAT to make this dream a reality. One of the earliest tasks VITA took on was to build a digital communications experiment (DCE) payload that was to fly as part of UOSAT-2, the follow-up mission for the University of Surrey's UOSAT-OSCAR 9 satellite. UOSAT-2 became UOSAT-OSCAR 11 after its successful launch on March 1, 1984. The DCE has been fully commissioned for some time now, and it boasts users from Antarctica, Australia, England, South Africa, the United States, and most recently, the Soviet Union. This experiment serves as proof of the efficacy of LEOs for packet-radio store-and-forward messaging service. The partnership between VITA and UOSAT has continued as two additional packet-radio satellites are now under construction at the University of Surrey. UOSATs D and E will be launched with the Microsats. This brings to six the total number of amateur satellites to ride into orbit on one launch vehicle.

Meanwhile, following the successful launch of UOSAT-OSCAR 11, JAMSAT (AMSAT-NA's sister organization in Japan) decided their first internal satellite project would contain both a packet-radio store-and-forward mode based on the concept being considered for our packet-radio satellite (PACSAT), as well as an analog linear transponder. This satellite, Fuji-OSCAR 12, was launched August 12, 1986, and is still operational.[4,5] Its digital mode, Mode JD, has four uplink channels in the 2-meter satellite subband and a single downlink channel in 70-cm satellite subband. The analog mode, Mode JA, operates with an uplink passband for SSB and CW transmissions in the 2-meter satellite subband, and a downlink passband in the 70-cm satellite subband. This configuration is much like the Mode J transponder JAMSAT built for inclusion on OSCAR-8 (which is no longer operational). FO-12's Mode JD uses Manchester-encoded FSK at 1200 bit/s on the uplink and BPSK at 1200 bit/s on the downlink.

From its earliest days, this satellite has been plagued by a negative power budget. (The satellite uses power faster than the solar cells can recharge the batteries.) A number of factors, including an overestimate of the efficiency of the solar arrays that power the spacecraft, an overestimate of the capacity of the batteries on board, as well as the slow deterioration of the solar panels because of continuous exposure to the harsh environment of space, have contributed to the power budget problem.

After 2½ years of service, what began as an annoying problem has become a serious one. Because of these difficulties, FO-12, produced with major funding from the Japanese Amateur Radio League (JARL), has had difficulty meeting its vast potential. Nevertheless, FO-12 has a large worldwide user base and has prompted the construction of equipment necessary to operate through it. This equipment is available in North America primarily from TAPR.[6] In Europe, a modem by G3RUH is available from AMSAT-UK.[7]

Microsat is Born

The design of FO-12's digital communication circuitry is sound. The satellite's user base is a group that AMSAT engineers decided to support rather than abandon. In November 1987, at the AMSAT-NA annual meeting and space symposium in Detroit, Michigan,[8] a late-night session took place involving Jan King, W3GEY, perennial leader of AMSAT-NA satellite projects, Tom Clark, W3IWI, Bob McGwier, N4HY, and Phil Karn, KA9Q. It was one of those magic moments that make this facet of our hobby so exciting. Jan King and Gordon Hardman, KE3D, had thought a bit about how to make a very small satellite. It was Jan's opinion that solar array efficiencies were now approaching the level where tiny satellites, with high-power transmitters, could be built with a positive power budget. At that time, he said he believed a good mechanical structure could be built out of trays, where individual modules would form the structure of the spacecraft. By 4 AM, the bleary-eyed group had picked a model for the computer, calculated power budgets, and chosen transmitter power levels based on these preliminary calculations. Indeed, the group had estimated the size, mass, and total power budget for each of the modules. Sleep had been pushed aside by a rush of excitement; we were on to something that would change the amateur satellite program for a long time to come.

Our early excitement paid off. A meeting was held in December 1987 at AMSAT headquarters. Participating in this meeting were representatives from TAPR, SANDPAC[9] and AMSAT-NA. Our early excitement was enhanced at this meeting by a nearly complete mechanical design, accomplished using wonderful new computer tools by the deft hand of AMSAT stalwart Dick Jansson, WD4FAB. A large collection of first-rate design drawings enabled those gathered to get a good visual picture of the satellite and allowed many critical construction decisions to be made.

The group considered carefully the question of whether we should try a new (better) modulation standard on these satellites. Thinking that we would be launching within a year, and knowing the effort that would go into such a design (getting together equipment for ground stations), the decision was made to use the currently existing digital mode adopted by the Japanese for FO-12. This guaranteed a built-in user base at the time the satellite was to be launched. Further, we decided to again place these satellites in Mode JD, with 2-meter channels up and 70-cm channels down.

Little did we know, we were on to something greater than originally imagined. During early 1988, Vern "Rip" Riportella, WA2LQQ, then president of AMSAT, was busy talking to several groups about getting involved in the Microsat project. Junior de Castro, PY2BJO, president of BRAMSAT (AMSAT Brazil), had wanted to loft a package on a satellite for many years. It was his dream to build and orbit the ultimate educational tool for young children to learn more about space science. Educational tools in the amateur satellite service are nothing new. UOSAT-OSCARs 9 and 11 are examples of such educational satellites. They have been good tools for educational purposes, but de Castro wanted to target children younger than those being addressed by existing satellites. PY2BJO also wanted to be able to support this spacecraft's operation with inexpensive ground station equipment. The Microsat project was perfect for his needs, and AMSAT-NA possessed the technical expertise to make his dream a reality. BRAMSAT's project is called DOVE.

Rip had also been trying to interest Arturo Caru, LU1AHC, in a project for some time. AMSAT-LU, under the leadership of Carlos Huertas, LU4ENQ, had begun discussing an inexpensive packet digital repeater for orbit. Upon hearing a description of the Microsat project from Rip, Arturo and Carlos came to the Dayton HamVention® in 1988 for technical talks with W3GEY, W3IWI and N4HY. They left Dayton with two dozen PSK modems from TAPR and a firm conviction to join us in producing a duplicate of our Mode JD satellite, now known as LUSAT. It will be functionally nearly identical to PACSAT. There are interns from AMSAT-LU working with us in Boulder, Colorado. Hams in Argentina are getting ready for operation of the spacecraft, and technical visits to the Boulder facility are common.

Weber State College in Ogden, Utah has, for some time, been interested in small spacecraft. They constructed NUSAT-I. It was launched from the space shuttle Challenger on April 29, 1985. NUSAT-I is the first satellite launched from a Get-Away-Special canister aboard a shuttle vehicle. AMSAT and Weber State had begun discussing ways in which they could help us with our long-term goal of launching a geosynchronous satellite, which we call Phase IV. Upon learning about the Microsat project, they knew this was a project for them. Weber State's Center for Aerospace Technology (CAST) took the project to heart and is participating in the construction of a Microsat of its own.

What is a Microsat?

Before we describe each mission in detail, let us consider the features all four satellites on this launch have in common. The Microsat spacecraft bus structure is composed of five aluminum modules, or trays, framed into a stack. This stack is almost cubical, measuring 230 × 230 × 213 mm. WD4FAB, W3GEY and Jeff Zerr are primarily responsible for the mechanical design. This structure has been flight qualified for any of the world's currently available launchers. Fig 2 gives you an idea of just how small the new Microsats really are.

Smaller is Better

One of the things happening in electronics today is making the old axiom, "the nicest things come in small packages" truer than ever. W3IWI has taken particular advantage of this in two major subsystems in the Microsat design. The core of all the satellites' receivers is the Motorola MC3362 single-chip FM receiver operating at a 10.7 MHz IF. It follows a high-quality 15-kHz IF filter. Following the MC3362's FM discriminator are two sets of filters, each made of one section of TL274 op amp. These 2-pole Butterworth filters are optimized for 1200- and 4800-bit/s data transmission. Early in the design, we decided to allow for a speed increase (after the initial run at 1200 bit/s using currently existing equipment). The satellites (with the exception of DOVE) can operate receivers and transmitters at data rates of up to 4800 bit/s, and all are independently controllable. This part of the receiver was designed by W3IWI, with help from Eric Gustafson, N7CL. In the front end, we have a GaAsFET with large gates to withstand the rigors of space, and a dual-gate MOSFET mixer with a local oscillator (LO) of 100 MHz. The output of the mixer (40-50 MHz) drives five emitter followers to provide good channel isolation between the five FM IF stages. Jim Vogler, WA7CJO, and W3IWI designed this part of the receiver. The entire five-channel receiver draws only 180 mA.

Motorola makes another useful chip, the MC14469F addressable asynchronous receiver/transmitter (AART). Veterans of amateur satellite construction complain the most about one job—wiring harnesses. Determined to circumvent the wiring harness chore in this spacecraft, we are making use of many of the AART's features. It has increased the number of possible telemetry points, giving us more command over individual aspects of this spacecraft than we have ever had, yet it operates on only five wires! The on-board computer controls the modules and gathers telemetry by talking to the AART on each module. The telemetry values are selected by sending a command to the appropriate AART and telling it to place the correct signal on the analog signal wire. The CPU module samples the telemetry value through an A/D converter. Commands are sent in a similar fashion. This module, designed by W3IWI and Bob Stricklin, N5BRG, has greatly reduced the complexity of the wiring harnesses and allows the use of standard software modules to command the AARTs.

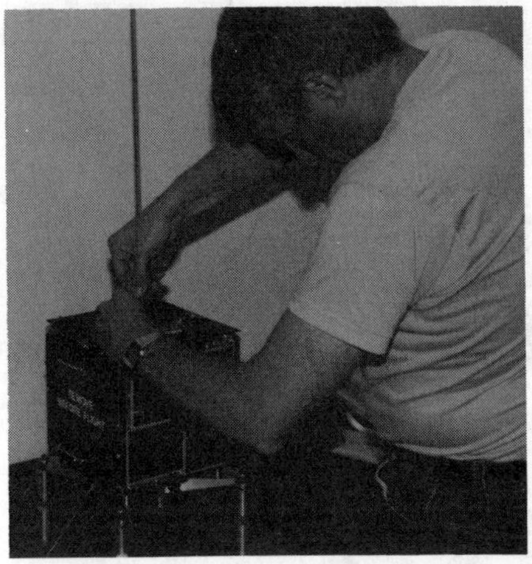

Fig 2—AMSAT's Vice President of Engineering, Jan King, W3GEY, removes protective plates from the Microsat mechanical model, exposing the small solar panels that power the satellite.

Power System

Probably the most important system in any spacecraft is the power system. At the heart of the system is the battery charge regulator (BCR) and the power regulators. The BCR takes the fluctuating input from the solar arrays, conditions it, and charges the batteries. Also in the power system are the regulators that produce 5 V and 7.5 V as needed to power the spacecraft. Work on the BCR circuitry is being done in the ARRL Lab by Jon Bloom, KE3Z, with help from Bruce Hale, KB1MW. The solar panels make use of high-efficiency silicon cells with back surface reflection to recapture some of the photons that made it through the silicon on the first pass. The solar panel electrical and mechanical design was done by W3GEY and WD4FAB. The panels are being produced under contract by Solarex.

Space-rated NiCd batteries are priced to fit budgets of major corporations, but not those of nonprofit organizations like AMSAT. Larry Kayser, VE3PAZ, and a group in Ottawa (working with him) have devised an ingenious testing procedure for space-qualifying commercial-grade batteries. His techniques have been proven in practice: A set of batteries chosen by these procedures has performed well in UO-11. The power subsystem will produce about 8 W (orbit average). This may not sound like much, but it is adequate for a powerful transmitter design.

Transmitters

The transmitters are all designed and built by Matjaz Vidmar, YT3MV. Matjaz is a well-known Amateur Radio talent in Europe. We found out what we had been missing when he became a Fulbright scholar this year. He is doing graduate work in electrical engineering at the University of Colorado. Fortunately, the Microsat project is underway nearby in Boulder, under the direction of W3GEY. Matjaz has designed some highly efficient transmitters for 2 meters (for the DOVE spacecraft) and 70 cm (for the other three spacecraft). The high-efficiency designs, acceptable for 70-cm PSK, are based on principles derived from the early work of Karl Meinzer, DJ4ZC, called high efficiency linear amplification by parametric synthesis (HELAPS). HELAPS has flown on several spacecraft built by AMSAT-NA and AMSAT-DL, including OSCAR 10 and OSCAR 13. Remarkably, the new 2-meter FM transmitter displays a whopping 85% efficiency. Understandably, the 70-cm transmitter displays a slightly reduced—yet commendable—efficiency in the 65% range.

YT3MV and WD4FAB did the mechanical layout of the transmitters. These transmitters produce 4 W at maximum power, with the ability to operate at reduced power levels on command. Again, this may not seem like much, but considering that the loudest signal from FO-12 is powered by a 1-W transmitter, you can see that the Microsat signals will be quite strong. The downlink will be usable with an omnidirectional antenna (with a good bit error rate at 1200 bit/s, and probably 4800 bit/s as well).

All of the satellites except DOVE will produce binary PSK at rates varying from 1200 to 4800. The satellites will start life at 1200 bit/s. In addition to these transmitters, YT3MV is building an L-band (1269-MHz) receiver and an S-band (2401-MHz) transmitter for the digital transponder. The 1269-MHz receiver is based on the receiver core designed by W3IWI, described earlier. In all, with the new L-band stages, this is a four-conversion superhet. A GaAsFET has been chosen for the front end. The exact uplink channel has not yet been selected. The S-band transmitter is again based upon the earlier 70-cm PSK transmitter. The mixer LO is replaced with a chain of multipliers (four in all) to give us the final mix to 2401 MHz. The final amplifier is an Avantek AV-8140; it produces 2 W at 32% efficiency. Using this downlink will be a real challenge for most receivers and modems, considering the total Doppler swing is in excess of 100 kHz during a 15-minute pass. As with the L-band receiver, the exact frequency has not yet been determined.

Computer Hardware and Software

Among team members who are computer builders and programmers, these satellites are considered to have a lot of hardware (for an orbiting computer). Departing from earlier AMSAT designs, the CPU is the primary payload. The model

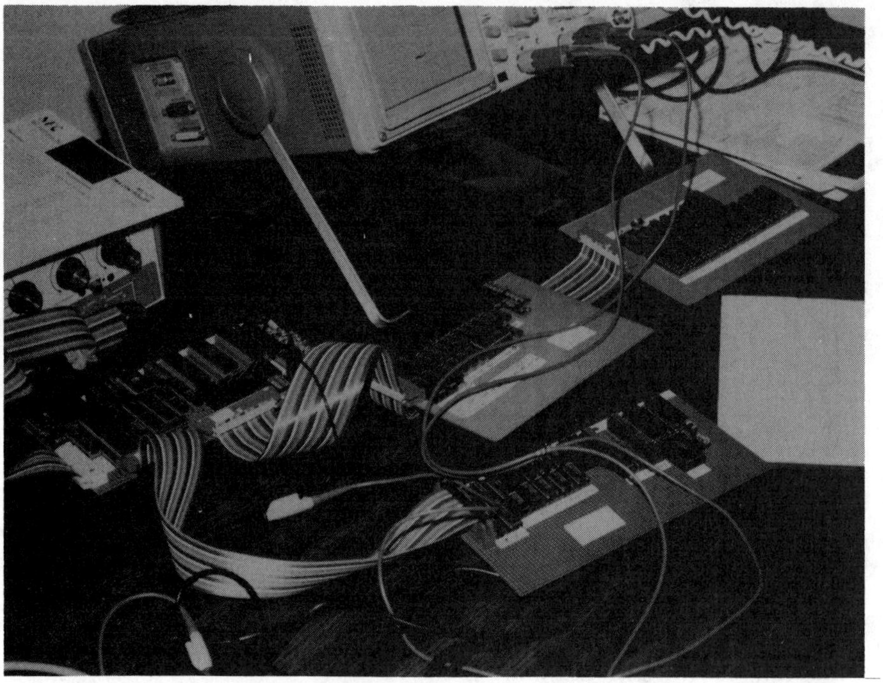

Fig 3—Prototype of PACSAT's CPU. *(N4HY photo)*

for the computer needed to be chosen with great care. Fortunately, shortly before the meeting in Detroit, SANDPAC had produced the PS186[10] computer for packet-radio networking. It is a fast, 80C186-based computer with lots of high-speed memory and HDLC serial controller chips, Zilog 8530s. N4HY was honored to receive one of these from SANDPAC in order to aid the development of packet-radio networking just two weeks before the November 1987 meeting. This greatly influenced our thinking about the way the CPU should look and operate.

The PS186 was delivered at the December 1987 meeting, where all agreed it was the type of CPU we wanted. Lyle Johnson, WA7GXD, one of the primary designers of the TNC 1, the DSP-1[11,12] and other TAPR projects took on the task of designing the CPU.[13] Lyle chose the NEC V-40 (an 80C188 look-alike). His design included lots of EDAC (error detecting and correcting) memory for storage of programs and critical data, and a whopping 8 MB of mass storage for a RAM disk. Also included are several sections of bank-switched, full-speed memory. This enables us to switch experiments in and out of the NEC V-40 bus so that maximum possible access to the experiments is afforded the satellite developers. WA7GXD and Chuck Green, NØADI, did the design and construction of the first prototype. Mike Brock, WB6HHV, is designing the fire-code reset devices so the command stations can hit the panic button if the software crashes. Jim de Arreas, WA4ONG, suggested the design for the mass memory and has also been instrumental in obtaining the hard-to-find memory chips for this project. Fig 3 shows a prototype of PACSAT's CPU. This is an incredibly dense set of circuit boards. There are well over 500 ICs to fit into one of the small modules. Fortunately, integrated circuit evolution has allowed us to do incredible jobs of packing lots of electronics into small places with surface-mount technology. For this reason, the flight units are being laid out professionally by Tex Engineering in California, and the parts will be placed on the CPU board by GMI, Inc in North Carolina.

Harold Price, NK6K, was one of the leaders of the software development for the TAPR TNC 1. He was also a primary member of the DCE development and software team. Harold has had a long interest in packet radio and computer networking—packet satellites in particular. Harold writes multitasking kernels primarily for smart serial I/O cards for Quadron, Inc. Quadron has donated the use of their multitasking kernel and the use of Harold's time to get the flight software developed. Harold will be writing the heart of the software system for the spacecraft.[14] The AX.25 software, which is a part of this kernel and other networking software such as TCP/IP, will be based on Phil Karn's (KA9Q) networking software. The device drivers, for talking to the serial data streams, are being designed by Skip Hansen, WB6YMH. The command and control software and telemetry collection software is being designed by N4HY. Harold will be writing the basic BBS software, and all the software team members will be adding the bells and whistles to what the user will actually see in this BBS. As any software writer will tell you, bugs never entirely disappear. The only piece of software that simply must work each and every time it is called upon is the bare-bones reset bootloader. Hugh Pett, VE3FLL, wrote the bootloader that saved the mission on UO-11. We decided such a track record should be put to work for us, and Hugh is writing the bootloader program that will be flown in ROM and will be executed upon reset.

This is a complex spacecraft system, and one that will take daily management by a dedicated team of volunteer command stations. Courtney Duncan, N5BF, has begun to put together plans for command stations and command operations. This will include gathering telemetry, PBBS sysop duties, and occasional uploading of new software. Courtney is being aided by Ralph Wallio, WØRPK. In addition, Weber State is putting together a command station that can be used for all spacecraft, when needed, and will be a professional operation with students, faculty, CAST members, and volunteers doing the operations duties.

Our Microsat discussion continues next month, when we cover operating frequencies, orbital data, and a detailed rundown of the Microsat missions.

Notes

[1]AMSAT-NA is The Radio Amateur Satellite Corporation, PO Box 27, Washington, DC 20044, tel 301-589-6062.

[2]TAPR is the Tucson Amateur Packet Radio Corporation, PO Box 12925, Tucson, AZ 85732.

[3]Several papers in the proceedings of the Second ARRL Amateur Radio Computer Networking Conference. These papers appear in the proceedings of *ARRL Computer Networking Conferences 1-4*, available from ARRL for $18 (plus $2.50 postage and handling, or $3.50 for insured Parcel Post or UPS) or from your local dealer.

[4]Talk given by Mori Ohara at the Third Space Symposium and AMSAT Annual Meeting, November 1985.

[5]T. Clark, "FO-12 Modems", *Proceedings of the AMSAT-NA Fourth Space Symposium and Annual Meeting*, November 1986.

[6]TAPR PSK modem kits are available from TAPR (see note 2) for $110 plus shipping/handling.

[7]AMSAT-UK, 94 Herongate Rd, Wanstead Park, London E12 5EQ, England.

[8]*Proceedings of the AMSAT-NA Fifth Space Symposium and Annual Meeting* are available from ARRL for $12 (plus $2.50 postage and handling, or $3.50 for insured Parcel Post or UPS) or from your local dealer.

[9]SANDPAC is the San Diego Packet Radio Association.

[10]M. Brock, et al, "A High Performance Packet Switch," *6th Computer Networking Conference*, August 1987. Copies of these proceedings are available from ARRL for $10 (plus $2.50 postage and handling, or $3.50 for insured Parcel Post or UPS) or from your local dealer.

[11]T. Clark and B. McGwier, "The DSP Project Update," *Proceedings of the Sixth AMSAT-NA Space Symposium and Annual Meeting*, November 1988. Copies of these proceedings are available from ARRL for $12 (plus $2.50 postage and handling, or $3.50 for insured Parcel Post or UPS) or from your local dealer.

[12]L. Johnson and C. Green, "Microsat Project—Flight CPU Hardware", *Proceedings of the Sixth AMSAT-NA Space Symposium and Annual Meeting*, November 1988.

[13]L. Johnson, "The AMSAT/TAPR DSP 1 Project: Hardware Design," *Proceedings of the Sixth AMSAT-NA Space Symposium and Annual Meeting*, November 1988.

[14]H. Price and B. McGwier, "PACSAT Software," *Proceedings of the Sixth AMSAT-NA Space Symposium and Annual Meeting*, November 1988.

Microsat: The Next Generation of OSCAR Satellites—*Part 2*

With this year's launch, the next generation of amateur satellites take to the sky. Will you be ready for OSCAR 20?

By Doug Loughmiller, KO5I and Bob McGwier, N4HY

President, AMSAT-NA
Fairway Drive
Paris, TX 75460

Assistant VP Engineering, AMSAT-NA
15 Cherrybrook Ln
East Windsor, NJ 08520

AMSAT is launching the Microsats on an Ariane 4 rocket from Kourou, French Guiana. This large South American space facility was designed by the European Space Agency and is operated by Arianespace, its commercial arm. Our satellites will be secondary payloads with the SPOT-2 satellite, a French earth-resources satellite with a high-resolution camera on board, capable of resolving surface objects only a few meters in diameter.

AMSAT approached Arianespace with the idea of launching small, secondary payloads. Iterations of the idea went back and forth. The result: Microsats will ride on a small shelf just below the main payload as shown in Fig 4. [When we say small, we mean small! Fig 5 shows a full-scale mechanical model of a Microsat sitting on a desk blotter.]

The SPOT launch will put its payload into a sun-synchronous orbit. This type of orbit was used for UO-9 and UO-11, both launched into sun-synchronous orbits on Delta launchers from Vandenburg Air Force Base. (These satellites are still functional.)

A sun-synchronous orbit is a predictable, nearly polar orbit. The earth is not a perfect sphere, and thus, it perturbs the orbit of a spacecraft from its initial value. If these perturbations are used advantageously, it's possible to achieve a fly-over of the spacecraft at nearly the same time every day. The microsat launch gives us a 10:30 AM-PM sun-synchronous orbit: The best pass each day will occur around 10:30 in the morning and evening, *local* standard time. It will vary slightly, but the average time for the best orbit will be around this period. As they fly over the US, the Microsats will be traveling essentially south to north, or vice versa. See Table 1 for a sample listing of the orbital elements for these microsats. These elements are good only if the satellite is launched on June 15, 1989. (These are not the actual elements; the microsats will most likely be launched in the fourth quarter of 1989.) It is, however, easy to modify the figures to make the orbital element set valid for any launch date, ensuring the availability of orbital elements, regardless of when the launch takes place. The only caveat is that the launcher must perform the insertion as planned!

Table 1
Sample Orbital Elements for a Microsat Launch

Epoch 06/15/89 (time of launch)	014213 UTC
Inclination	98.7376°
RAAN (changes with day of launch)	240.17746°
Eccentricity	0.001338
Argument of Perigee	108.2°
Mean Anomaly	257.5°
Mean Motion	14.19889
Drag	0.0000001

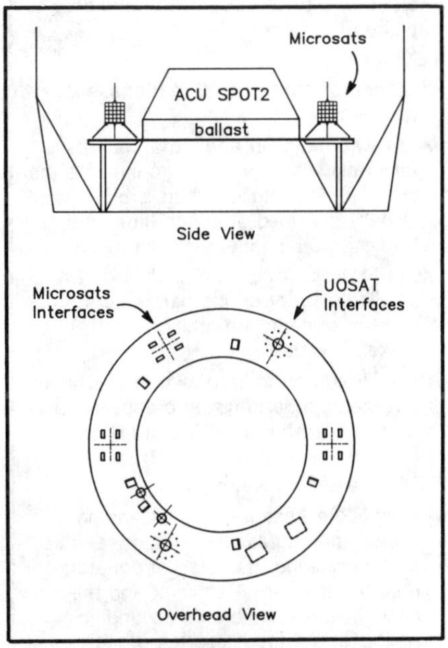

Fig 4—Partial view of Ariane 4 spacecraft interface. The Microsats are launched from a small shelf located just below the SPOT 2 satellite (see upper illustration). The lower illustration is an overhead view of the payload portion of the Ariane 4 vehicle. *(Drawing courtesy of Arianespace.)*

The variables in the orbital information are the right ascension of the ascending node (RAAN) and the date of the launch (not the time). The RAAN is the longitude of the orbital plane on the celestial sphere coordinate system where the orbit crosses the equator going from south to north. As the earth revolves about the sun, this number must change in a predictable way to keep overhead passes occurring synchronous fashion with the sun.

$$RAAN = 77.50451 + 0.98561228\,T \text{ degrees}$$

where T is the number of days between January 1, 1950 at 0000 UTC and the date of the launch.

This will be a night launch. The valves on the first stage are scheduled to be opened at 01:42:13 UTC. The launch window is a short ten minutes. The launch may be visible from the East Coast of the US during its ascent. We will also be able to hear from the satellites soon after their launch, rather than having an agonizing delay of several hours wondering if "we made it."

The Missions

PACSAT and LUSAT are digital store-and-forward satellites.[15] They will allow

Fig 5—This full-scale mechanical model of a Microsat indicates the extreme small size of our newest satellites. The internal circuit density is quite high. Microsats are the most technologically advanced OSCARs to date.

open access to a packet-radio bulletin board by any amateur who has the necessary equipment. They will use AX.25, HDLC, and NRZI as produced by any standard TNC. Because these are operated in orbit, however, you need to use a better modem than the Bell 202 AFSK modems that are standard in most TNCs.

Both satellites will operate in Mode JD. Mode JD, as defined by the Japanese, is Manchester-encoded FSK on the uplink and BPSK on the downlink. The user will need to have a 2-meter FM transmitter and a 70-cm SSB receiver. A special modem, available from a number of sources,[16,17] is needed to operate at 1200 bit/s. We are planning to move the data rates to 4800 bit/s as the mission progresses (meaning, when the modems are ready!). Fortunately, an effort is under way which guarantees access to the modems needed to operate at 4800 bit/s.[18,19] A number of networking experiments are planned, and the packet-radio mission will evolve over time. We are aiming for a simple BBS to be operational on the day of launch with enhanced capabilities to follow. You will recognize the WØRLI/WA7MBL BBS interface. We are planning for these satellites to augment the terrestrial packet-radio message-forwarding system.

On PACSAT, there will be an L-band receiver and a 1-W S-band transmitter. On LUSAT, there will be a 70-cm experimental transmitter and data beacon, constructed in Argentina by AMSAT-LU under the guidance of Carlos Huertas, LU4ENQ.[20] The navigational system on LUSAT is slightly different from that on the other Microsats. On all Microsats, the navigational system is composed of simple bar magnets. On LUSAT, the poles of the magnets are inverted from the configuration used on the other satellites to better optimize it for use in the Southern Hemisphere.

Digital Orbiting Voice Encoder (DOVE) is the dream of PY2BJO. It will use a narrow-band, 2-meter FM transmitter to transmit stored voice messages (output from a Votrax chip) or Bell 202 AFSK tones to send telemetry to command stations. Rather than designing a different receiver and transmitter, we decided to place both the uplink and downlink on 2 meters. The DOVE transmitter will be

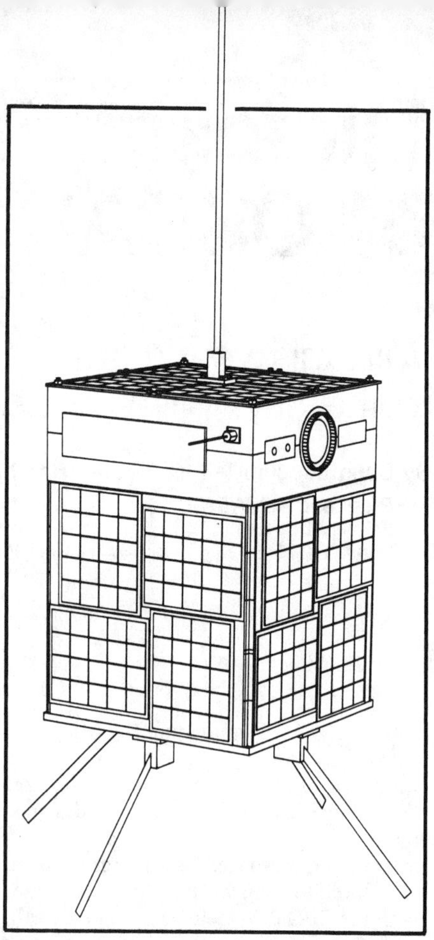

Fig 6—An exterior view of WEBERSAT, a product of the cooperative venture between AMSAT-NA and Weber State College. Note the CCD camera lens in the upper module. See text for the operational details of WEBERSAT. *(Drawing courtesy WD4FAB)*

Microsat Glossary

AFSK: Audio Frequency Shift Keying.

Argument of Perigee: The polar angle locating the perigee point of a satellite in the orbital plane; drawn between the ascending node, geocenter and perigee; and measured from the ascending node in the direction of satellite motion.

AX.25: Amateur packet-radio link-layer protocol approved by ARRL Board of Directors in October 1984.

BBS: Bulletin Board System.

Bell-202: A 1200-baud modem standard with 1200-Hz mark, 2200-Hz space, used for VHF FM packet radio.

BPSK: Biphase Shift Keying.

Eccentricity: A parameter used to describe the ellipse that constitutes the orbit of a satellite.

EIRP: Effective Isotropic Radiated Power.

Epoch: A reference time at which parameters describing satellite motion that vary are specified.

Flash A/D Converter: Analog-to-Digital conversion accomplished using multiple comparator circuits. Flash A/D conversion is much faster than the more conventional technique known as "successive approximation."

Geosynchronous Satellite: A satellite that orbits the earth at an altitude of approximately 22,300 miles, with an orbital period of 24 hours. To an earth-bound observer, the satellite appears to be fixed overhead, hence the term geosynchronous.

HDLC: High-level Data Link Control Procedures as specified in ISO 3309.

Inclination: The angle between the orbital plane of a satellite and the equatorial plane of the earth.

LEO: Low-Earth Orbit.

Manchester-encoded FSK: Biphase-L Frequency-Shift Keying.

Mean Anomaly: An angle that increases uniformly with time, used to indicate the position of a satellite on its orbit. Usually specified at epoch time when Keplerian orbital elements are used.

Mean Motion: A constant included in a satellite's set of orbital parameters. The number of complete orbits a satellite makes in one day.

NRZI: Nonreturn to zero inverted. A binary baseband code in which output transitions result from data 0s but not from data 1s.

PSK: Phase-Shift Keying.

RAAN: Right Ascension at Ascending Node. The angular distance, measured eastward along the celestial equator, between the vernal equinox and the hour circle of the spacecraft's ascending node. One of the Keplerian orbital elements.

TCP/IP: Transmission Control Protocol/ Internet Protocol.

TNC: Terminal Node Controller. A device that assembles and disassembles packets.

turned off periodically to listen for possible commands. We are planning to use its huge RAM disk to store digitized voice using 4-bit differential encoding. These 4-bit quantities will be fed through an integrator to reproduce the digitized waveform. We also have the ability to run straight 4-bit digitized data with no encoding, bypassing the integrator. Authorized command stations will be able to uplink voice messages, bulletins and other digitized waveforms.

Rich Ensign, N8IWJ, is working closely with PY2BJO to devise an educational program based upon DOVE's capabilities. Rich has produced a packet of material for educators who are interested in using this satellite in the classroom.[21]

The design of the speech encoder experiment was done by W3IWI and N4HY. The software to drive the experiment is by N4HY. The DSP project will be supplying the necessary hardware to do the digitization and encoding of the speech for the stored messages.

WEBERSAT, AMSAT's cooperative mission with Weber State College, will have all the capabilities of LUSAT and PACSAT and an extra module on board for some interesting experiments. This satellite, shown in Fig 6, will have a CCD TV camera in the top module. Its lens will "peek out" the side of the satellite through an opening. The TV image is sent to a high-speed flash A/D converter which will digitize the video signals at a 10-MHz sampling rate. The digitized pictures will be processed by the on-board CPU and stored in the RAM disk. This is an example of an experiment which sits in the V40 memory bus when commanded to switch its bank of memory into the CPU bus. This allows for high-speed transfer and manipulation of video data. The CCD camera has a mechanical iris which is also controlled by the CPU. The camera's field of view will be approximately a 350-km square (from the intended orbit). Also included in this experimental module is a simple spectrometer and some other experiments devised by students working with CAST. An L-band receiver can also be connected to the digitizer, enabling pictures to be taken on the ground and digitized. Extreme EIRP will be needed for this procedure, but we do not hesitate to point out that this infrequent uploading of pictures is done only in short bursts. The Weber State/CAST team includes Bill Clapp, Bob Summers, Stan Sjol, Bob Twiggs, and Chris Williams along with several students. The operating frequencies for all four satellites is shown in Table 2.

Table 2
Operating Frequencies

Mission	*Downlink*	*Uplinks*
PACSAT	437.050 MHz	145.900, 145.920, 145.940, 145.960 MHz.
DOVE	145.825 MHz	not announced
LUSAT	437.150 MHz	145.840, 145.860, 145.880, 145.900 MHz.
WEBERSAT	437.100 MHz	not announced.

Also on board this launch will be the University of Surrey's third and fourth satellites, UOSATs D and E. UOSAT D will carry a packet-radio experiment that will be operating using a special polling protocol, in addition to AX.25. This protocol will run in your computer through a TNC running AX.25 and a special modem. This satellite will operate 9600-bit/s FSK. The modems needed are K9NG compatibles and are available from TAPR and G3RUH.

AMSAT-NA has recently learned that the follow-up mission to FUJI-OSCAR 12, JAS-1B, is scheduled to take place in early 1990. This satellite, with design enhancements for an improved power budget, will round out the current deployment of OSCAR satellites planned for the year's end.

The Microsat group is a large team of talented people. This is as much their story as it is an attempt to describe the new satellites. Other volunteers in AMSAT, TAPR, ARRL, CAST and elsewhere have patiently watched us work and delayed other projects so the tight timetable could be met. TAPR has generously donated funds to cover the cost of PACSAT's electronics (many members of the Microsat team are TAPR members). We appreciate the generosity of the ARRL in allowing the use of the ARRL Lab and personnel to do some critical work on this project.

In addition to these teams, we have recently signed an agreement with AMSAT-I, our sister society in Italy, to produce another Microsat, with construction largely taking place in that country. Alberto Zagni, I2KBD, is the project leader for AMSAT-I.

The future for Microsat is bright. With its small mass and size, it can be launched as a secondary payload on almost any orbital launch. In the not-too-distant future, you should be able to access a packet satellite at any hour of the day or night. OSCAR 20, here we come!

Notes

[15]T. Clark, "AMSAT's MICROSAT/PACSAT Program" (see note 18)

[16]TAPR PSK modem kits are available from TAPR (see note 2) for $110 plus shipping/handling.

[17]AMSAT-UK, 94 Herongate Rd, Wanstead Park, London E12 5EQ, England.

[18]T. Clark and B. McGwier, "The DSP Project Update," *Proceedings of the Sixth AMSAT-NA Space Symposium and Annual Meeting*, November 1988. Copies of these proceedings are available from ARRL for $12 (plus $2.50 postage and handling, or $3.50 for insured Parcel Post or UPS) or from your local dealer.

[19]L. Johnson and C. Green, "Microsat Project—Flight CPU Hardware, *Proceedings of the Sixth AMSAT-NA Space Symposium and Annual Meeting*, November 1988.

[20]Mode-L receiver and Mode-S transmitter frequencies for PACSAT and WEBERSAT have not been finalized as of this writing. The 70-cm frequency for the AMSAT-LU experiment has also not been finalized.

[21]You may obtain these information packets by contacting Rich Ensign, N8IWJ, 421 N. Military, Dearborn, MI 48124.

Conducted By
Vern "Rip" Riportella, WA2LQQ
P.O. Box 177, Warwick, NY 10990

Antennas for Working OSCAR

It seems likely man has always looked skyward in search of inspiration. Today, when amateurs seek to expand their vistas, they naturally look skyward toward OSCAR. What antennas do they use?

A typical OSCAR station is equipped for three or perhaps four Modes: A, B, J and maybe L.[1] This implies the station has antennas for 10 m, 2 m and 70 cm. A fully equipped station may also include a 24-cm antenna for Mode L. What kind of antennas are typical on each band?

For 10-meter Mode A reception, there are several approaches. With a 10-meter beam and preamp, you'll hear the Russian amateur satellites well. However, when the RS satellites are overhead, your beam's low elevation pattern is a disadvantage. Supplement your 10-meter beam with another type of 10-meter antenna. Several selectable sloping dipoles help. A turnstile is easily built and surprisingly effective for overhead passes. A horizontal dipole stapled to a bedroom wall will even suffice, but a vertical is generally a poor choice.

Two-meter OSCAR antennas are used for Modes A, B, J and the future JL mode. Antennas for VHF and above can be interesting and occasionally baffling.

Recent OSCARs, such as AO-10, use circular polarization (CP). CP can be thought of as a mixture of vertical and horizontal polarization. AO-10 is spinning and what might be vertically polarized one moment could be horizontal the next. Moreover, radio waves passing through the geomagnetic field have their polarization rotated in passing. This is called Faraday rotation. The polarization of the downlink at your QTH is not only unpredictable, but it's rapidly varying! A CP antenna solves this problem by (ideally) being equally effective in both horizontal and vertical planes.

CP comes in two "flavors" (engineers call them senses): Right Hand (RHCP) and Left Hand (LHCP). A handy visualization tool for CP is to imagine you could see the plane waves launched by your CP antenna. Imagine a ribbon-like plane wave twisting off regularly into space. The rate of twist of the ribbon would be exactly one turn per wavelength of travel. The direction of the twist is the sense. If a mouse were to run down the RHCP ribbon (away from you), the mouse would appear to be rotating clockwise as he scampered off into the distance. Conversely, a mouse running down a LHCP ribbon would appear to be rotating counterclockwise.

Many antennas can generate CP, but few of them do it really well. Two CP figures of merit are gain and circularity (axial ratio). Circularity is the relative sensitivity of the antenna to RF energy in various planes. Gain for CP antennas is analogous to linearly polarized Yagis.

A typical Mode B OSCAR antenna system—a pair of 2-meter crossed Yagis and a single 70-cm crossed Yagi. See text for details.

The easiest way to get CP on 2 meters is with a helical antenna. The 2-meter helix tends to be bulky, but it can be fun to build and is very forgiving of lax dimensional tolerances. Several types of helices are described in the *Satellite Experimenter's Handbook* (SEH).[2] Helices tend to be a little lower in gain than you might want for 2 meters.[3]

The most popular solution for the Mode B downlink is crossed Yagis. The Yagis can be on different booms or they may share a common boom. They are oriented at right angles to each other and fed so that the resultant wave acts like that imaginary ribbon. This can be done by equally splitting power to the two Yagis and then delaying the power to one Yagi by 90 degrees. The result will be either RHCP or LHCP, depending on which antenna is leading and which is lagging. An alternative is to have both Yagis on a common boom but to offset them physically on the common boom by ¼ wave. Then they can be fed in phase to generate either RHCP or LHCP. To reverse the sense, a ½-wave delay line is inserted in one feed or the other. AO-10 uses RHCP for all its antennas except the 2-meter omni, which is rarely used. Experience has shown it very advantageous to be able to switch your station antennas between the two senses (RHCP to LHCP).

OSCAR antennas for 70 cm are currently used for Modes B and L. In the future, they will be used for Modes JL and S. Helices and crossed Yagis are very popular here, too. Gain of 14 or 15 dBic can be obtained with a single crossed Yagi of modern design. You'll see the quagi antenna also used on 70 cm. Some work has been done on a CP version of a quagi which, in its original version, was linearly polarized.

For Mode L at 24 cm, Yagis, loop Yagis, quagis, helices, dishes and some other rare varieties enter the picture. F9FT (Tonna) has made an excellent Yagi array for Mode L, and many are using it. It produces linear polarization. Consequently, users may observe some spin modulation.[4] Currently experiencing a surge in popularity on Mode L are loop Yagis.[5] Some designers claim close to 20-dBi gain for the longer versions. Arrays are in use producing 24 dBi or more. KØRZ has had excellent results with an array of four long-loop Yagis for Mode L. Spectrum International sells a shorter version that seems to work quite well. These antennas are very lightweight, have low wind drag and are relatively easy to construct. Dimensional tolerances need to be precisely held however. The loop Yagis are also linearly polarized and show some spin modulation effects. Also used at 24 cm are small- to medium-sized parabolic dish antennas of the 4- to 8-foot class. (We'll cover these in a subsequent column).

Let's take a quick look at a fairly typical Mode B OSCAR antenna installation. The photo shows a pair of 2-meter crossed Yagis and a single 70-cm crossed Yagi. The 2-meter Yagis are spaced at about 9 feet. The 70-cm Yagi is more than a ½ wavelength (at 2 meters) from the 2-meter antenna. The elements of the 70-cm Yagi are at 45 degrees to the 2-meter elements to improve isolation. The boom is off-center to increase the distance of the 70-cm antenna from the mast. Top guys are used to lower mechanical stresses on the elevation rotor caused by the off-center arrangement. The top guys are of nylon 150-pound-test line with turnbuckles. The feeds for the antennas all approach from the rear to avoid pattern distortion caused by running the coax and its associated field through the elements. The boom is, of course, nonconductive fiberglass. This is a must! The preamps for each band are mounted in the two black boxes just below the elevation rotor.

When Galileo first turned his telescope on the skies, a whole new world opened to him. What will *you* find when you turn your antennas skyward?[6]

Next time we'll discuss ways of keeping your OSCAR antennas accurately pointed: tracking.

Notes

[1] Transponder modes were delineated in Table 1 in the September 1985 column.

[2] Available from ARRL and AMSAT.

[3] For 2-meter OSCAR work, you want at least 12-dBic gain.

[4] Spin modulation is the received signal amplitude modulation that results from the spin of the satellite and the consequent satellite antenna-pattern rotation. The effect is akin to a low-frequency (approximately 100 Hz) amplitude modulation impressed on signals.

[5] J. Reisert, W1JR, "VHF/UHF World," *Ham Radio*, Sept. 1985, pp. 56-62.

[6] Information about getting started on OSCAR is available for an s.a.s.e. to the author at the address above.

QST

Conducted By
Vern "Rip" Riportella, WA2LQQ
P.O. Box 177, Warwick, NY 10990

Basic Satellite-Tracking Themes

Establishing and maintaining knowledge of the whereabouts of satellites is called tracking.[1] There's a keen interest in tracking OSCAR. And I think I know why.

It's the mystery that shrouds the movements of these artificial planets that makes their movements so fascinating, their reappearance almost mystical. It makes those who accurately predict their appearance rather shaman-like figures in the community.

Most satellite shamans have replaced their icons with IBM®, their crow's feet with Commodore®, their mushrooms with MacIntosh® PCs. The great caldron is first loaded with Kepler stew and feverishly stirred. Soon it yields up a magnificent information porridge richer by far than any gypsy's tea leaves: a forecast of heavenly events to come ... the rise of a great friendly star, OSCAR!

There are two fundamental reasons one needs to keep track of OSCARs. First of all they move—some fast, others not so fast. Since you must use a beam of some sort, you need to know where to point to catch the little bugger as it goes by. Second, most folks would find it rather onerous to sit by a radio and wait several hours for a satellite to show up. That would be an awful waste of time, and could be hazardous to your health besides. The soothing effect of the white noise emanating from the receiver has been known to induce a condition known to medicine as radiosomnia: nodding off at just the wrong moment.[2]

To avoid entirely this potentially debilitating condition, one needs to know when the satellite of interest will appear. Then, one can leisurely go about one's (presumably) less somniferous business to return to the shack at just the right moment to catch the bird on the rise.

Thus, there are two fundamental functions of your OSCAR tracking effort: position determination and scheduling. There are other functions one might envision (and those will be discussed subsequently), but these two functions are clearly most basic.

To track OSCAR requires four things:

1) You need information about the OSCAR you want to track: its precise location and rates of movement at a precisely defined instant.

2) You must know your location.

3) You must know the time of day reasonably accurately.

4) Most important, you need a contrivance to make sense of the first three items.

The contrivance, or tool, can be an OSCARLOCATOR, Satellipse or similar manual tracking device.[3] Or it can be a number engine: a modern-day icon, crow's foot or mushroom. The manual locators are sufficiently accurate for most applications, and can cost under $20. Obviously, the crow's feet are somewhat more dear (ask any crow).

Let's look first at the manual locators. In the usual arrangement, you get an equidistant azimuthal projection map centered on the North Pole. A series of clear-plastic overlays is supplied. The ground-track overlay relates the path of the satellite to the map of the earth. The ground-track overlay pivots around a rivet positioned at the North Pole. In this way, it denotes various paths the satellite can take. Another overlay, called a spiderweb because of its resemblance to same, provides azimuth and elevation pointing information to the satellite from your QTH.[4] Time hacks on the ground-track overlay signify where the satellite will be at selected times after a reference is crossed. The satellite's motion (rates and angles) are factored into your plotter and determine the shape of the curves on the overlays. Different satellites usually have different orbits. That means you need a separate ground-track overlay for each satellite.[5]

To make the manual plotters work you need an accurate reference point, a precise reckoning of where the satellite was at a selected instant. With low earth-orbiting (LEO) satellites, which have very nearly circular orbits, the reference used is the time and longitude of the satellite's northbound equator crossing. More precisely, *the* reference orbit (the one most often used for reference purposes) is the *first* northbound equator crossing of the UTC day.

The reference orbit consists of the time and longitude of the equator crossing. Orbit number is sometimes also included. To track subsequent orbits you increment the longitude of the reference orbit by a fixed amount (given in the bulletins). Similarly, the time increment is given. So, given a reference orbit together with the longitude and time increments (orbital period), you have sufficient information for accurate tracking for several weeks, at least.

With elliptical orbiting satellites such as AMSAT-OSCAR 10 (AO-10), things are a bit more complex. Since both the velocity and altitude of AO-10 change constantly, the shape of the ground-track overlays seems at first a bit bizarre. The earth is rotating at a fixed rate, but the motion of the satellite is variable. The interaction of the two motions yields a ground track that doubles back on itself. Moreover, the shape of the ground-track overlay must be updated periodically to account for changes in the orbit geometry. Finally, when used for AO-10, the manual trackers most often use the time and location (both latitude and longitude) of apogee as a reference rather than the equator crossing time.[6]

Locators used for both circular and elliptical orbits have several things in common: They depend on well-defined graphs of the satellites' movements, and they require a reference time and position input to get started tracking. These reference inputs can be obtained from several sources. W1AW transmits reference orbits as part of its regular bulletin regime. AMSAT nets carry extensive orbital information, including the reference orbits and reference apogees.[7] *Amateur Satellite Report* (ASR) also contains the required information.[8]

So far, we've looked at two of the four items mentioned above that you need. We've looked at the position and motion information you need, and we've mentioned one form of tool (contrivance) to garner some meaning from the information. Now for the easiest two requirements: your location and the precise time.

You can determine your location from an atlas or a good road map. You should be able to determine your location easily to within a tenth of a degree of both longitude and latitude. If you have difficulty, try calling your municipal airport for help. As for time of day, the National Bureau of Standards station WWV can be tuned in on 2.5, 5, 10, 15 and 20 MHz whenever conditions allow. Time hacks are given every minute. You should have an accurate clock, preferably digital, closely synchronized with WWV.

Manual locators have much to recommend them. They're inexpensive and completely adequate for most tracking applications. In fact, they are fun to use, if a bit confusing at first to the newcomer. Designers of AO-10 trackers (K2ZRO, W2GFF and K2UBC) spent years working out the details to produce some excellent, affordable instruments.

Expert DXers know where and when to point their beams, based on years of experience. Tracking satellites is similar in some ways, yet starkly different in others. It *does* take experience to become a proficient satellite tracker and to really understand what is going on. In this way satellite trackers and DXers are similar. On the other hand, DXers have to shrug their shoulders at the vagaries of the F2 mode when overwhelmed by too many variables; simple unpredictability. Thankfully, predicting OSCAR access is much, much more precise. There is enormous satisfaction in dumping a bunch of numbers into a computer, pushing a few buttons and being presented with a piece of paper that says an object traveling at 18,000 miles per hour is going to pop over your horizon in precisely 38 minutes and 22 seconds. And then it *does!* Shamans, man your caldrons!

Next time, we'll conclude the tracking theme with a look at the icons, crow's feet and mushrooms (computer number crunching) tracking methods.[9]

Notes

[1]Tracking in a general sense can mean all those measures one employs to locate the object of interest. In a narrower sense, tracking, as with radar, can involve an exchange of information, either cooperatively or passively, between the tracker and the target. When we speak of "tracking" OSCARs, we generally mean the broader sense of the word. Tracking OSCAR most often reduces to predicting its position in space and time as discussed (in the text) rather than exchanging location information with it.

[2]Symptoms include a red mark on the forehead caused by frequent, percussive contact with the operating position.

[3]See the June 1985 column.

[4]See! There really are mystical allusions here.

[5]For satellites of the same family, however, you can use a single overlay. For example, for RS-5, RS-7 and RS-8 (all the currently operating Russian satellites), a single ground-track overlay is sufficient. Separate overlays are required for UoSAT-OSCAR 9 and UoSAT-OSCAR 11 because of their disparate altitudes.

[6]Apogee is the highest point in a satellite's orbit; the point at which it's farthest from earth.

[7]Net times and frequencies were given in the June 1985 column.

[8]See the June 1985 column.

[9]A free catalog of AMSAT Software Exchange tracking programs is available for an s.a.s.e. to the author at the address above.

Conducted By
Vern "Rip" Riportella, WA2LQQ
P.O. Box 177, Warwick, NY 10990

Basic Satellite-Tracking Themes—Part 2

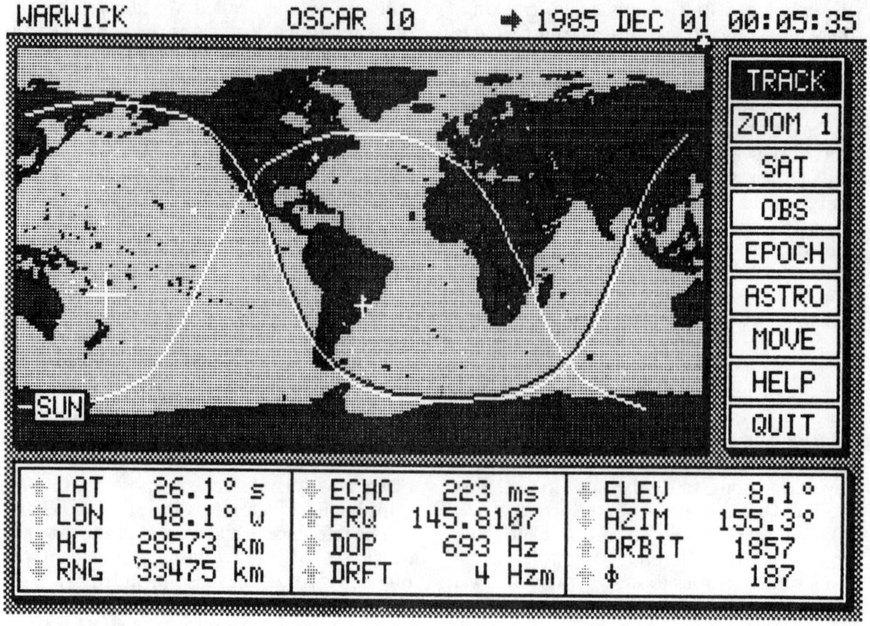

Examples of the newest and best graphics tracking abilities of the GRAFTRAK II software of Silicon Solutions (l-r): a footprint of AO-10 over South America and western Africa while the sun is centered north of New Zealand (left).

Last month, we talked of manual satellite tracking (locator) systems. This month, we conclude the basic tracking discussion with a review of computer tracking methods.

Computer programs designed to track satellites usually have a common set of "guzintas" (inputs) and a variety of "comsoutas" (outputs). The inputs are almost always in the form of the NASA orbital prediction bulletin. The prediction bulletins provide precise data on the position of the satellite at a reference instant (epoch), and are velocities and accelerations for the satellite. Based on the values supplied, the well-designed tracking program can output a wealth of information.

The output can be presented on your TV or CRT monitor, it can be printed or it might even steer you antennas for you by controlling the rotors through a suitable interface adapter. In the most elementary programs you get an output that tells you where the satellite is and which way to point to aim your beam at the satellite.[1] Advanced programs can dazzle you with maps showing the position of one or more satellites, and can forecast DX paths with selected QTHs that will be within view of a given satellite concurrent with you.

There have been three generations of programs. The first generation simply gave you a tabular display (or printout), i. e., time, azimuth and elevation and SSP of the chosen satellite for a selected period. For example, the computer could figure the pointing angles for OSCAR 9 for the next four hours.

The second-generation programs added graphics. Those developed by WØSL, GM4IHJ, W6WNK and others presented you with a Mercator projection map of the earth. Depending on the program, you would see the relative position of one or more satellites projected on the map. Provided is a table that tells which way to point to "look" at the satellite.

The first of the third-generation programs does all of this and much more. A system developed by W5SXD and WB5CCJ is a remarkable combination of slick graphics and enormous flexibility. It provides tools for the satellite operations planners as well as users. And it runs with the 8087 math coprocessor, so it is very fast.

What to Expect

What can be done besides merely giving you pointing angles to the bird?

1) Tracking from your location: Provides azimuth and elevation from your QTH for a selected satellite if the satellite is above the horizon. Advanced programs allow you to track several satellites simultaneously. Some will allow you to adjust the time step size to better resolve motion. Others let you set the horizon value so you are alerted to satellites just below the horizon where they can occasionally be worked. Most programs will tell you how far along its orbital path the bird has progressed on the current orbit. This is displayed in terms of phase or mean anomaly (MA). This is important because some satellites, AO-10 in particular, operate in different modes according to where they are along their orbital path.

2) Scheduling: This allows you to select a broad time window and ask the computer to display each rise and set of the selected satellite within that window. More advanced programs allow scheduling of more than one satellite.

3) Mutual visibility: Time and pointing information for any two stations you select that will be simultaneously within view of the chosen satellite.

4) Satellite off-pointing angle: This new feature, this facility tells you how far off from your QTH the satellite's beam antenna is pointing. This is significant with AO-10 since it uses high-gain beams and occasionally the satellite's orientation is adjusted for better sun-angle. The algorithm for doing the off-pointing calculations was developed by Bob McGwier, N4HY, and is in several versions of his QUIKTRAK program.

5) Graphics: The addition of graphics distinguishes the second-generation tracking system from the first. Advanced graphics have handsome maps with detailed land mass outlines. The simplest programs will track but one satellite on the map. The best graphics capabilities I've seen are in the W5SXD/WB5CCJ GRAFTRAK II package. Here you can watch the satellite's SSP traverse the map (as with the others) or you can plot the "footprint" (coverage zones). You can even zoom in to get more detail. Or you can do a special spherical projection to see what the earth looks like from the satellite at that instant. This, combined with its number crunching speed, distinguish GRAFTRAK II as the first (and for the moment only one) of the third-generation programs.

6) Autotrak: KØRZ homebrewed one of the first systems whereby the computer controls the antenna position directly without human intervention. Although fewer than 1 in perhaps 500 satellite users today have autotrak systems running now, they will become very popular in the future.

7) Special features: GRAFTRAK II has a fast mode that allows you to watch the ground track and coverage zone move across the map at selectable high rates. This helps to plan access times to various QTHs you might want to chat with.

While tracking a satellite is a fascinating and instructive exercise, there are those who would just as scon treat the media as transparent and get on with the fun of QSOing. For them, computer-aided tracking and eventually autotracking is definitely the way to go. The ease of use and tremendous information content afforded, especially from those programs such as GRAFTRAK II with advanced graphics capability, make satellite use all the more enjoyable.

Next time we'll discuss the ultimate in easy-to-track satellites: AMSAT's plans for a fully geonsynchronous satellite system, which just hangs in the sky with no apparent movement at all; just set your antennas and weld them in place. Next month: Phase 4 Satellites. The future is here![2]

Notes

[1]The satellite's position is usually given in terms of the latitude and longitude of its sub-satellite point (SSP). The SSP is the point on the surface of the earth lying on a line connecting the satellite and the center of the earth. In other words, the SSP is the point right "beneath" the satellite. The position information given may also include the elevation above the earth and the range to your QTH.

[2]A free catalog of AMSAT Software Exchange tracking programs is available for an s.a.s.e. to the author at the address above.

Conducted By
Vern "Rip" Riportella, WA2LQQ
PO Box 177, Warwick, NY 10990

Fun, Games and (Hopefully) Technical Challenges on OSCARs

Viewed as "sport," Amateur Radio inspires some to reach new heights. But taking this "radiosport" competition to the OSCAR satellites raises both new challenges *and* risks.

OSCAR transponders are especially vulnerable to the abuses intense competition seems to foster. Consequently, AMSAT has carefully limited on-satellite competition. Power "hogging" of limited transponder power by ardent contesters is the basic problem; it's the essence of what precludes "contests" on OSCARs.

Competition also means awards. Awards programs differ from contests in meaningful ways.

First, contests tend to be short, high-intensity events. Awards (eg, DXCC) tend to be of lower intensity and are usually long-term pursuits.

Second, contests pit operators against each other in a dueling environment. Awards present arbitrary milestones (eg, 100 countries). The absence of head-to-head combat seems to reduce abuse levels.

There is a third class of competition, which I call techno-sport. It lends itself nicely to satellites and embraces the essence of the Amateur Space Program. Techno-sport emphasizes technical acumen over physical endurance, mind-food over monastic chanting and ken over kilowatts! The now-defunct Frequency Measuring Test (FMT) and the Fox 'n' Hound (F 'n' H) hidden-transmitter events are familiar examples.

The FMT challenged the participant to determine precisely the frequency of a CW signal. The more accurate the judgment, the higher the award. Today's F 'n' H events pit clever foxes against portable, sophisticated equipment and are more fun than ever.

The desire to instill sound engineering principles and advanced techniques through the incentive of competition, combined with its fundamentally benign character, is the motivation for AMSAT's developing a series of techno-sport competitions. The first techno-sport competition held on AMSAT-OSCAR 10 (AO-10) in 1985 was a receive-sensitivity test. The participant merely copied a moderately weak CW signal transmitted through AO-10. If the characters were copied correctly, the participant was awarded a certificate. If a still weaker signal was received, the competitor would receive an endorsement to the award. Each time a weaker signal was copied, a more prestigious endorsement would be granted. This form of competition is simple and technically stimulating, too. It promotes improved "ears" through better station engineering, essential in OSCAR use.

AMSAT's receive-sensitivity test is called the K2ZRO Memorial Station Engineering Award. In the ZRO Test, the participant monitors AO-10's downlink. A calibrated CW signal sends a five-digit number group in 10-wpm Morse code. The participant notes it. Then the test director reduces the signal power level by half (−3 dB). A different code group is sent. The participant notes it. Power is cut in half again. This process is repeated until nine different power levels are sent: Z_0 through Z8. The lowest level is 24 dB below the first signal (see Table 1).

Conducting the test is also a challenge. Fig 1 shows the equipment used in the transmitter chain. The power meter is used only to gauge general power levels. Its accuracy (±5%) is insufficient for the test. In the future, a directional coupler and a precision Boonton microwattmeter with digital readout will be used. The isolator stabilizes the impedance the attenuator output sees. Attenuator accuracy hinges on the maintenance of a 50-ohm line, and the accuracy of the entire test depends on the accuracy of the attenuator.

Choosing the test time is as important to the accuracy of the ZRO Test as the instrumentation. The critical factors are satellite location, perspectives and attitude (orientation). Test fairness must be assured in three ways:

1) Each participant must have the same downlink energy to work with (uniformity).

2) No test session should be easier than another (precision repeatability).

3) Increments must be close to −3 dB (accuracy).

To assure uniform illumination levels, the test session is scheduled at (or near to) apogee, the highest point on the satellite's orbit. During this time, the difference in path length (and path loss) between participants is minimal. Also, when the satellite is at apogee, the differences attributable to downlink antenna-beam variations are minimized.

To assure repeatability, the benchmark for each session is the observed strength of the satel-

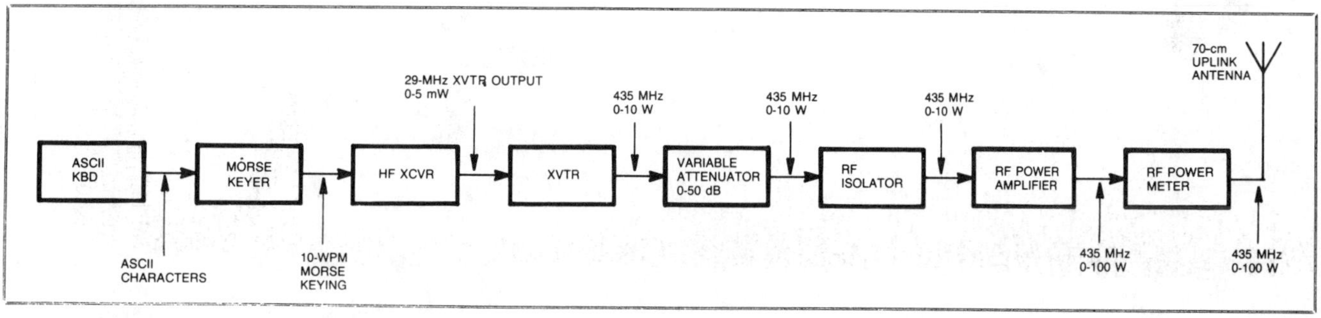

Fig 1—ZRO Test transmit chain.

Table 1

ZRO Test Typical Operation Levels

Z Level	*Relative Level (dB)*	*Measured RF to Feed Line*		*EIRP**	
0	0	20 W	(13 dBW)	316 W	(25 dBW)
1	−3	10 W	(10 dBW)	158 W	(22 dBW)
2	−6	5 W	(7 dBW)	79 W	(19 dBW)
3	−9	2.5 W	(4 dBW)	40 W	(16 dBW)
4	−12	1.25 W	(1 dBW)	20 W	(13 dBW)
5	−15	625 mW	(−2 dBW)	10 W	(10 dBW)
6	−18	312 mW	(−5 dBW)	5 W	(7 dBW)
7	−21	156 mW	(−8 dBW)	2.5 W	(4 dBW)
8	−24	78 mW	(−11 dBW)	1.25 W	(1 dBW)

*Antenna Effective Isotropic Radiated Power, assuming 1.0-dB feed-line loss and 13.0-dB gain.

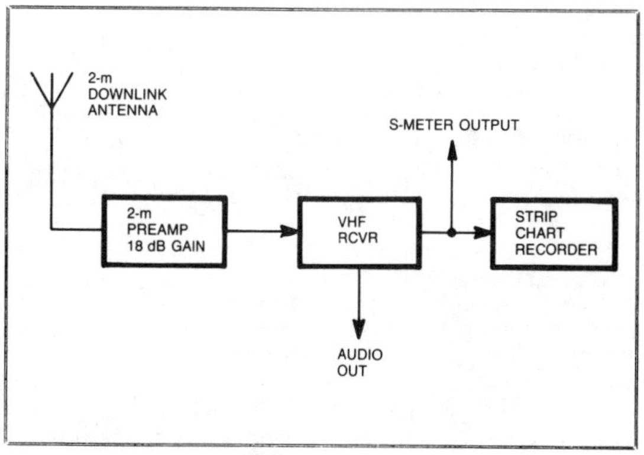

Fig 2—ZRO Test receive chain.

lite's beacon transmitter rather than, say, a carrier sent through the transponder. To assure accuracy of the −3 dB increments, a precision attenuator is used.

To calibrate a test shot, the test director carefully adjusts the uplink power such that the downlink signal exactly equals the observed beacon amplitude. This, then, becomes the reference Z_0 level for the test session (316 watts effective isotropic radiated power [EIRP] uplink in the session typified in Table 1).

Setting the Z_0 level is often difficult; it is the reason for using the strip chart recorder in the receiver chain of Fig 2. With spin modulation and variable transponder loading to complicate matters, careful observation is required before the baseline Z_0 level can be established.

Choice of the transponder test environment is essential to the success of the test session. The transponder loading must be moderate and stable. Too few users means statistically unacceptable variations in transponder loading such that a single, strong signal could modulate the test levels. Too many users reduces the effect of individual users, but may mean QRM and demand more uplink power than the power amplifier can provide in its linear operating range.

Once the benchmark Z_0 is set, it is simple to reduce power levels in 3-dB increments using an attenuator. One of the significant results to date is that it is *much* easier to attain Z8 on Mode L (70-cm downlink) compared to Mode B (2-m downlink)! There's a message here.

When Phase 3C is launched, two new techno-sport activities will be introduced. The satellite-based FMT will add a challenging new dimension to the traditional HF versions since OSCAR moves with respect to both the signal source and the test participant. Doppler shifts will complicate measurements for the competitor.

An OSCAR-based F 'n' H event is conceived as an analogue of the remarkable SARSAT/COSPAS search-and-rescue transponders on US and USSR satellites. In the AMSAT version, the "Fox" (QTH unknown) is a "cooperative" beast. To aid the hounds, the fox retransmits the WWV time standard through the transponder. By comparing the arrival time of the direct WWV signal (via the ionosphere) to the arrival time of the WWV signal, as relayed by the satellite, a curve is determined. A series of measurements narrows the unknown QTH to a region.

The FMT and F 'n' H events are in the planning stages and will be described more fully in a subsequent column. Next time, we'll look at what it takes to be successful in the ZRO test.

[Write to AMSAT for *free* information about getting started with OSCARs. An SASE to AMSAT, PO Box 27, Washington DC, 20044 will do the trick.—Ed.] QST

Conducted By
Vern "Rip" Riportella, WA2LQQ
PO Box 177, Warwick, NY 10990

Fun, Games and (Hopefully) Education on OSCARs—Part 2

Last month, we discussed how AMSAT performs its receive sensitivity test, the ZRO Test. This month, we'll examine what it takes to do well in the competition.

There's no single piece of equipment or technique that will assure you of being among the top performers in the ZRO Test. Rather, it's a combination of factors that makes the difference. But if there's any common thread that unites the top performers, it's that they all have paid scrupulously careful attention to detail.

When striving for better receiving sensitivity, the primary obstacle is noise. The ability to hear anything is dependent on the power of the signal you're trying to hear compared to the power of the noise in the monitored bandwidth. This is most commonly called the in-band signal-to-noise ratio, or the S/N ratio.

The receiving system consists of two basic components: an antenna, which couples a weak electromagnetic field to your receiver, and a receiver, which converts the RF to AF and couples the resultant audio to your brain. Some important ancillary equipment consists of the preamplifier (actually an extension of your receiver), the transmission line connecting the antenna to the receiver, and the speaker (or earphones), which couples the receiver to your ears.

Here are the basic requirements. Capture as much of the signal as possible at the antenna while rejecting as much extraneous noise as possible. Get the signal to the receiver intact. Convert the signal to audio while limiting the bandwidth to as narrow a slice as possible to allow the desired signal to stand out prominently from the noise, ie, increase the S/N ratio.

A preamp is essential, although where it's placed depends on several factors. In essence, the preamp should be placed ahead (on the antenna side) of any significant losses such as might be incurred in transmission lines. Why?

Picture your transmission line as a noise source (because it is). It's lossy and warm.[1] Any losses incurred between the antenna and the preamp contribute greatly to overall receiver S/N degradation. This is *the single most important thing you can do!* Get the preamp close to the antenna. How close? If there is a 1 dB loss between your antenna and the preamp, you're at the limit of what I consider a reasonable tradeoff. Keep in mind that at 2 m a 1 dB loss is incurred in about 40 feet of RG-8 foam cable (in new condition). At 70 cm, you incur 1 dB loss in about 25 feet of the same coax.

For weak-signal space work, you should have as much gain as possible generated by your antenna array. How much is enough? Start with a single Yagi. Point it to the zenith. Does the needle of your receiver's S meter come off the peg or does it sit there listlessly? If the receiver is in good shape and you have a good, low-noise preamp, the needle might be just off the peg. If not, try to borrow another preamp for a test. Put the second preamp in line. Now, the S meter should be well up-scale and your receiver's speaker should be erupting with the rushing sound of white noise. If the noise is not prominent, you may need a new receiver. If a single preamp gives you noticeable, but slight, needle movement, then chances are you have enough gain in the active components (preamp and receiver). Next you need to concentrate on the passive components, specifically the antenna array. You can add a second Yagi. If you separate it at the proper distance from the first antenna, you will reduce the beamwidth of the resulting array.

The sky is full of noise sources. When you add antenna gain, you are, in effect, increasing the S/N ratio in two ways. First, since the gain of the antenna goes up, it couples more energy to the preamp. Thus, the ratio of the desired satellite signal energy from the antenna increases in proportion to the undesired noise energy unavoidably generated in the preamp. The S/N ratio is improved. Second, and somewhat more subtly, when the antenna gain is increased, the total sky area that is within the beam of the antenna decreases in direct proportion. So all those noise sources in space you don't care to hear are out of the beam. What you *do* want to hear, the satellite, stands out more clearly against the omnipresent noise background.

In general, therefore, once the receiver AGC begins to be "tickled" by the sum of sky noise plus preamp noise plus the noise of everything else ahead of the receiver, as indicated by very slight S-meter movement, it's time to increase antenna gain as far as practical.[2] More antenna gain is added until the target signal exceeds the total noise by an acceptable margin.

What about other noise sources? Noise from distant thunderstorms, the bane of DX HF work, is virtually nonexistent at VHF and above because the ionosphere rarely reflects VHF signals. Thunderstorm noise simply passes out into space for the most part. Automobile ignition noise and noise from urban industrial centers is less of a problem with VHF/UHF space communications because the antennas are generally pointed skyward. You thus turn a "deaf ear" toward the terrestrial noise sources.

But, there are noise sources much closer to home that can degrade your station's performance. Your azimuth and elevation rotators probably contain noise-generating electric motors. Slewing these motors probably increases your local noise. Computers and related digital equipment (such as packet radio TNCs) can generate noise into the GHz range. Turn them off when possible. If not, place them in a thoroughly RFI-proofed box. Turn off all TVs and microwave ovens.

Don't use BNC connectors if you can avoid them, and never use them outdoors. The bayonet connections are notoriously noisy when corroded. Use type "N," TNC or SMA connectors instead. Tighten all antenna hardware. In the most modern designs, the elements are insulated from the boom to avoid the intermittent contact and noise that results from inevitable corrosion of parts exposed to the weather. Make certain all station grounds and bonding straps are clean and tight. A poor ground can doom your otherwise excellent station to virtual deafness.

Is your receiver itself a significant noise source? If it uses a synthesizer as a frequency source, it could be. So-called phase noise can be a problem with some VHF/UHF radios just as this has recently become recognized as a factor in the noise floor of HF radios.[3]

Another way to improve the S/N ratio is to reduce receiver bandwidth. This can mean merely using the narrowest CW filter available commensurate with the signal spectrum of interest. In the ZRO Test, 10-WPM CW is sent so even the 200-Hz filters some top-notch radios offer are practical. Still, more improvement can be obtained by using advanced variable bandwidth audio filters. Some ZRO Test participants, using audio filtering, have successfully copied CW signals others couldn't even begin to detect.[4]

What is in use at the top stations? On 2 m, the top stations are using antennas with gains of 18 or 19 dBi, and a preamp with a noise figure in the 1 dB (or less) range and gain of 18 to 20 dB. A median good station generally runs 12 dB antenna gain and approximately the same preamp as the top station. For 70 cm, the top stations use antennas providing 20 or 22 dBi gain with a preamp in the 0.6 dB noise figure range, while yielding gain in the 18 dB range. A median good station on 70 cm runs about 13 or 14 dBi gain on the antenna and about the same preamp as the top stations. In all cases the preamp is at the antenna.

Especially at 70 cm and up, the sky is generally quiet and even a relatively weak signal from a satellite clearly stands out against the cold sky. For example, it is not uncommon for a first-rate ZRO competitor to be able to hear a milliwatt-level 70-cm downlink signal at a range of 22,000 miles!

At the low end of the capabilities scale, many regular satellite users get by with just 10 dB of antenna gain and 4-5 dB noise figure on both 2 m and 70 cm. They can hardly begin to hear the weak QSOs. The ZRO Test demonstrates how much room for improvement there is at some stations.

When we recognize how easy it is to have a station that hears well, it seems strange indeed that some would hog-tie themselves with ineffective or no measures at all to hear all that's on the satellites. The ZRO Test seeks to provide a means of evaluating both objectively (in absolute terms) and relatively (compared to one's peers) how well one's satellite station really hears. In that sense it has been an outstanding success.

Not only will the ZRO Test continue as soon as possible on AO-10 and Phase 3C, but, as mentioned last month, the ZRO Test is destined to foster a whole new breed of on-satellite competitions in the tradition of techno-sport. Next time we'll look forward to the new breed of techno-sport activities planned for the future.

Notes

[1]Any device that is above absolute zero degrees (−273° C) generates noise that is attributable to thermal agitation of its molecules and other lesser effects.

[2]When your receiver is sufficiently sensitive and quiet, such that sky noise comprises the majority of the noise to which it is subject, the receive system is said to be "sky noise limited." This is the point of departure for further improvements obtained through increased antenna gain.

[3]G. F. McCanless, Jr, KA4GSQ, "Using *QST*s to Choose an Old HF Rig," *QST*, Feb 1987, p 20.

[4]Jeff Bishop, W7ID, holds the world record. He is the only one ever to earn a Z8 rating on the Mode B (2-m downlink) session of the ZRO Test. He used special home-brew antennas, but we suspect his real advantage was in the very narrow (about 40 Hz) audio filter and earphones he used.

Information about satellites and AMSAT can be obtained for an SASE to AMSAT NA, PO Box 27, Washington DC 20044.

Conducted By
Vern "Rip" Riportella, WA2LQQ
PO Box 177, Warwick, NY 10990

Fun, Games and (Hopefully) Education on OSCARs, Part 3

Last month I explained what was required to excel in AMSAT's receive sensitivity test, the ZRO Test. This month let's pick up a new direction within the general topic of satellite techno-sport.

Amateur Radio has, at its heart, the notion of public service. Indeed, in the public consciousness, the image of amateurs rallying to provide vital communications during emergencies is one we actively promote. And in no small measure is that image unwarranted. In the future, Amateur Radio satellites could play a significant part in emergency communications in any of several ways. AMSAT's Phase 4 geosynchronous satellite plans include a significant public service component at their heart.[1]

There are possibilities and opportunities for experiments leading to real life-saving techniques that can commence now using current satellites. To dramatize this, to gain experience and proficiency in the field and to promote productive use of space resources, AMSAT is considering broadening its techno-sport base well beyond just the ZRO Test I've addressed over the past two months. In the future, satellite users can look forward to a fascinating new type of techno-sport that is both fun and fairly easy, but has some important implications for the whole field. I am talking about radiolocation by satellite.

In a techno-sport context, radiolocation by satellite is simply the game of trying to locate a hidden transmitter by using its satellite uplink signal together with special information about the satellite. In a real-world emergency, this technique can be used to locate downed aircraft or other vehicles in distress. In 1975, AMSAT pioneered a similar concept using the AMSAT-OSCAR 7 spacecraft. This led to the development of NASA's Search and Rescue Satellite (SARSAT) system.[2,3]

SARSAT made its first save after locating a downed Canadian aviator on September 10, 1982. Since then, SARSAT and its Russian counterpart, COSPAS, have together saved over 500 lives, mostly in remote territory. The principles are simple and, as will be shown, can be easily and reliably transported to Fuji-OSCAR 12, the newest OSCAR, which was launched in 1986.

Most aircraft and many ships have emergency locator transmitters (ELT) aboard. In an emergency the ELT is automatically activated. When its signal is detected by a SARSAT/COSPAS-equipped satellite, the ELT's location can be determined almost immediately, depending on the precise circumstances. Rescue units can then be dispatched quickly to the scene. The essential elements to this scenario are these: The lost vehicle has a radio aboard, but it is out of range of terrestrial VHF or UHF direction-finding (DF) equipment. But the SARSAT/COSPAS satellites, listening on the ELT frequencies of 121.5, 243 or 406 MHz, easily pick up the ELT transmissions and relay them to ground analysis sites. Here the Doppler shift of the ELT signals heard by the SARSAT/COSPAS satellites is analyzed, and a position is computed for the vehicle in distress.

The ELT's emissions can be detected anytime an ELT is within the satellite's footprint, which is about 4000 miles in diameter. Once an ELT emission is detected, the signal is transponded (relayed) to a Local User Terminal (LUT) in real time for analysis and computation of the ELT's QTH. Using the older version's system, the relay takes place in real time, requiring both the ELT and the LUT to be in the footprint concurrently. On newer versions, the satellite makes a time/frequency record of the ELT and dumps the record to the LUT on command. The LUT can thus obtain Doppler data on ELTs that the satellite has "seen" previously in its travels. Moreover, on the newer systems, the potential ambiguities inherent in the data provided by the older versions are quickly resolved within a few minutes from a single satellite.[4]

The SARSAT/COSPAS satellite contains a simple transponder that listens on 121.5, 243 or 406 MHz and regenerates the downlink at 1544.5 MHz. The analysis sites, established by the US, USSR, Canada and France, subject the resulting Doppler shift to careful scrutiny. The result is a quick determination of the ELT QTH, even in extremely rugged terrain.

Doppler shift is related to the closing or diverging velocity of the satellite to or from the ELT. Fig 1 shows the general shape of the curve of frequency versus time resulting from a SARSAT/COSPAS satellite approaching and then diverging from an ELT. The SARSAT/COSPAS ground station would receive a set of frequency and time data such as that which produced this curve. At acquisition of signal (AOS), the Doppler shift is maximum and positive; the signal heard on 1544.5 MHz is upshifted.[5] The Doppler shift decreases until the satellite reaches its closest point to the ELT at the Time of Closest Approach (TCA). At this point, the satellite moves in a tangential line to the ELT. Thus, the satellite is neither converging nor diverging from the ELT and the observed frequency is the actual ELT emission frequency, F0. Then, the satellite begins to move away from the ELT and the Doppler effect causes the observed frequency to be below the actual frequency as shown in the figure. Finally, at Loss of Signal (LOS), the Doppler shift has caused the observed frequency to be at its lowest.

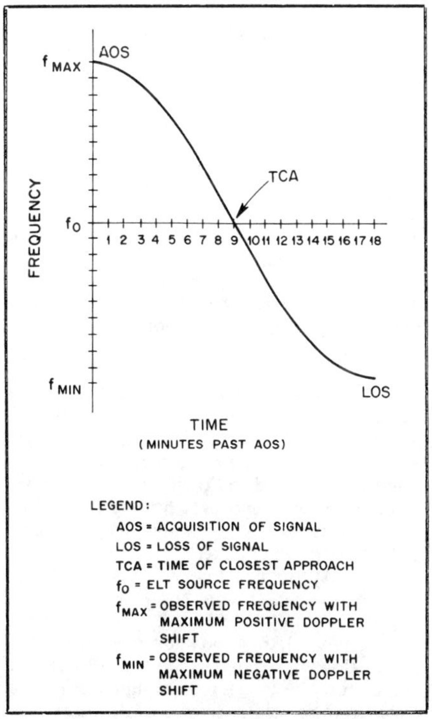

Fig 1—ELT typical Doppler-shift curve as observed by a typical SARSAT.

The mathematics underlying the ELT QTH determination are fairly simple. Knowing the ELT frequency, the observed frequency and the position of the satellite at various times is sufficient. The angle between the path of the satellite and the ELT at any instant is found by calculating the arc-cosine of the ratio of observed frequency to ELT frequency multiplied by the ratio of the speed of light to the satellite's velocity.[6]

Using the same principles, SARSAT/COSPAS radio-location techniques can be performed on FO-12. FO-12 has an uplink on 2 m and a downlink on 70 cm. Using the Mode-JA transponder, it should be possible for a clever, well-equipped amateur to locate a hidden transmitter to within a small region in just a few minutes.

To test this theory, AMSAT will begin a series of demonstrations on how the technique works in the near future. Simultaneously, AMSAT will publish a guide to calculations and required instrumentation. At a minimum, the equipment required will include a precision frequency counter to measure the downlink frequency, a digital clock and a computer to display the position of the satellite and to provide a detailed ephemeris of its time and position.

To make the demonstrations more interesting, AMSAT will format the event in the guise of a techno-sport competition. Certificates will be offered and the most accurate participants will be specifically cited for their achievements.

Next month we'll investigate yet another radio location by satellite technique using the so-called time-difference of arrival (TDOA) principle. For more information about AMSAT and OSCAR satellites, send a business-sized SASE to AMSAT, PO Box 27, Washington, DC 20044.

[1]J. King, V. Riportella and R. Wallio, "OSCAR at 25: The Amateur Space Program Comes of Age," *QST*, Dec 1986 and Jan, 1987.
[2]*AMSAT Satellite Report*, No. 43/44, Oct 11, 1982.
[3]*AMSAT Newsletter*, Vol VIII, No. 1, Mar 1976.
[4]A more detailed system analysis will appear in a future edition of *QEX*, the advanced experimenter magazine from ARRL and AMSAT.
[5]Assuming the ELT is on 406 MHz and the 1544.5-MHz downlink Doppler shift is subtracted out, the net Doppler shift for the ELT, as heard from SARSAT/COSPAS, is about +10 kHz, maximum. Satellite velocity in orbit is about 4.5 miles per second.
[6]The *QEX* article will discuss potential ambiguities and how in practice they are eliminated or mitigated.

Conducted By
Vern "Rip" Riportella, WA2LQQ
PO Box 177, Warwick, NY 10990

Fun, Games and (Hopefully) Education on OSCARs, Part 4

Last month, I introduced the idea of hidden-transmitter location using OSCARs and the SARSAT/COSPAS series of international satellites. This month, I'll continue with the theme of locating a hidden transmitter using a satellite. As before, this discussion is within the context of Techno-Sport, an AMSAT concept for learning interesting and useful tools and methods in radio and space technology while having fun in the process.

Measuring the Doppler shift of an emitter (such as Fuji-OSCAR 12) or a reflecting object (such as your automobile when illuminated by the local constable's radar) is a convenient and easy means of detecting relative motion. The problem is that when the relative motion is low (in terms of wavelength and velocity), Doppler shift is low, too. Thus, with police radars, there is a lower limit to the relative velocity that can be measured. Similarly, if the frequency of a satellite source is low enough or its relative motion is sufficiently low, the Doppler shift may be too low to measure with any useful degree of accuracy.

For example, when AMSAT-OSCAR 10 was first launched, one of the first orders of business was to locate it precisely. This was not as easy as it may seem, because, even though the Air Force's SPACETRACK system can and does track thousands of objects the size of AO-10 at geosynchronous altitudes,[1] the most sensitive tracking systems are reserved for important defense missions. The more common, lower-priority tracking systems are hard-pressed to track an object the size of AO-10 several tens of thousands of miles distant. So, AMSAT engineers devised their own means of tracking AO-10 that did not rely on radar, per se. Because AO-10 moves relatively slowly (especially at apogee, the highest point in its orbit), the Doppler shift method is not suitable. Instead, AMSAT engineers measured the round-trip transit time for pulses originated on the ground.

This system is simple in concept and, except for the sophisticated number-crunching techniques applied to the resultant data, simple in practice. A pulse is sent to AO-10 on its 70-cm uplink. Simultaneously, a clock is started. The AO-10 Mode B transponder receives the pulse and regenerates it on the 2-meter downlink. The returned pulse is received by the originating station and the clock is stopped. Because the transponder delay time is known (from prior measurements made on the ground), and the propagation velocity of the radio wave is known, it is easy to convert the measured round-trip transit time into a range (distance) from the earth station to the satellite at that instant. The result of this measurement does not determine the position of the satellite, merely a range. To be slightly more precise, the satellite has been determined to lie on the surface of a sphere, the radius of which is the measured range.

To isolate the satellite's position to a relatively small domain on the surface of the sphere requires more measurements. One approach is to make additional measurements from other locations. Thus, a series of incongruent spherical surfaces is determined. Ideally, they all will intersect at a point—the location of the satellite at that instant. A real-time computer analysis could, in theory, provide real-time tracking this way. In practice, however, the measurements are fed into a computer program and the orbital characteristics themselves are determined.[2] Given this, the position of the satellite can be predicted at any time in the future, because the motion is fully understood in time and space.

The uncertainties in measuring range to the satellite and reducing range to location are many and varied. Moreover, because of irregularities in the data and miscellaneous uncertainties, what normally results is a series of onion-skin-like probability densities. The outer shell represents high probability that the satellite is contained within the volume of that shell. That is, the more precisely one says he knows the location, the more likely he is to be wrong. Conversely, it's easy to say the satellite lies within a 1000-mile sphere, but quite difficult to say it's within a 10-mile sphere. As more data is added and the measurements are refined, the volume of space representing an arbitrary uncertainty value decreases. If the process of data collection and analysis were to continue indefinitely, the onion would shrink to a point of 100% certainty.

Using these and similar methods, AMSAT engineers were able to locate AO-10 to within a few cubic miles over a range of about 25,000 miles.[3] A more advanced version of this technique may be employed in the future.

What would happen if we turned the situation around a bit? In the foregoing example, the locations of the tracking stations were well known, but the orbit was initially unknown. Suppose the opposite were the case. Let's say the orbit is well known, but your location is unknown. Could you determine your own location? The answer is definitely *yes.* In fact, a vast array of satellites (called Global Positioning Satellites, GPS) is in use by the government and private sectors for precisely that purpose. With GPS, several satellites are in view of your location at any given time. You have a special receiver with a powerful portable computer built in. The GPS send precise time signals. The computer in your receiver measures the arrival time of the signals. By comparing the arrival time of the signals from several satellites, whose precise orbits and positions the computer knows, the computer can work backwards to determine *your* position to within a few dozen feet.[4]

By rearranging the knowns and unknowns a bit, one can structure an interesting Techno-Sport challenge for those OSCAR enthusiasts who like to test their technical talent in an interesting and educational event. By adding some accuracy incentives, a healthy competitive event results. This is how it might be structured.

An "unknown uplinker" sends a signal on the uplink of AO-10 (or Phase 3C). You're listening on the downlink. You know exactly where AO-10 is (from your AMSAT orbital data and your computer), thus you know how long it took for the downlink signal to reach you.[5] But, you don't know how long it took the uplinker's signal to reach the satellite, so you can't locate him.

Now suppose the signal is one that carries special timing information. Let's say the uplinker takes a WWV signal he receives on HF and retransmits it on the uplink. You listen to WWV on one receiver, and the downlink on the other receiver. *Voilà!* The difference in arrival times of the signal direct from WWV and the signal as relayed by the uplinker through the satellite contains most of the information you need to determine the uplinker's location.

The other piece of information needed is your distance from WWV. More precisely, you need to know the radio path distance from your location to WWV. Because you probably hear WWV via skywave, the exact path length may be difficult to ascertain. This adds one of the major uncertainties to the determination of the uplinker's location. But, with reasonable care in measurement, an estimate of the location should be possible in an hour or less of measurements. Moreover, by combining your measurements with someone else's at a widely disparate location in a cooperative determination, the uncertainties involved should be reduced.

The solution to the problem lies in establishing the distance from the uplinker's location to the satellite, because all of the other distances are known.[6] When you hear the WWV signal relayed by the satellite, you can determine how far away from the satellite the originator is. Because the satellite is moving, if but slowly, the transit time between the satellite and the uplinker changes, too. By carefully logging the changes in path length, the uplinker can be located by using a succession of intersecting spheres as described earlier. With time, the uncertainty in the exact location is reduced until a good guess can be made as to where the "unknown uplinker" is.

I'll be off until September. When I return, I'll discuss in more detail the workings of this newest technique in radiolocation by satellite in the Techno-Sport context. To get more information on this and other AMSAT satellite projects, write to AMSAT at the address given below.[7]

Notes

1 About 22,300 miles.

2 An ephemeris is generated that provides a mathematical means for describing the satellite's position along with the time it will appear at that position. The Keplerian data provided by NASA via AMSAT is a special form of this data.

3 That is, a few cubic miles out of a potential volume of over 60 trillion cubic miles of space!

4 Several automobile manufacturers have demonstrated GPS systems in prototype cars. A receiver, computer and special map projection on a CRT show your exact location even while you're moving. Other companies are mounting devices on their vehicles that will report their position to headquarters so each vehicle can be closely monitored.

5 Radio waves travel at about 186,300 mi/s in a vacuum. That works out to about 1 foot per nanosecond, or about 1017 feet per microsecond. Measuring a microsecond in your typical ham shack is a lot easier than it formerly was, thanks to inexpensive digital counters.

6 Your location, the satellite's location, WWV location and all the distances between them can be determined.

7 Information about AMSAT can be obtained by sending a business-size SASE to AMSAT, PO Box 27, Washington, DC 20044.

Conducted By
Vern "Rip" Riportella, WA2LQQ
PO Box 177, Warwick, NY 10990

Prospects for Mobile and Portable OSCAR Operation

Never is the advantage of using OSCAR satellites more obvious than when the sunspot cycle is at its low ebb. While the MUF hovers in the 15-MHz range, and would-be 10- and 15-meter band users reluctantly slide into the ever-more-crowded 20-meter band, satellite use goes merrily on its way!

OSCARs historically have used frequencies that were only mildly affected by F2-layer density. Mode A transponders, such as those used on AMSAT-OSCARs 6, 7 and 8 and all the Russian RS-series, use a 2-meter uplink and a 10-meter downlink. Occasionally, during periods of high solar activity, the ionosphere becomes sufficiently radio-opaque to noticeably attenuate 10-meter radiation through the ionosphere. Listening to AO-7 or RS-1 as it passed "behind" various attenuating zones while its apparent signal strength varied by 10 dB or more was an educating experience. It was as if a buddy of yours were groping through the fog with a flashlight. One moment he could be seen fairly clearly, the next only dimly.

There are, however, more reasons to want to move up in OSCAR frequency than just to avoid the occasional highly attenuating ionosphere. Spectrum capacity and obtainable antenna directivity are two other very strong motivations for moving to the UHF regime in future satellites. In fact, the current AO-10 satellite has set the course with its combination Mode B and Mode L transponders.[1] Future satellites such as Phase 3C, to be launched later this year, will use a combination of Modes B, J, L and S (see Table 1).

Table 1
Phase 3C Transponder Frequencies

Mode B

Uplink: 435.425-435.575 MHz
Downlink: 145.975-145.825 MHz
General Beacon: 145.8125 MHz
Engineering Beacon: 145.975 MHz

Mode JL

L Uplink: 1269.575-1269.325 MHz
L Downlink: 435.725-435.975 MHz
General Beacon: 435.650 MHz
J Uplink: 145.82-145.86 MHz } Option 1
J Downlink: 435.93-435.97 MHz }
or
J Uplink: 144.44-144.48 MHz } Option 2
J Downlink: 435.93-435.97 MHz }

Digital Mode L (RUDAK)

Uplink: 1269.675 MHz
Downlink: 435.675 MHz

Mode S

Uplink: 435.625 MHz
Downlink: 2401.337 MHz
S Beacon: 2401.267 MHz

Notes

(i) It is currently undecided which of the two J input options shall be implemented. In either option, there is an overlap whereupon signals originated at 24 cm and 2 meters can result in a downlink between 435.93 and 435.97 MHz.
(ii) RUDAK is a digital-only transponder that will use PSK.
(iii) Mode S will be a soft-limited FM transponder that can also accommodate up to four SSB signals.
(iv) Although minor revisions in frequency may be anticipated, the frequencies presented are those currently planned.

Never is it as obvious why it is strongly desirable to move up in frequency with OSCAR than when one closely looks at future satellite systems. Many future satellites will continue the high-orbit tradition begun with AO-10. In its high, elliptical orbit, AO-10 can relay signals originating from nearly a hemisphere, putting in contact all those within its view. And it can do this for hours on end. Phase 3C will continue this tradition in another elliptical orbit with improved characteristics for the higher latitudes. Discussions have begun regarding orbital options for a possible follow-on called Phase 3D. Some very clever combinations of two or more satellites in true Molniya (elliptical) orbits yield many of the desirable characteristics of a geosynchronous orbiting satellite while reducing substantially the cost and engineering burden of the latter. In any case, the future high-flying satellites will glimpse much of the earth during the course of their orbit.

Thus, while viewing so much of the earth's surface, it is necessary to have a QSO capacity (spectrum) commensurate with the potential user-load. Where can the necessary spectrum of several hundred contiguous kilohertz be found? Quite plainly, the only option is in the UHF regime.

Another reason for the appeal of UHF use with OSCAR is the reduced size of highly directional antennas as compared with VHF or HF antennas of comparable gain. Using large, heavy antennas on a spacecraft is not just inconvenient, it's impossible. Launcher constraints of size, mass and cost limit the types of antennas to be used aboard OSCAR. From a high-flying OSCAR such as AO-10, the earth subtends an angle of about 16 degrees when viewed from apogee. So it's notably wasteful to scatter RF across the cosmos using an antenna with, say, a 45-degree 3-dB beamwidth. Rather, one wants to concentrate all the RF toward the earth. Given the constraints mentioned, one can best achieve this using UHF or above and the compact, highly directional antennas achievable there.

A similar situation exists with your ground station. You want to concentrate as much power as possible in the direction of the spacecraft and, conversely, avoid spraying the sky with RF that misses the target. Again, this is most effectively achieved with a given-sized array when the wavelength used is relatively small, ie, the frequency is in the UHF (or higher) regime. "Well," you might retort, "I've got a few acres of real estate here and don't mind putting up a real monster antenna to work OSCAR." But even though you might thoroughly enjoy merely the prospect of establishing an aluminum monster to work future OSCARs, and even if we ignored the strong spacecraft engineering motivations for using UHF and above, using VHF and below would make much less likely one of the most striking and powerful future prospects of OSCARs: portable and/or mobile OSCAR use. Using UHF and SHF equipment now becoming available, it is conceivable to have highly portable or even mobile-in-motion OSCAR QSOs on a regular basis in the not-too-distant future, say 3 to 4 years. The gating technologies are just about available, and early conceptual designs for both Phase 3D and Phase 4 (geosynchronous) systems suggest a strong potential for portable and/or mobile use. But the concept rests totally on using UHF and SHF frequencies to achieve the link budgets required for reliable communication.

With just a smidgen of imagination one can envision satellite-portable terminals being erected at remote locations for emergency communications or even sport. Imagine pulling into a major disaster zone with your four-by-four truck, unloading a few modest shipping containers, assembling a half dozen connectors, setting up a tripod, aiming at the sky and being in touch with the hemisphere within a half hour of arriving! Further, imagine connecting a portable FM repeater to your satellite terminal making it a gateway terminal and affording local 2-meter emergency communicators a channel to the satellite and hundreds of other stations as required. Or, by interfacing a portable linear translator to your terminal, provide integrated digital and voice services in/out of the affected area. Here we might find high-speed packet data working side by side with voice QSOs linking the affected area with support activities across the hemisphere.

Perhaps the ultimate in OSCAR technology will be attained when OSCAR mobile-in-motion QSOs are regularly afforded. Yet the day when this too will be reality is fast approaching. The enabling technology may be available as derivatives of NASA's so-called MSAT-X project. Later this year the FCC is expected to rule on several commercial applicants' proposals to implement a mobile satellite communications system. It is a distinct possibility that amateurs may obtain this capability nearly concurrent with commercial applications.[2]

Whether for spectrum availability, ionospheric transparency or reducing the size of antennas, the move to higher satellite frequencies is both desirable and inevitable. The prospect of promoting smaller, more efficient earth stations for use by mobile, portable and apartment-dwelling amateurs is a highly attractive one. And the prospect of using gateway access and integrated digital/voice channels over future OSCARs builds on concepts now being architected.[3]

Next month we'll take a closer look at what a gateway is and how it functions.

Notes

[1] Mode B uses a 70-cm uplink and a 2-meter downlink. Mode L uses 24 cm up and 70 cm down.
[2] Interestingly, one of the commercial proposers for MSAT-X would use technology first used aboard AO-10. Thus, in this sense, Amateur Radio satellites are carrying on a venerable tradition of ham radio dating back decades, ie, technologies developed by amateurs finding commercial applications.
[3] Information on getting started on OSCAR may be obtained from the author for a business-sized SASE to the address shown above.

Conducted By
Vern "Rip" Riportella, WA2LQQ
PO Box 177, Warwick, NY 10990

Waves in Rotation: The Challenge of Circular Polarization

Few topics in Amateur Radio elicit the intense fascination of antennas. But the "field" really becomes interesting when antennas designed for space communication are factored in.

In space communications, the earth's magnetic field can dramatically affect radio waves traveling over long distances. The effect is to rotate the plane of polarization. To reduce the adverse effects of this polarization rotation, antennas designed for space communication often employ a special form of polarization called "circular polarization" (CP), a combination of the familiar vertical and horizontal polarization generated by common antennas. What makes CP desirable for space communications?

It was known early in the 19th Century that some substances are optically active; the plane of polarization of light passing through these substances is rotated. In 1845, Michael Faraday discovered that some substances, which normally show no optical activity, can be made to rotate by subjecting them to a strong magnetic field. This came to be known as the "Faraday Effect."

Radio waves and light waves are basically the same phenomenon. Early radio experimenters soon found that the Faraday Effect was detectable in low-frequency radio waves where the geomagnetic field works to rotate polarization. The amount of rotation of the wave's plane of polarization depends on its frequency, how far the wave travels in the magnetic field, how strong the field is, and the wave's angular relation to the magnetic field lines. Briefly, the degree of wave plane rotation *increases* with:

1) increasing magnetic field strength

2) increasing path length the wave travels along the field lines

3) increasing alignment of the wave plane and field lines.

The degree of wave plane rotation *decreases* with increasing frequency, ie, VHF is affected less than HF, UHF less than VHF, SHF less than UHF, and so on.

To someone watching TV Channel 7 at a range of 50 miles, the Faraday Effect is negligible. But take roughly the same frequencies (around 200 MHz) and stretch the path over 10,000 or 20,000 miles, and Faraday Effect rotation (or simply Faraday Rotation, FR) can greatly affect received signal polarization.

The problem arises when, owing to random incoming wave polarizations, the wave and the receive antenna are not in the same plane. The result is a widely varying received signal strength because of cross-polarization losses. Cross-polarization losses are familiar to anyone who has had difficulty using a horizontal Yagi to access a vertically polarized repeater antenna. An orbiting spacecraft transmitting to earth over a long path using UHF could very well originate a signal using horizontal polarization only to have it arrive vertically polarized. Frequently, the case is that the arriving wave's polarization is essentially random and changing at any instant.

The solution most often used for reliable space communications is two-fold. Since FR is less of a problem with increasing frequency, space communications are best accomplished at the highest practical frequency. And, when FR at the chosen frequency can still be a problem, CP is used.

In a practical sense, the frequencies between 0.1 to around 2.0 GHz is the range where CP finds its greatest utility. Frequencies below 0.1 GHz are seldom used for space communications; frequencies above 2.0 GHz are affected by FR only minimally. But, since many of the OSCAR users' prime frequencies lie in the area where FR is significant (0.1 to 2.0 GHz), CP antennas must be employed for best results.

The CP antenna puts equal amounts of RF in each plane. The result is that the effects of FR are nullified. The price paid, however, is that the power in any given plane is less than if linear polarization were used. If one knew what the polarization would be all the time, one would use linear polarization and ensure the receive antenna was well aligned with it. But since the factors that control FR may all be varying at once, putting power into all planes with CP assures that when the signal is received on a CP antenna, the *average* received signal power will be higher than if linear polarization had been used.

Moreover, with OSCAR satellites in particular, the additional QSB caused by the spinning of the spacecraft most often makes CP doubly desirable. Indeed, many antennas built into OSCAR satellites are specifically designed for CP to reduce both FR and spin caused by QSB.[1]

CP is somewhat more difficult to generate than linear polarization. A CP antenna combines vertical and horizontal components in a particular time relation or "phase." This is accomplished most easily using an antenna not encountered in HF work, but quite familiar in the space communications context: the helix. The corkscrew-like radiating element of the helix radiates axially a wave whose plane of polarization rotates as it leaves the transmitting antenna. Imagine a ribbon twisting off into the distance as the wave travels away from the source helix. The appearance of the twisting ribbon gives us a clue as to why CP works well in space communications. If the receive antenna is linear, no matter what its current orientation, the wave will never be cross polarized for very long. If the receive antenna is CP, the wave is always in the "right" plane as it's received. In other words, a CP antenna "hears" equally well in all planes.

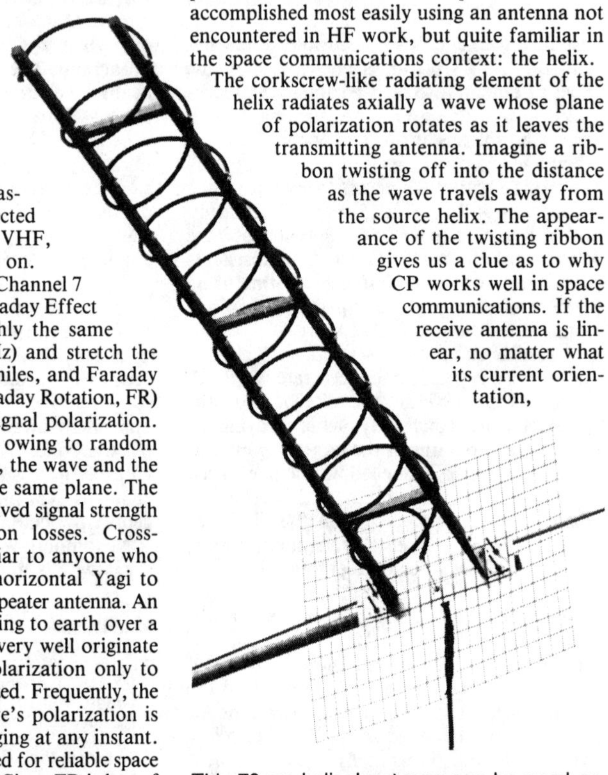

This 70-cm helical antenna can be used as part of a switchable system that provides both types of circular polarization.

The direction the ribbon twists is called the "sense" of the wave. Right Hand CP (RHCP) rotates clockwise as seen from behind the source antenna, and Left Hand CP (LHCP) rotates counterclockwise. Thus, the twist of the imaginary ribbon is either clockwise or counterclockwise, corresponding to RHCP or LHCP, respectively. The rate of twist is one complete turn (360 degrees) per wavelength. For best results, both the transmitting and receiving antennas should have the same sense.

Helices may be the easiest way to generate CP and one of the most popular types of homebrewed satellite antennas. It's not the only way to get CP, by far. Many OSCAR users employ a pair of specially phased Yagis to generate CP in the 2-m through 24-cm bands. The two identical Yagis have their elements mounted orthogonally (at right angles; thus "crossed Yagis"), either in two separate antennas side by side or two separate Yagis sharing a common boom.

CP can be generated by a variety of antenna types. The use of CP antennas for space communications is essential in many cases. Moreover, the bizarre shapes and configurations used to generate CP serve to enhance the already entrenched mystique that antennas enjoy with amateurs.[2]

[1]The QSB caused by the spinning of the satellite is called "spin modulation." On frequency, it sounds like rapid amplitude modulation, or flutter, of the downlink, and depends on the angular velocity of the spacecraft about its spin axis and the specific antenna pattern involved.

[2]To learn more about some of the interesting aspects of Amateur Radio space communications, write to AMSAT for free information about getting started with OSCARs. An SASE to AMSAT, PO Box 27, Washington, DC 20044 will do the trick.

Conducted By
Vern "Rip" Riportella, WA2LQQ
P.O. Box 177, Warwick, NY 10990

Working OSCAR—The Basics

The fascinating thing about Amateur Radio satellites is . . . well, quite frankly, there's not just one thing but rather an array of features that make working OSCAR today among Amateur Radio's most fascinating, challenging and rewarding activities. Last time (June 1985 *QST*), we highlighted a few of the many activities and modes to be found on OSCAR. Now let's look a little closer at what it takes to get started using OSCAR satellites.

There are four basic topics you'll need to be familiar with to succeed on OSCAR:

1) When and where to point your antenna (tracking).

2) Basic transponder characteristics (frequencies and modes).

3) Basic station characteristics (transmit power, receive sensitivity).

4) Basic operating practice (band plan, protocol, courtesies).

First, you need to know when and where to look for the satellite (tracking). In essence, you need to know when the satellite you're interested in working is within view of your QTH. If you've got one of the new, little personal computers, AMSAT has a tracking program that makes (tracking) life very straightforward and easy. A review of the ARRL's *Satellite Experimenter's Handbook* (SEH) is recommended for a basic understanding of what's going on with the satellite—that is, its motion around the earth. But, just as you don't need to understand hydraulics to use the automatic transmission in your car, you don't need to understand Kepler's equations to use a computer to track OSCAR. But it helps conceptually to have a basic grasp of the motion of the satellites across the sky.

Several manual means of satellite tracking are also available. These aids are available from ARRL (OSCARLOCATOR), ZRO Technical Devices (Satellipse, Satellabe), and others.[1] The manual devices resemble circular slide rules with maps and various curves on them. When you enter a reference time and position for a certain satellite, the locators will tell you where the same satellite is at the time you select. Significantly, it will also tell you which way to point your antennas (azimuth and elevation) to zoom in on the OSCAR you want to work. Although the manual tracking aids or locators lack the accuracy, speed and general pizzazz of computer tracking methods, they are inexpensive and fairly easy to learn to use.

On the other hand, our first tracking computer was a Sinclair ZX-81, which I purchased for $29.95 plus an extra $10 for more memory. I got the AMS-81 tracking program from the AMSAT Software Exchange for $10 and had an old TV monitor just perfect for the job.[2] So for $50 and no sweat at all, I had a first-rate tracking computer system that gave me high accuracy and did nothing but plot orbits for me.

Second, you need to know what frequency to transmit on and what frequency to listen on. The popular current mode of operation on AMSAT-OSCAR 10 (AO-10) is called Mode B. That means you transmit your signal to the satellite (uplink) in the vicinity of 435.1 MHz, and you listen for your signal (downlink) from the satellite on about 145.9 MHz. Moreover, since you are operating crossband, you operate full duplex—that is, you transmit and receive concurrently. Why crossband? The hardware required to provide sufficient isolation for in-band, full-duplex operation (similar to a terrestrial FM repeater) would be too massive to fit aboard a cramped-satellite. So the traditional satellite solution is to have cross-band, full-duplex operation. OSCAR satellite modes are listed in Table 1. A Mode B band-plan chart is shown in *The 1985 ARRL Handbook*, page 23-6.[3]

Table 1
OSCAR Operating Modes

Mode	Uplink Band	Downlink Band
A	2 m (145 MHz)	10 m (29 MHz)
B	70 cm (435 MHz)	2 m (145 MHz)
L	24 cm (1269 MHz)	70 cm (436 MHz)
S	70 cm (436 MHz)	13 cm (2401 MHz)
J	2 m (145 MHz)	70 cm (435 MHz)
LJ	2 m/23 cm	70 cm
K	15 m	10 m

Third, you need to have a basic understanding of how to establish a station to use AO-10 in the mode you choose. You will need information to help you decide what equipment need be added to your existing shack to make it OSCAR-compatible.

Fourth and finally, you need to be familiar with the operating practice and operating schedule for the satellites and modes you choose to operate. Operating schedules can be learned from AMSAT newsletters and nets.[4] Operating practice can be learned from many reference sources, including the ARRL's *SEH* and AMSAT's beginner's manual.

Each of these topics will be covered in detail in future columns. Meanwhile, here's something you can do to get started right away. Simply take the first small step: Listen for AO-10. Make an attempt to hear AO-10 on its next available pass. All you need is a 2-meter all-mode receiver and antenna. Having a 2-meter preamp is not absolutely essential, but it makes a very, very significant improvement. Borrow or purchase one if you can. Then write or call the AMSAT Area Coordinator in your region and ask for a copy of the latest orbital predictions for your area. (You should offer to contribute to the postage costs.) Ask the Area Coordinator to help you point your beam in the right direction if AO-10 is in view then. Check to see if it's in Mode B or Mode L. You want Mode B if you want to listen to the 2-meter downlink. If you don't know who your Area Coordinator is, you can find out by calling toll-free to the Chief Area Coordinator, Jack Somers, WA6VGS, at 1-800-421-6631.

If you're lucky, the Area Coordinator will be close by, and a short drive to his QTH will result in your acquiring the key tracking data for your area. The computer-tracking printouts will tell you the azimuth and elevation to point your antenna to track AO-10 for the next several days. Most newcomers don't have an elevation rotor. In that case, you may have some difficulty hearing AO-10 when it's above 20- or 30-degree elevation. As a start, you might select a listening period during which AO-10 is within 20 degrees or so of the horizon.

Start out by listening to the general beacon on 145.810 MHz. The frequency may be slightly different because of the Doppler shift

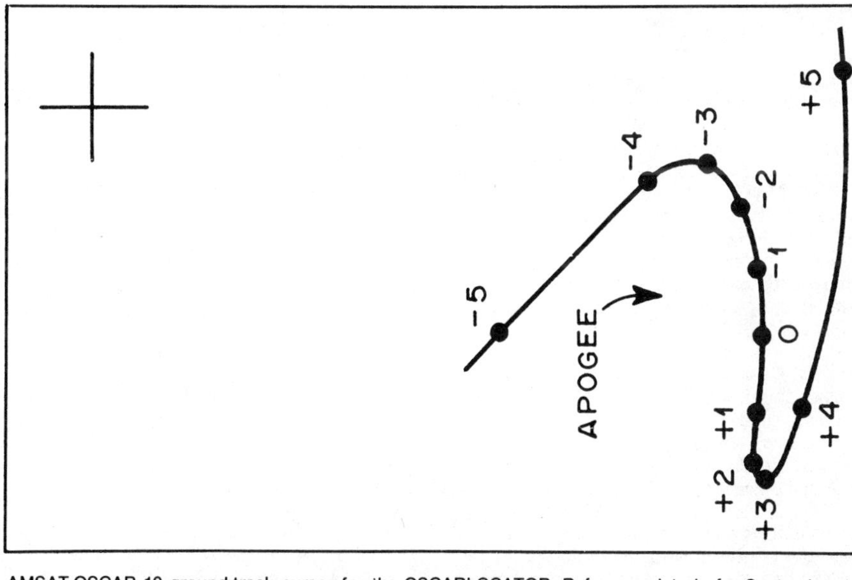

AMSAT-OSCAR 10 ground-track cursor for the OSCARLOCATOR. Reference data is for September 1.

effect exhibited by the fast-moving satellite. Use your receiver's USB or CW mode to listen. You may hear a buzzing sound, which is special phase-shift-keyed (PSK) telemetry, or you may catch the CW or RTTY bulletins, depending on exactly when you listen. The beacon changes mode in recurring half-hour patterns (beacons will be detailed in a subsequent column).[5]

Chances are, if you don't use a preamplifier, you will hear the beacon weakly or not at all. A good preamp is really very helpful, especially if your antenna is not terribly good or is in poor repair. Also, if you have a long run of transmission line between your antenna and your rig, the preamp will help most if mounted at the antenna and remotely powered from the shack. For a short test, you might consider battery powering the preamp and locating it at the antenna, just to see how well it works that way.

In any case, try tuning up to center band, 145.900 MHz. If the transponder is on, you should hear dozens of CW and SSB signals in the transponder passband. Use the USB position to receive. The convention on all the transponders is to use an uplink mode that produces USB on the downlink. Since AO-10 Mode B is an inverting linear transponder, LSB on the uplink results in USB on the downlink.

If your 2-meter station consists of a 2-meter beam with at least 10-dB gain and you have a preamp, if the transponder is on, you'll be hearing lots of activity from local as well as DX stations. And at this point, you will have linked yourself for the first time into the worldwide network of satellite users.

But if you're disappointed in what appear to be weak signals on the 2-meter downlink, take heart. There really *is* a lot of 2-meter signal there, but your everyday, off-the-shelf 2-meter rig may need some help with the AO-10 signal. Most of the 2-meter radios sold have only marginal receiver front ends and really perk up with the addition of a new GaAsFET preamp out front. "Wow," you'll exclaim, "What a difference!"[6]

It is often helpful to a have a standard frame of reference or benchmark to determine just how well you *are* hearing on 2 meters. To provide just such a benchmark, AMSAT began a series of on-the-satellite tests last spring. The tests are similar to the ARRL's frequency-measurement tests (FMT), except AMSAT's test works in the amplitude domain while ARRL's obviously works the frequency domain. AMSAT's receive sensitivity tests offer a convenient way to establish how well your station is performing both in an absolute sense and compared to other operators. For those who demonstrate various levels of proficiency on the test, an AMSAT Technical Achievement Award, called the ZRO Memorial Station Engineering Award, is available. The test frequency is 145.840, and the next scheduled event will be later this month.[7]

First steps in a new endeavor are often long remembered. Many new OSCAR enthusiasts assert that their first OSCAR QSO was even more exciting than their first-ever QSO. Of course, you'll have to find that out for yourself. Meanwhile, your portable ionosphere whirs overhead, awaiting your signal. Once you hear OSCAR's beckoning call, you'll be hard pressed to resist for long!

Next time, we'll take a look at the antennas used in OSCAR work.

Notes

[1]ZRO Technical Devices, P.O. Box 11, Endicott, NY 13760.

[2]AMSAT Software Exchange, P.O. Box 27, Washington, DC 20044.

[3]A copy of the Mode B band plan is available free for a business-sized s.a.s.e. to the author at the address at the top of this column.

[4]See notes to the June 1985 column for nets and newsletter information.

[5]A free handout showing the general beacon program schedule is available from this column conductor for a business-sized s.a.s.e.

[6]Ads for 2-meter preamps are found in this *QST*. Refer to the ad section.

[7]A free information booklet about receive sensitivity and the AMSAT ZRO-Memorial Technical Achievement award is available for a business-sized s.a.s.e. with 39¢ postage affixed. Request from this column conductor at address above.

Amateur Satellite Communications

Conducted By
Douglas A. Loughmiller, KO5I
PO Box 247, Brookston, TX 75421

A Look at Satellite Modes

In response to a large number of questions recently asked by newcomers, this month's column examines one of the most basic concepts of satellite operation—satellite modes.

As with the rest of Amateur Radio, OSCAR operation has its own jargon. And to effectively participate, you'll need to become familiar with the lingo. One term that seems to confuse many OSCAR newcomers is the term "mode."

Part of the confusion may stem from the fact that the term mode usually refers to the type of emission used in an amateur transmission—such as CW, SSB or SSTV.

For satellite operations however, the term mode takes on a new meaning. Unlike traditional HF operation, satellite QSOs require the simultaneous use of two frequencies in different amateur bands. In fact, standard satellite operations are full duplex—the operator transmits on one band while receiving on another, monitoring his signal through the satellite's transponder.

The signal transmitted to the spacecraft is called the uplink, and the signal received from the spacecraft is known as the downlink. The term mode identifies the various uplink and downlink combinations used by today's OSCARs. It's a quick way for operators around the world to recognize the operational requirements of the satellite in question. As the Amateur-Satellite Service has evolved, various groups around the world have experimented with a variety of frequency combinations.

A satellite operator referring to Mode A (2-meter uplink, 10-meter downlink), for instance, is much like an HF operator referring to 20 meters—it's a reference to a specific point in the spectrum. Remember, in satellite work, a mode designator does not refer to the station's emission type, it refers to the "band" being used, or more correctly, the combination of bands being employed.

Table 1 outlines the mode designators for the various combinations of bands used by amateur satellites to date.

Although Table 1 provides an analytical answer to the question "What do all of those letters mean?" a look at the origins of the mode designators might be of interest to OSCAR newcomers and old-timers alike.

In the Beginning...

Defining mode designators for satellite transponders didn't become an issue until the launch of OSCAR 7, the first OSCAR to have more than one transponder aboard.

LOOK IN THE BOOK AND SEE IF THAT'S A RIGHT-HAND OR A LEFT-HAND HELIX FOR THE UPLINK!

Initially, choosing a mode designator was straightforward. Because the transponder that used the 2-meter uplink and the 10-meter downlink had previously flown on OSCAR 6, it became known as Mode A. The second transponder, with the new 70-cm uplink and 2-meter downlink, became known as Mode B.

Following the successful launch of OSCAR 7, attention turned to the construction of OSCAR 8. Because of the heavy use of 2 meters for terrestrial communications in Japan, our Japanese colleagues proposed a new transponder configuration that inverted the Mode B uplinks and downlinks, making the signals more accessible to Japanese satellite enthusiasts. This new transponder, with a 2-meter uplink and a 70-cm downlink, was designated Mode J.

Later advances in digital store-and-forward techniques demonstrated with the launch of Fuji-OSCAR 12 produced even more refined Mode J capabilities. Operations via FO-12's linear transponder were designated Mode JA (for analog), while the digital store-and-forward mode became known as Mode JD (for digital).

Other transponder configurations were labeled according to their geographic origins. In 1987, RS-10/11 was launched by our Soviet colleagues. This satellite was built at the Tsiolkovskiy State Museum of the History of Cosmonautics in Kaluga, USSR.

This unique spacecraft contains a multiple transponder suite, including two configurations that were flown for the first time. The first became known as Mode K. It uses a 15-meter uplink and a 10-meter downlink. The second transponder configuration became known as Mode T. It uses a 15-meter uplink and a 2-meter downlink. The mode designators were taken from the names of the city and the institute where the spacecraft was developed.

Rounding out the growing list of transponder designators are Modes L and S. These designators were chosen because the transponders use frequencies in the microwave spectrum. Above 1 GHz, various blocks of microwave frequencies are identified by letter designators. In the case of the Mode L transponder, its uplink is located in the 23-cm L band at 1.2 GHz. Likewise, the Mode S transponder's downlink appears in the 13-cm S band at 2.4 GHz.

There are several designators that use two letters. These are combinations of transponders that share a mutual uplink or downlink.

I hope this brief look at satellite terminology has cleared up any misunderstanding you might have had about the various satellite modes or their designators. As the state of the art progresses and ham satellites use higher and higher frequencies, the question is: What will the next amateur satellite mode be called?

If you are one of the many newcomers entering the realm of the OSCARs and need more information, feel free to write to AMSAT for a free information package. Our address is AMSAT, PO Box 27, Washington, DC 20044. Until next time, 73, and see you on the birds! QST

Table 1
Amateur Satellite Mode Designators

Mode	*Uplink*	*Downlink*	*Comments*
A	2 m	10 m	
B	70 cm	2 m	
J	2 m	70 cm	
JA	2 m	70 cm	Analog, same as Mode J
JD	2 m	70 cm	Digital Mode J
JL	2 m & 23 cm	70 cm	Combination J & L
K	15 m	10 m	
KA	2 & 15 m	10 m	Combination K & A
KT	15 m	10 & 2 m	Combination K & T
L	23 cm	70 cm	
S	70 cm	13 cm	
T	15 m	2 m	

Conducted By
Vern "Rip" Riportella, WA2LQQ
PO Box 177, Warwick, NY 10990

On the OSCARs: Coping with Dr Doppler

One person I know refers to working OSCAR as the "English muffins of Amateur Radio . . . full of nooks and crannies of delightful surprises." He's referring to some of the fascinating phenomena and modes encountered in OSCAR work. Perhaps this is why so many who've grown weary of everyday, standard QSOs elsewhere find OSCAR work so refreshing and full of vitality. Last month, we looked at some of the lesser-known OSCAR operating practices and phenomena. This month, we'll focus on the natural phenomenon that is chief in the minds of most OSCAR operators: Doppler shift.

The effect known as *Doppler shift* or the *Doppler effect* was first described in 1842 by Johann Doppler (1803-1853). He predicted the frequencies of received sound waves were dependent on the motion of the source and the observer relative to the propagating medium. Experiments using trains as the moving source soon proved his prediction. Later, in his Special Theory of Relativity (1905), Einstein showed that for light waves, the Doppler shift depended on the velocity of the source relative to the observer. The Doppler effect accounts for the redshift seen by astronomers in receding galaxies. And Doppler shift similarly affects radio waves.

A handy way to visualize the way Doppler shift affects radio waves is to picture the waves as originating from an OSCAR and traveling across thousands of miles to your antennas. Let's say the frequency at which you receive the wave depends on the number of wave crests received in a given time. Since we know the speed of radio waves in a medium is constant, if the satellite is moving towards you, you'll receive more wave crests in that time period, and the frequency of the wave will be slightly higher. Conversely, if the satellite is moving away from you, the number of wave crests heard in that time will be fewer.

From the satellite's perspective, a similar argument could be made for signals you transmit to the satellite. If the satellite is moving towards you, it will hear your signal slightly higher than your actual transmit frequency. And, if the satellite is going away from you, the satellite will hear your transmitted signal downshifted slightly.[1]

Table 1 shows the Doppler Shift for some currently operational satellites; however, it shows the *one-way Doppler* shift only. Use the BASIC program listing in Table 2 to calculate other Doppler-shift combinations for various operating frequencies and spacecraft heights. (The program is based on sample problem 10.1 of the *Satellite Experimenter's Handbook.)*

When you have a two-way link, ie, an uplink and a downlink, Doppler shift affects both links. How it affects what you hear depends on the design of the transponder itself. Some of the early transponders—and particularly those that use Mode A (2 meters up and 10 meters down)—are noninverting. That means that a rise in frequency in the uplink results in a rise in frequency of the downlink. USB signals on the uplink result in USB signals on the downlink.

Mode B transponders (70 cm up and 2 m down) use inverting transponders. A rising

Table 1

Maximum Doppler Shift Magnitude For Current Spacecraft*

	Shuttle	*UO-9*	*UO-11*	*RS-10/11*	*FO-12*	*AO-13*	
Height	*(Or Mir)*					*Perigee*	*Apogee*
km	*330*	*495*	*700*	*1000*	*1500*	*2500*	*36,000*
(miles)	*(205)*	*(307)*	*(435)*	*(621)*	*(931)*	*(1552)*	*(22,356)*
Freq	*Maximum Doppler Shift (One-Way Link) in kHz*						
21 MHz	0.51#	0.49	0.47#	0.44	0.40#	0.34#	0.03#
29 MHz	0.71#	0.68	0.65#	0.61	0.56#	0.47#	0.04#
145 MHz	3.54@	3.41	3.27	3.07	2.78	2.33	0.22
435 MHz	10.6#	10.3	9.81	9.22#	8.35	6.98	0.67
1269 MHz	31.0#	29.9#	28.7#	26.9#	24.4#	20.4	1.95
2401 MHz	58.7#	56.6	54.1	50.9#	46.1#	38.5	3.69
10.5 GHz	257#	247	237#	222#	202#	168#	16.1#

Notes

*The Doppler shift shown includes only the Doppler shift contribution due to the motion of the satellite. An additional Doppler shift component is contributed by the motion of the earth relative to the satellite. The magnitude of this component depends on the observer's latitude and may be computed using equations provided in Chapter 10 of the *Satellite Experimenter's Handbook* (see note 1).

This frequency is not actually used on this satellite. The Doppler magnitude is shown for reference purposes only. Use it as a guide to the Doppler shift expected from the spacecraft at the height indicated.

@ This value indicates the Doppler shift experienced during the SAREX (Shuttle Amateur Radio Experiment) when a 2-meter transceiver was used on the shuttle by astronauts Owen Garriott, W5LFL, and Tony England, WØORE.

Table 2

(Adapted from the *Satellite Experimenter's Handbook,* Table 10.1.)

```
1Ø KEY OFF : CLS
2Ø C = 3E + Ø8
3Ø K = 3.986E + 14
4Ø R1 = 6371
5Ø INPUT "What is the satellite height in km" ;H
6Ø PRINT : PRINT
7Ø INPUT "What is the operating frequency in MHz" ;F1
8Ø F2 = F1 * 1ØØØØØØ!
9Ø R2 = (R1 + H)
1ØØ V1 = SQR(K / (R2 * 1ØØØ))
11Ø V2 = V1 * (R1 / R2)
12Ø F3 = (V2 / C) * F2
13Ø PRINT : PRINT : PRINT
14Ø PRINT "Satellite Height (km)", "Operating Freq (MHz)", "Doppler Shift (Hz)"
15Ø PRINT
16Ø PRINT TAB(8) H;:PRINT TAB(35) F1; : PRINT TAB(57) F3
17Ø END
```

frequency on the uplink results in a falling frequency on the downlink in an inverting transponder. LSB on the uplink produces USB on the downlink. A benefit of the inverting transponder scheme is that it reduces Doppler shift. For example, the effective Doppler-shift frequency for a Mode B transponder is the *difference* between its uplink and downlink frequencies. Thus, for AO-13 Mode B, the effective Doppler shift frequency is 435 − 146 = 289 MHz. If a noninverting transponder had been used, the effective Doppler shift would have been 435 + 146 = 581 MHz. Thus, the use of inverting transponders reduces the effective Doppler frequency by one half for Mode B.

Operating OSCARs in a Doppler-shifted frequency environment can be unsettling at first, but most operators find it no real bother after a bit of experience. At most, the greatest "inconvenience" encountered amounts to sending a few CW dots on the uplink to allow you to hear the dots on the downlink. Occasionally, however, this can be tricky, especially if you're trying to drop into an open frequency between two QSOs without swishing through the activity.

Some of the new dual-tracking VFO, full-duplex radios (such as the Yaesu FT-736) allow you to assess the Doppler shift by plopping down a test signal in an unoccupied portion of the band. You then lock the transmit and receive VFOs in such a way that when you hear a station you want to call—or find an open spot you wish to occupy—you can transmit and know your downlink signal will be exactly where you're listening. This is a boon to rapid QSY with minimal disruption to others. Inexperienced operators spend a lot of time swishing through on-going QSOs making for unnecessary disruption and QRM.

For more information on getting started on OSCAR and information on AMSAT membership and membership benefits, call AMSAT at 301-589-6062 or write: AMSAT, PO Box 27, Washington, DC 20044. Please include business-size SASE.

A Calculated Approach

M. W. "Maury" McMahon, K4GMJ, uses a home-brew method of ensuring he'll know precisely where his downlink will appear even before he keys his transmitter. His method doesn't require the dual-locked VFOs available on the new radios. Rather, he determines the net effect of Doppler shift and radio calibration first in a test in a vacant part of the passband. He knows that the sum of the uplink and downlink frequencies is constant, so he develops a local standard for it and uses it to calculate frequencies. Maury says the results are quite accurate and allow you "to QSY and be precisely on [the desired] frequency." To be most useful using the K4GMJ method, your radios should have a digital readout with at least 100-Hz resolution.

K4GMJ describes his general method as follows.[2] "First determine the uplink-to-downlink frequency relationship. This will account for both Doppler shift and frequency calibration errors in your radios. To do this, select a frequency well away from other operators. Use an OSCAR frequency chart to roughly determine what your uplink frequency should be to generate a downlink in the open area you've chosen. First, use a CW tone on the uplink to locate your downlink. Then, switch to SSB and speak in a normal voice. Tune your receiver so that you hear your voice in a normal pitch. Always use earphones to prevent audio feedback."

Maury says to carefully note the uplink and downlink frequencies required to produce a normal voice pitch. Let's say your uplink frequency was 435.4241 MHz and it produced a downlink at 145.9751 MHz. Convert both these numbers to kilohertz, discard the numbers to the left of the commas and add the remaining numbers together. Thus, 435.4241 MHz = 435,424.1 kHz; 145.9751 MHz = 145,975.1 kHz. And 424.1 + 975.1 = 1399.2. This error-corrected constant forms the basis of your frequency calculations.

For example, let's say you want to plunk down on exactly 145.9455 MHz. Simply convert this to kilohertz (145,945.5), discard the 145, leaving 945.5. Then subtract this from the corrected constant of 1399.2. So: 1399.2 − 945.5 = 453.7. You would then know that your transmit frequency (in kilohertz) should be 435,453.7, or simply 435.4537 MHz.

Conversely, if you have your transmitter set at 435.4567 MHz, where will the downlink appear? Convert to kilohertz (435,456.7) and discard numbers to the left of the comma, leaving 456.7. Then, subtract this from the corrected constant: 1399.2 − 456.7 = 942.5. You would then know your downlink will appear at 145,942.5 kHz (145.9425 MHz).

Knowing the corrected constant value, it's a simple matter to determine ahead of time where your downlink will appear, given a selected uplink. Conversely, if you see an open downlink frequency, you will be able to select the precise uplink frequency to land on that spot before you even key the transmitter, thus averting unneeded QRM.

Maury uses an inexpensive calculator to keep track of the numbers. He uses the calculator memory to store the corrected constant. Then all he does is subtract either the transmit or receive frequency's least-significant digits to learn the unknown frequency's least-significant digits. If he subtracts the transmit frequency, the receive frequency is revealed. If he subtracts the receive frequency from the memory, the transmit frequency is yielded.

Maury says: "Once the calibration has been made, you need only to check it periodically to see if the Doppler rate has changed. Also, since the calibration accounts for drift in your radio's frequencies as well, if they are still warming up, you'll need to re-calibrate more frequently." Maury says his method is "simple, fast and easy." He points out that while your computer program can provide a reasonable estimate for the Doppler shift to expect at that instant, the "computer tracking programs are not usable, as they don't factor in the calibration errors in your transmitter and receiver."

Next month we'll examine AO-13's Mode S transponder.

Notes

[1]A complete description of the Doppler effect as it affects satelite radio links is provided in Chapter 10 of the *Satelite Experimenter's Handbook*, (Newington: ARRL, 1984).

[2]The method presented is based on K4GMJ's. It has been modified slightly for clarity.

Conducted By Jeff Ward, G0/K8KA
The Flat, Flexford House
Guildford Surrey, GU3 2JP, England

Tune in to Telemetry

Is it cold in space, or is it hot? Bright or dark? Quiet or packed with QRM and QRN? When I first started tuning the amateur satellite bands, these questions fascinated me. I'm sure that many who are now old AMSAT hands were initially drawn in by the question, "What's it like up there where no one can hear you scream?"

A high school or college physics course will teach you that it's (very) hot and bright in the sun and (very) cold and dark in the shade. You'll probably also learn that convection isn't available in the vacuum of space, so heat moves only by conduction and radiation. But what do these things really *mean*, and how can you quiet the little voice inside you that says "prove it?" (That's the voice that first convinced you to cut a bit off a dipole to see if the resonant frequency would really change.)

Fortunately, amateur satellites continuously send back the answers to these questions. The answers come down from orbit in the *telemetry beacons* that are a feature of all OSCARs and RS satellites. "Telemetry" means "measurement at a distance," and designers include telemetry beacons on satellites to measure the space environment and to monitor satellite health. Monitoring telemetry is an exciting and educational facet of amateur satellite communications.

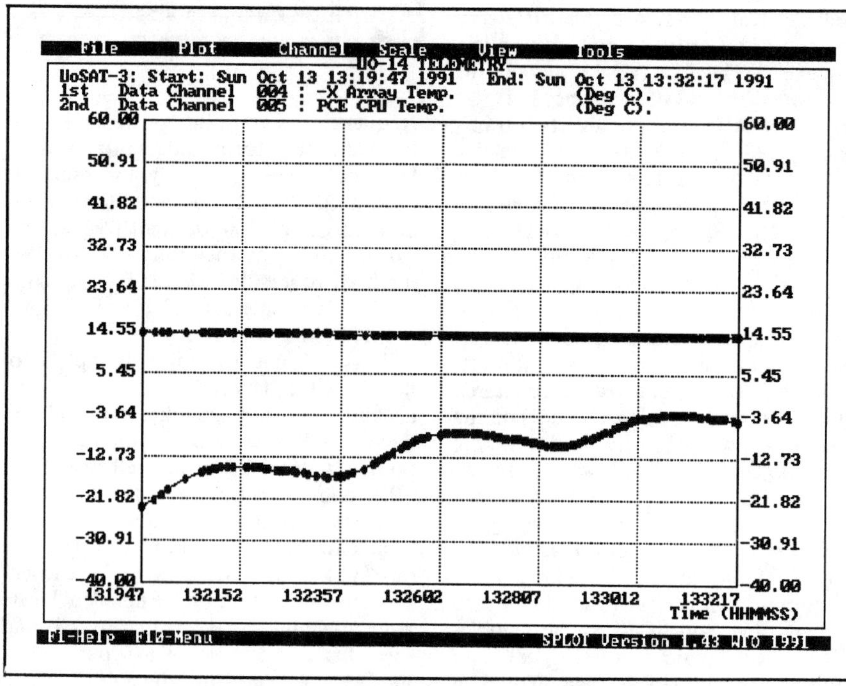

Fig 1—A UO-14 telemetry plot showing internal temperature (flat line plot) and the temperature of the satellite's solar power array. See text for details.

Telemetry transmissions come in many types: CW, AFSK, FSK, PSK and even digitized voice. CW telemetry from the Soviet-built amateur satellites (called "RS" for "Radio Sputnik") makes a perfect introduction to satellite reception—you can tune in to RS-10/11 or RS-12/13 with your HF rig on 10 meters.

OSCARs and RS satellites also transmit CW beacons on the 2-meter band. If you're already a packet radio operator, you can receive DOVE-OSCAR-17 telemetry with your standard (AFSK-FM) packet radio TNC on 145.825 MHz. More advanced transmission modes used include 400 bit/s PSK, 1200 bit/s PSK and 9600 bit/s FSK.

Telemetry Glossary

Whichever satellite and mode you choose to monitor, you'll need to know a bit about how telemetry is gathered and formatted for transmission. The same concepts apply to the telemetry from most amateur satellites.

Each point in the satellite measured by the telemetry system is called a telemetry *channel*. Some channels measure analog quantities, such as temperature, current and voltage. In some (nonamateur) satellites, the analog signal is directly converted to a varying tone and transmitted on the satellite downlink; on OSCAR-1, the satellite's temperature varied the speed at which the beacon sent the CW characters "HI." In a modern satellite with 50 or more analog channels, this is hardly practical!

Modern systems sample each channel using an analog-to-digital converter and transmit the sample using one of the familiar digital modes (CW, packet or RTTY). The output of the A/D converter is called a telemetry *count*, and these counts are what you'll get when you first copy telemetry off the air. Just as OSCAR-1's CW speed wasn't 100 WPM at 100 degrees, telemetry counts aren't directly equal to the measured quantity. They have to be entered into a *calibration equation* before they become degrees, volts, amps or whatever. Once the telemetry count has been put through the calibration equation, it's called an *engineering value*.

Fortunately, most telemetry calibration equations are simple. The usual form is:

Engineering Value =
(Telemetry Count) * SCALE + OFFSET

Tables of SCALE and OFFSET values for every channel are published widely. Once you have the calibration equation, a pocket calculator or a simple computer program can convert the telemetry counts to engineering values.

Some satellite systems are simply ON or OFF and don't require complicated telemetry channels. Switch positions, relay closures and computer output ports require simple one-bit measurements called *digital status points*. A modern amateur satellite with several transponders, an onboard computer and some experiments may have a hundred status points or more. To interpret status points, you use a list that relates the bits you receive on the downlink to specific relays, switches, etc, on the satellite.

Periodically, a circuit or computer on the satellite measures all of the analog channels and digital status points and transmits the measurements as a *real-time telemetry frame*. Real-time telemetry frames provide a quick, complete look at the health of the satellite. Telemetry frame formats vary from satellite to satellite because each was customized to get the best from a particular satellite's hardware and software.

Within this proliferation of protocols, however, there are some common features. Frames usually start with a recognizable *frame marker* that tells the person or program receiving the telemetry that a new frame is about to start. The frame marker is followed by the telemetry samples—one for each channel, in a strict, well-known order. Some telemetry frame formats contain checksums so you can detect reception errors, and the newest satellites use the standard AX.25 packet protocol.

Free Satellite Station With Every HF Station!

If your code speed is up to it, the easiest way to begin receiving telemetry is to listen to one of the RS satellite beacons on 10 meters. You can use a simple wire antenna (perhaps a sloping dipole) and your HF rig. It takes some practice to tune for Doppler shift with one hand and copy CW with the other, but at least you won't have to manage antenna azimuth and elevation rotators.

So that you'll know what to expect, here's one of the telemetry frames I copied:

RS10
SS81 GR00 RD12 DG45 GU45 SW00
RK00 RO00
WS32 UR24 UD35 UG31 WU00 UW00
WK46 UO89

It's good for CW practice, anyway. To decode this, I used information found in *The Satellite Experimenter's Handbook*. I learned that the temperature of the 2-meter transmitter was at 14°, while the 10-meter transmitter was at 25°—presumably because one was turned on and the other off. Oddly, both of the transmitter power-output channels showed 0, even though I was listening to one of them! You learn strange things when you eavesdrop on telemetry....

The Other End of the Spectrum

During the RS pass, I copied two complete frames of telemetry, each of which took one minute to transmit. UoSAT-OSCAR-14, on the other hand, sends a frame of 49 analog channels and 108 digital status points every five seconds—it uses the remaining 4.9 seconds for PACSAT service. Telemetry frames captured during a UO-14 pass provide a detailed look at the satellite's characteristics and the way they change. Figure 1 is a graph showing two temperature channels, one on a solar panel and the other inside the satellite. The solar panel temperature undulates as the satellite spins and rises gradually during the pass (UO-14 had just come out of the Earth's shadow and was still warming up). The internal temperature channel is flat, showing that the satellite's thermal design provides a safe, even operating temperature inside. With 47 other channels available, there's a lot to learn.

Resources

Even if you use your existing equipment to monitor telemetry, you'll need the calibration equations and other details before you can interpret what you hear. The best single resource for such information (and for everything you need to know when getting started on amateur satellites) is *The Satellite Experimenter's Handbook* by Martin Davidoff, K2UBC, published by the ARRL. This book also includes a list of online BBSs where you can expect to find up-to-date information on all OSCARs and RS satellites. Another book, *Decoding Telemetry for Amateur Satellites* by G. Gould Smith, WA4SXM, is available from AMSAT, which also has software for receiving and decoding non-CW telemetry. Write for a catalog: AMSAT Headquarters, 850 Sligo Ave, Silver Spring, MD 20910. QST

Conducted By
Vern "Rip" Riportella, WA2LQQ
PO Box 177, Warwick, NY 10990

Gateways: Keys to Opening New Communication Doors

A gateway is a portal between two domains or regions. For example, in computer networks, a gateway is a facility where different networks meet. Data from one can be transferred to the other. In Amateur Radio, packet-radio gateways illustrate the concept. A station having transceive capabilities on both VHF and HF, and the equipment to switch traffic, could function as a gateway. Thus, the packet gateway functions as a portal to VHF networks for HF network users, and vice versa, as shown in Figure 1.

Similarly, in Amateur Space Program jargon, a gateway is a facility where a terrestrial network interfaces a space network.[1] For example, a terrestrial repeater with its user community could interface AMSAT-OSCAR 10 and its network of satellite users, the Amateur Radio space-communications community. The facility providing this network interface is a gateway. A typical satellite gateway facility might look as simple as Figure 2.

Conceptually and functionally a satellite gateway is straightforward. Typically, signals originated by 2-meter FM users are converted to baseband audio by the repeater's receiver. Then, by any one of several means, the audio is linked to the satellite station's uplink transmitter. Conversely, satellite downlink signals are received at the ground station, converted to baseband audio and then shipped back to the repeater's transmitter. From there they go out on FM just as if they were a normal repeater signal.

The overall system (including the gateway, the repeater, the satellite ground station and the users in both the terrestrial and space communications networks) is functionally identical to normal satellite systems used by individuals, except the user on one end has an extra link inserted to "remote" him from the satellite station. Indeed, regular satellite users might be unaware they were talking to someone quite apart from a regular satellite station. You might be strolling down the street in sunny Orlando, Florida with your 2-meter hand-held radio and chatting with a chap in Honolulu or Sardinia. And, except for the repeater squelch tail, no one would suspect the unique nature of the QSO in progress. But dozens of these types of gateways have operated since AO-10 was launched in 1983. Two years ago, the first transcontinental QSO via AO-10 using hand-held radios took place when two gateway stations hooked up and hand-held users in West Virginia and California QSOed through the gateways in their vicinity.

Two types of gateways have been used with AO-10. The first and most basic type provides single channel access through a local repeater on one end and a fairly standard AO-10 ground station on the other end. The second type of gateway is slightly more complex. It takes a few dozen kilohertz at one frequency and translates it to the AO-10 uplink frequency. The uplink could contain several mixed SSB and CW signals spread across, typically, 40 kHz. This rarer type of gateway uses what is called a linear translator.[2] Yet again, AO-10 users might be totally unaware that the person they are talking with is using a gateway to access AO-10.

Gateway operation through AO-10 requires skilled operators; completely automatic control is still in the future. With AO-10, antennas must occasionally be aimed and Doppler shift corrections must be made. While the control operator of a simple gateway has only to manage a 2.5-kHz chunk of AO-10 spectrum, linear translator operators need be much more skilled. The relative challenge is comparable to the difference between steering a canoe and a barge through a narrow channel.

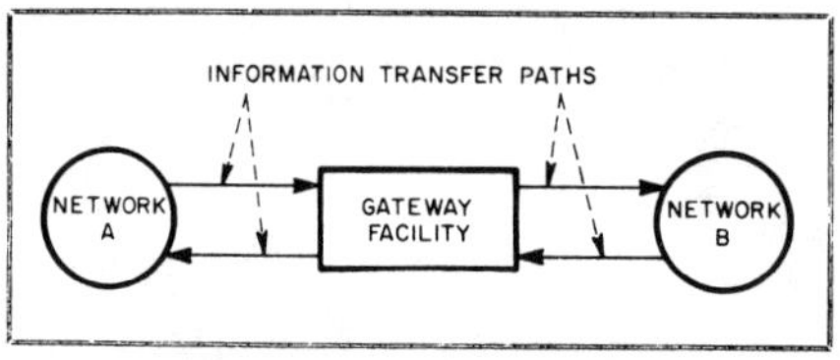

Fig 1—The gateway as a bridge between networks.

The advantages of using a gateway to access AO-10 are many. Apartment dwellers unable to field the modest antennas required for direct AO-10 access can still enjoy the occasional thrill of working true DX by using a gateway. Mobile operators can enjoy intercontinental QSOs on VHF even before the new generation of satellites is born.[3] Demonstrations at conventions and hamfests might be greatly enlivened with the addition of a gateway operation to show off Amateur Radio's "high ground." Emergency communications might be enhanced if a trunk line to the affected area passed via a gateway and AO-10 to master command centers and logistics-support areas. Many more classes of uses might be imagined.

But one of the most important aspects of gateway operation is the facilitation of demonstrations to the uninitiated of the thrill and challenges presented by today's Amateur Radio in a space context. Moreover, if you surveyed hams today, you'd probably find that if they had just one radio, it would likely be a 2-meter hand-held radio. Thus, with a gateway to use, a newcomer with hamdom's most basic equipment, a hand-held radio, could try out hamdom's highest achievement—AO-10! *That* is a significant capability bridge that should further spur gateway use.

Yet some veteran satellite users have expressed dismay and concern with some aspects of gateway operation. The concerns most often fall in one of two categories. The first is a turf issue. "They'll use up all the spectrum and available power." The second is more subtle. "If gateways are really good,

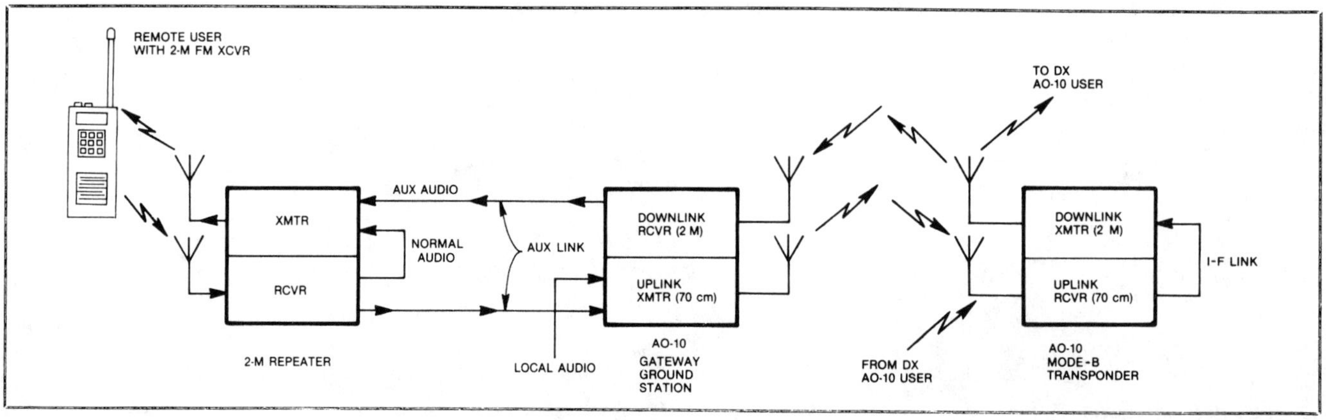

Fig 2—Gateway functional block diagram. The aux link between the repeater may be any convenient mode such as telephone line or aux RF link. Even 24-GHz Gunnplexor tranosoivors have been used.

there'll be no reason to obtain one's own satellite station, people will ignore the desired space education aspects of getting to know how to track and use satellites, and so forth. And if they don't need to know anything, they won't need AMSAT to provide information. AMSAT membership will drop and it won't be able to build satellites anymore!"

Fortunately, none of this has happened. In the first case, the number of gateway operations has not been excessive. The very fact that AO-10 does not always present itself for use at convenient times has tended to limit gateway operation since few find it sufficiently compelling to warrant rising at, say, 3 AM.

On the second issue—the matter of diminished AMSAT membership with increased gateway use—again, fortunately the issue has remained mostly academic because gateway operations have not proliferated. Moreover, many gateway users have found AO-10's challenge so appealing they have obtained both their own OSCAR equipment and AMSAT membership to boot.

In addition, the built-in constraints on gateway operation seem to work to encourage truly interested individuals to do more, to learn more. Individuals accessing the satellite through a gateway often find it so fascinating they want to get more flexibility in who they talk with on the satellite and when they operate through it. This strongly impels them toward obtaining their own stations and to become full-fledged AMSAT members. Those who remain occasional gateway users are perhaps content to queue up for a short QSO on AO-10 through the gateway and that's that. These folks have had fun, enjoyed the tryout and will probably tell friends about it. They can continue to be AMSAT's guest on the satellite even though we hope they will eventually help to support new satellite construction by joining.

Gateway operation is a great way to taste the wine before purchasing the bottle. And it offers some nontrivial benefits and experience to many who try it. See if there is an experienced AO-10 operator in your area and a cooperative, knowledgeable repeater operator, too. You might suggest that these folks get together for a gateway experiment. Your friends may never forget the experience of their first AO-10 contact made from the comfort of their "whatever"![4]

Next month, we'll take a first look at Japan's first homebuilt Amateur Radio satellite, JAS-1. Employing both digital and voice transponders, JAS-1 will be launched late this summer.[5]

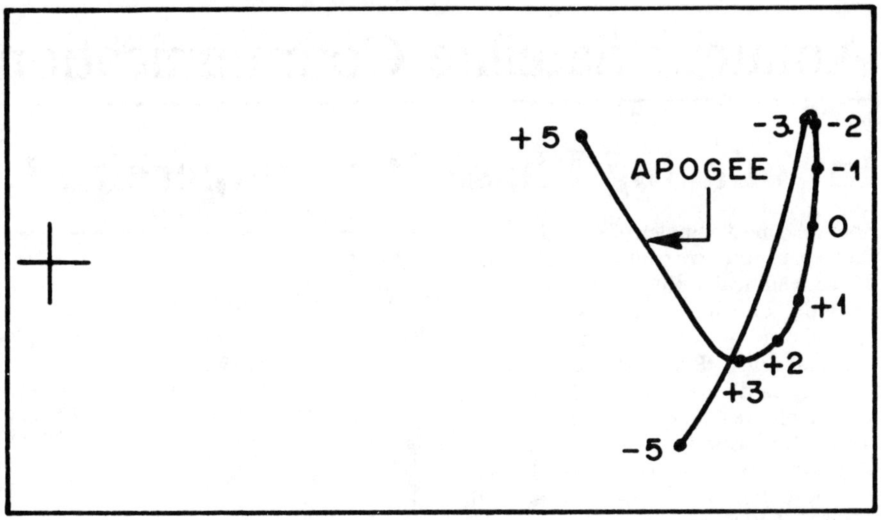

AMSAT-OSCAR 10 ground-track cursor for the OSCARLOCATOR. Reference data is for May 15. QST

Notes

[1]The term "teleport" is also applied to the interface of space and terrestrial networks.

[2]Functionally, a linear translator is very similar to the linear transponder employed by AO-10.

[3]See last month's column on prospects for mobile satellite work.

[4]A revised booklet on gateway operation is available for a $5 donation to AMSAT. Checks only, please, made payable to "AMSAT." Send to AMSAT, PO Box 27, Washington, DC 20044. Mark your envelope "Gateway" to speed your request.

[5]Free information on satellite-tracking software, AMSAT satellite nets and how to get started on the satellites can be obtained by sending a business-sized SASE (with postage commensurate with your request) to the column conductor at the address above.

Conducted By
Vern "Rip" Riportella, WA2LQQ
PO Box 177, Warwick, NY 10990

Introducing Phase 3C: "Superbird" Soon!

Soon, the most complex piece of Amateur Radio hardware ever built will be lifted into a high, elliptical orbit. This hardware will provide enormous communications capabilities for those equipped to take advantage of it. But what does it take to get "on board" the new Phase 3C satellite? This month we'll look at a typical "starter" station for Phase 3C.

As detailed last month, Phase 3C[1] will employ four distinct modes of operation: B, JL, S and RUDAK. Each mode refers to a set of uplink/downlink band pairs and/or modulation types (see Table 1).[2]

To operate Mode B, you need to know five key facts:

1) Where the satellite is
2) When its Mode B transponder is on
3) What frequency to transmit on
4) What frequency to receive on
5) Basic operating practice

Determining the satellite's location, item 1, is called *tracking*. Since high-gain antennas are required, you need to properly aim them at the satellite. Tracking tells you *where* to aim. Tracking techniques and equipment have been covered in this column previously, and will be repeated in an upcoming column.

Item 2 is a matter of scheduling. The operating schedule of Phase 3C will be announced after launch. You can learn the operating schedule by tuning to W1AW bulletins, or by obtaining official AMSAT net bulletins via on-air nets,[3] packet-radio bulletin boards or from telephone bulletin boards.

Items 3 and 4 are addressed in Table 2. Although the table information might lead you to conclude that the passband is divided into many 10-kHz channels, this is not the case. For example, Table 2 shows that if your uplink is on 435.505 MHz, your downlink will be about mid-band on the 2-meter downlink, 145.895 MHz. But, you could just as well have transmitted on 435.507 and heard your downlink on 145.893 MHz. Table 2 merely shows the correlation of uplink and downlink frequencies across a continuous spectrum of available frequencies. Thus, there are no "channels" as such.

There is more to operating via an OSCAR than just turning on the transmitter, though! Item 5, operating practice, will be covered in a future installment. However, well before you turn on the rig, you need to know your basic station requirements to have a good chance of success on OSCAR. So, let's spend a few moments reviewing basic Mode B station requirements. Then you can determine how your shack stacks up and determine where any improvements need to be made.

Table 1
OSCAR Operating Modes

Mode	*Uplink Band*	*Downlink Band*	*Notes*
A	2 m (145 MHz)	10 m (29 MHz)	Traditional
B	70 cm (435 MHz)	2 m (145 MHz)	Current favorite
L	24 cm (1269 MHz)	70 cm (436 MHz)	First use: AO-10
S	70 cm (436 MHz)	13 cm (2401 MHz)	New; Phase 3C use
JL	2 m & 24 cm	70 cm (435 MHz)	New; Phase 3C use
JA	2 m (145 MHz)	70 cm (435 MHz)	FO-12 analog mode
JD	2 m (145 MHz)	70 cm (435 MHz)	FO-12 digital mode
K	15 m	10 m (29 MHz)	RS-10/11 use
T	15 m	2 m (145 MHz)	RS-10/11 use
KT	15 m	10 m & 2 m	RS-10/11 use
KA	15 m & 2 m	10 m (29 MHz)	RS-10/11 use

Table 2
Mode B Uplink Frequency Versus Downlink Frequency
(Preliminary Estimates)
(Frequencies in MHz)

Uplink		*Downlink*	
		145.975	— Engineering Beacon
435.425	——	145.975	— Passband limit, upper
435.435	——	145.965	
435.445	——	145.955	
435.455	——	145.945	
435.465	——	145.935	
435.475	——	145.925	
435.485	——	145.915	
435.495	——	145.905	
435.505	——	145.895	— Passband center
435.515	——	145.885	
435.525	——	145.875	
435.535	——	145.865	
435.545	——	145.855	
435.555	——	145.845	
435.565	——	145.835	
435.575	——	145.825	— Passband limit, lower
		145.8125	— General Beacon

Let's start at the interface to the satellite: the antennas. You'll need an uplink antenna for 70 cm (435 MHz) and a downlink antenna for 2 meters (145 MHz). How much gain should the antennas have? For the uplink, you want to aim for an effective isotropic radiated power (EIRP) of 27 to 30 dBW (0.5 to 1.0 kW EIRP). EIRP is calculated simply by adding the gain of your antenna in dBi to the power you feed to the antenna in dBW (dB relative to 1 W). Table 3 shows a conversion of watts to dBW. Depending on how much power you have in the shack to feed to the antenna, you can now narrow the range of antennas from which to select. As a rule of thumb, select a 70-cm antenna with at least 10 dBi gain. About 17 dBi gain is the upper limit of gain for practical Yagi or LP antennas used for OSCAR satellites.

Table 3
Converting Watts to dBW

dBW = 10 log (P), where P is expressed in watts

P (Power in watts)	*Equivalent in dBW (Decibels relative to 1 W)*
1	0
2	3
5	7
10	10
20	13
50	17
100	20
200	23
500	27
1000	30

Example: Assume you're feeding 50 W to a 12-dBi-gain antenna. What is the EIRP? Solution: From Table 3, 50 W equates to 17 dBW. Add this to the gain of the antenna in dBi to get: 17 dBW + 12 dBi = 29 dBW EIRP = 794 W EIRP. Similarly, 100 W to a 13-dBi-gain antenna, fed through a 3-dB-loss transmission line yields: 20 dBW − 3 dB + 13 dBi = 30 dBW = 1000 W EIRP.

Because the satellite receives and transmits using Right Hand Circular Polarization (RHCP), you'll get best results when your antenna is similarly polarized. A crossed-Yagi array with between 18 and 20 elements in each plane is the most common solution to the uplink antenna question. A linearly polarized Yagi can also be used, but the compromise will be evident in reduced performance in terms of increased fading, which tends to reduce readability.

For the Mode B 2-meter downlink, your antenna should have between 11 and 15 dBi gain with RHCP. Sure, you can get along with linearly polarized antennas, but fading could become bothersome. Most successful satellite operators use 2-meter crossed Yagis with between 7 and 11 elements in each plane for a total of between 14 and 22 elements. The longer-boom 2-meter antennas are generally very good performers, but elevating an antenna with a boom length of up to 20 feet can be difficult in some installations.

After many years of experimenting, I'm convinced it's a mistake to try to stack circularly polarized, crossed-Yagi antennas. Stacking helices is hard enough. Stacking linearly polarized antennas is a well-developed technology. Stacking crossed Yagis is so complex and sensitive to changes in frequency, polarization, spacing and power division that I strongly recommend you don't try it.[4] The best way to obtain more circularly polarized gain is to increase the antenna's boom length.

Before we move into the shack, there are a few more things we need to mention in conjunction with the antennas. An az-el (azimuth-elevation) rotator system is highly desirable, but not absolutely essential. If, for example, you're using fairly low-gain antennas with their correspondingly broader beamwidths, you can often get along without an elevation rotator as long as the antenna is set at a fixed elevation of some predetermined value, say 30 degrees above the horizon. That way, if your antenna has a half-power beamwidth of 60 degrees, which corresponds to a gain of about 10.5 dBi,[5] the signal at the horizon will be only 3 dB down from the main lobe. Similarly, the signal from the satellite at a 60-degree elevation will be down only 3 dB from the main lobe. Of course, you will need an azimuth rotator nevertheless.

Using a mast-mounted 2-meter preamplifier is very helpful for 2-meter Mode B downlink reception. If you use low-loss transmission line, you can probably put the preamp in the shack, out of the weather. In any case, you *should* use a preamp.[6]

In the shack, a Mode B station needn't be terribly elaborate. Essentially you need a good, stable SSB/CW-capable 2-meter receiver, and a clean 435-MHz SSB/CW transmitter and amplifier. I still use the setup I had 10 years ago for AMSAT OSCAR 7 Mode B: An HF transceiver (TS-820), a 10-meter-to-70-cm transverter (Microwave Modules MMT432-28S) and a 2-meter all-mode transceiver (TS-700S) form the central elements. The transverter feeds a solid-state 70-cm amplifier. If you've accumulated the usual assortment of radios typical of many modern shacks, perhaps you already have most of the gear you need. Otherwise, you may want to investigate several approaches to configuring a successful Mode B station.

Next month, I'll discuss Phase 3C operating schedules. In the meantime, you might want to tune in on the Phase 3C launch. It will be transmitted on a worldwide AMSAT Launch Information Network Service (ALINS).[7,8]

Notes

1Phase 3C will obtain its traditional OSCAR number only after having been successfully placed in operation.

2RUDAK is a German acronym for digital repeater. It uses a Mode L frequency pair of 24 cm up, 70 cm down.

3Active AMSAT nets are listed on p 64, Oct 1987 *QST*.

4The discussion of why stacking is unsatisfactory is beyond the scope of this column. Suffice it to say, I doubt you'll be happy with the results.

5M. Davidoff, *Satellite Experimenter's Handbook* (Newington: ARRL, 1984) page 6-3, eq 6.4.

6Although a mast-mounted preamp is *desirable* for the 2-meter Mode B downlink, it is *essential* for the 70-cm downlinks of Modes JL, JA and JD.

7Information on when ALINS will be on the air will be transmitted on all AMSAT nets and carried on W1AW bulletins as launch day approaches. See note 3.

8You can obtain free information on how to get started on Phase 3C—and information about AMSAT in general (including available tracking software)—by sending an SASE to AMSAT, PO Box 27, Washington DC 20044.

Conducted By
Vern "Rip" Riportella, WA2LQQ
PO Box 177, Warwick, NY 10990

Phase 3C: What Do You Need To Work It?

AMSAT's new Phase 3C satellite will be launched soon. As you know from previous columns, the spacecraft carries four transponders: Modes B, JL, S and RUDAK. This month, we'll look briefly at the ground station capabilities required to operate Modes B, JL and S.[1]

Beginning satellite users may be surprised to find that much of the basic ground station equipment is already in the shack or, with a little prudent shopping, can be found at a springtime flea market. Mode B operation on Phase 3C should be the easiest to achieve for the newcomer.[2] To work Mode B, you transmit to the satellite on 70 cm and receive signals from the satellite on 2 meters.[3] Table 1 provides suggestions for the minimum recommended equipment for working Phase 3C, Mode B.

Let's walk through the uplink requirements. The operating frequency is self-explanatory. "EIRP" is Effective Isotropic Radiated Power. You calculate this by adding the gain of your antenna (in dBi) to the power (in dBW) at the antenna feed point.[4] The recommended value of 21.5 dBW corresponds to 141 W EIRP. This can be obtained by feeding 10 W to an antenna having 12 dBic gain.[5] As shown, the polarization should be right-hand circular (RHC). As a compromise, linear polarization, either horizontal or vertical, can be used, but the results obtained may be less satisfactory because of spin modulation.[6]

For your Mode B receive system, the frequency and polarization requirements are self-explanatory. Although the minimum receive antenna gain recommendation is 10 dBic, several commercially available antennas surpass this value by 2 to 3 dB and should be considered. Selecting a higher-gain receive antenna is nearly always worth the cost since it relaxes requirements elsewhere in your system. The exception comes in when you have to elevate the antenna as well as rotate it in azimuth.[7]

The recommendations in Table 1 suggest a preamp is a good idea for Mode B. If you use a short run of good, low-loss transmission line such as Belden 9913, you can leave the preamp in the shack and needn't weatherproof it. Using an expensive preamp with a noise figure of anything less than 2 dB or so is a waste because the sky noise at 145 MHz far exceeds 2 dB. An inexpensive preamp with a gain of 18 to 20 dB should work just fine.[8] I'll talk about effective noise temperature and figure of merit in detail in a future column.

For the experienced satellite user, Mode JL should be the closest thing to perfection yet offered. Mode JL combines 24-cm (1269-MHz) and 2-meter uplinks to produce a 70-cm downlink. Mode JL's combination of low uplink power requirements, small antennas, low sky noise, low spin modulation, wide passband and so forth, should delight the heart of anyone who has ever wished for a broad-coverage DX satellite. Moreover, the combination of 2-meter and 24-cm uplinks means those living where 24-cm equipment is difficult to obtain can enjoy using 2-meter uplinks on this fine mode, just as many enjoyed using Mode J (2 meters up, 70 cm down) on AMSAT OSCAR 8 in the late 1970s. Table 2 presents the minimum recommended station capabilities for Mode JL use. As mentioned earlier, the exact operating frequencies will be published after launch.

Table 1

Minimum Mode B Station Requirements

Uplink

Frequency: 435.425 to 435.575 MHz.

EIRP: 21.5 dBW for 20 dB peak and 10 dB average SNR on downlink.

Polarization: RHC.

Suitable uplink components: 10 W to a 12-dBic gain antenna.

Downlink

Frequency: 145.975 to 145.825 MHz.

Polarization: RHC.

Minimum recommended antenna gain: 10 dBic.

Maximum receive system effective noise temperature: 625 K (NF = 5 dB).

Minimum figure of merit: –18 dB/K.

Table 2

Minimum Mode JL Station Requirements

Uplink

Frequency: Mode L, 1269.575 to 1269.325 MHz; Mode J: 145.840 MHz ±20 kHz or 144.450 MHz ±20 kHz.

EIRP: Mode L, 25 dBW for 20 dB peak and 10 dB average SNR on downlink; Mode J, 25 dBW for 20 dB peak and 10 dB average SNR on downlink.

Polarization: RHC.

Suitable uplink components: Mode L, 10 W to a 15-dBic gain antenna; Mode J, 20 W to 12-dBic gain antenna.

Downlink

Frequency: 435.725 to 435.975 MHz.

Polarization: RHC.

Minimum recommended antenna gain: 13 dBic.

Maximum receive system effective noise temperature: 290 K (NF = 3.0 dB).

Minimum figure of merit: –12 dB/K.

Again, the frequency requirements are self-explanatory. The RF power requirements for the uplinks at 24 cm and 2 meters are identical: 25 dBW, which corresponds to 316 watts EIRP. As shown in Table 2, you can get 25 dBW at 24 cm from a 10-W transmitter driving a 15-dBic gain antenna. A small, crossed Yagi or helix can yield the required 15 dBic quite easily. Many loop Yagis that yield 18 dBi and more are available, but they are linearly polarized. They may be used, although results on Phase 3C remain to be seen. For the 2-meter uplink on Mode JL, a typical setup might include 20 W fed to a 12-dBic gain antenna. If you have more antenna gain, you can roll back the power, and vice versa.

For your Mode JL receive system (see Table 2), good UHF practice is in order. That means a well-designed 70-cm crossed Yagi or helix antenna with RHC polarization. Stay away from those older-design crossed Yagis with the gamma-match feed! Most newer antenna designs use T-matches or folded dipoles with baluns to illuminate the array. Antenna designs have improved greatly in the last few years. You'll get much better results if you use an antenna of recent design. The recommended minimum gain of 13 dBic for your 70-cm receive antenna should be taken as a real minimum. You really don't want to compromise with your receive antenna. If you do, you'll always be wondering why others seem to hear more than you. Besides, some modern designs provide up to 15 dBic of gain in an antenna having a reasonable boom length, and if you invest in a good 70-cm antenna for Mode JL, it will pay off when using it on the Mode B uplink as well.

With Mode JL, you get the chance to field that nice, new GaAsFET preamp, too. On 70 cm, where the sky noise is much lower than on 2 meters, and RFI from terrestrial sources also mitigates, you can use a good, low-noise preamp. One with a noise figure of less than 1 dB is fine. It's a good idea to place the preamp right at the antenna. If, for example, you put 50 feet of transmission line ahead of your preamp and that transmission line has, say, 2 dB loss at 70 cm, you could just as well add that 2 dB to the noise figure of your preamp; the results are practically the same. In other words, you will have worsened the noise figure of your system by 2 dB and wasted much of the benefit you bought the preamp for in the first place.

If you use your 70-cm antenna for receive only (ie, you don't operate Mode

Table 3

Minimum Mode S Station Requirements

Uplink

Frequency: 435.625 MHz, ±15 kHz.

EIRP: Approx 27 dBW under average Mode B AGC conditions

Polarization: RHC

Suitable uplink components: 25 W to a 13-dBic gain antenna.

Downlink

Frequency: 2400.710 MHz, ±15 kHz.

Polarization: RHC.

Minimum recommended antenna gain: 28 dBic.

Typical antenna: 1.4-m dish, assuming 50% efficiency.

Maximum receive system effective noise temperature: 290 K (NF = 3 dB).

Minimum figure of merit: +3 dB/K.

B), you can simply patch your preamp into the transmission line at the antenna in a weatherproof container. If you want to use your 70-cm antenna for both receive and transmit (as most operators do), you'll need to isolate the preamp with transfer relays. In-line preamps with built-in relays are readily available, but cost more. As an alternative, you may opt to find and install your own relays. But placing the preamp at the antenna is most essential if you want to ensure that you'll hear the satellite well.

For the expert satellite user, Mode S offers the newest challenges. For the first time, an Amateur Radio transponder in space will use the S-Band at 2.4 GHz (13 cm).[9] Fortunately, getting on 13 cm these days can be as simple as patching together some basic building blocks. So, even a beginner can succeed if a modicum of care is employed in selecting the system components.

Mode S is designed primarily for a single, narrowband FM signal, but up to four well-spaced SSB stations can also be accommodated. Table 3 provides recommended minimum ground station capabilities for working Mode S.

Because of the high frequencies involved, the Mode S operating frequencies must be viewed as tentative only, and are subject to significant changes when the satellite is finally placed into operation in space. The frequencies shown, however, may be used for general planning purposes. For the 70-cm uplink, one estimate of the required FM uplink power is 27 dBW EIRP, assuming the FM threshold on the downlink is 10 dB. An uplink power of 27 dBW (501 W) EIRP can be generated using 25 W to a 13-dBic gain antenna, for example. If you go up to a 15-dBic antenna similar to one commercial model now available, you can drop the power back 2 dB to 16 W and still get the desired 27 dBW EIRP.

On the downlink side, you'll get to try out your UHF skills. First, a good, low-noise preamp is *absolutely essential.* You simply can't proceed without one *mounted right at your 13-cm receive antenna.* A reasonably priced 13-cm preamp has a noise figure of 1 dB or less. Get the best one you can afford.

This band is just about the lowest frequency where a dish antenna is clearly preferable to a Yagi.[10] A 1.4-m (4.6-ft) dish with a well-designed feed system should provide the minimum recommended gain of 28 dBic. This is about the smallest dish that can be used with obtainable preamp noise figures and this combination will consistently yield the minimum required figure of merit of +3 dB/K. A 1.9-m (6-ft) dish should provide about 30 dBic, and offer a little better FM margin, reduce the preamp requirements, or a little of both.

Notes

1 I'll cover RUDAK in a later column.

2 The new Russian satellite RS-10/11 offers an even more modest entry point, requiring only an HF transmitter and receiver to operate one of its modes. See prior installments of this column for details.

3 The exact frequencies will be published after launch, but approximate values were given in the March column.

4 Converting from watts to dBW was explained in the March column, and is also addressed in the *ARRL Handbook.*

5 dBic means decibels referred to an isotropic, circularly polarized source.

6 Spin modulation results when an elliptically polarized signal is received on a linearly polarized antenna or when a linearly polarized signal is received on an elliptically polarized antenna.

7 Highly directional antennas are specified for all satellite work. Consequently, the satellite user must accurately point the antennas both in azimuth (compass directions) and elevation. This applies to all modes addressed. Extremely long booms stress the rotators and often complicate installation.

8 Although your Mode B station will see no benefit from the low-noise performance of a 2-m GaAsFET preamp, the strong-signal overload characteristics of GaAsFETs may warrant their installation for those who operate in dense RF environments, ie, an urban area with numerous repeaters.

9 Several prior OSCARs have had beacons at 2.4 GHz and above, but Phase 3C is the first to have a *transponder* on this frequency.

10 Convincing arguments can be made that 13 cm and above is the domain of dish antennas, while the realm of the Yagi and helix is 70 cm and below; for the 24-cm band, it's a toss-up.

11 Additional information on Phase 3C may be obtained by sending an SASE to AMSAT, PO Box 27, Washington, DC 20044.

Conducted By
Vern "Rip" Riportella, WA2LQQ
PO Box 177, Warwick, NY 10990

Phase 3C Operating Schedules

Last month, I introduced AMSAT's new Phase 3C satellite. Launch is now scheduled for late May, so as you're reading this the launch process could be nearing its countdown stages. Last month, I said there are five key facts you need to know in order to operate the new satellite, and I explained some of them. This month, let's look at another important aspect of operating: operating schedules.

The operating schedule of Phase 3C is a means of planning *what* happens *when*. There are two primary determinants of an operating schedule: power budgets and technical compatibility of activities.

The power budget of the satellite is directly related to the availability of sunlight to the solar-cell arrays. Without sunlight, the satellite's batteries would soon be exhausted, and the satellite would be forever mute thereafter. Even though the high elliptical orbit of Phase 3C takes it out to 36,000 km (22,000 miles), there are occasions when the positions of the sun, earth and satellite are such that the satellite falls into the earth's shadow. These "eclipses" come and go in cycles. They can occur up to once per orbit, and can last only a few minutes; others stretch to durations of more than an hour.

In any case, the spacecraft cannot be safely operated with a negative power budget (more power being consumed than is being generated) for very long. During an eclipse, the on-board computer[1] and various other subsystems are powered from the battery, but the power-hungry transponders are shut down.

Because the satellite's Mode B receiver and the Mode-JL transmitter both use the 70-cm band, it's impractical to run Modes B and JL simultaneously.[2] Some arrangement needs to be made to tell which mode is in use. This arrangement takes the form of the operating schedule.

The most widely recognized terrestrial "standard" time is Coordinated Universal Time (UTC). When dealing with satellites, however, it's often most convenient to use the time as kept by the satellite as the frame of reference. Let's see how this works and why satellite time is employed in the first place. We'll examine this question by analogy to the earth year and earth day.

A "year" in earth time is simply the length of time it takes the earth to make its way around the sun and return to its place of origin. For smaller time intervals, we use the "day" and then divide it into successively smaller units. Significantly, the length of the day—the time required for the earth to rotate once—is unrelated to the length of the year. That's why the day is about 0.00273785 years (1 year = 365.25 days, approximately), and not some nice even number, say 0.001 (1 year = 1000 days). The rotation of the earth is not, to any degree we can detect, synchronized with the motion of the earth around the sun.

For example, in setting up an operating schedule for the baseball season, we could simply say the regular season runs from day 95 (April 4) to day 265 (September 21). The year's calendar begins with day 1, January 1. That's when we reset the clock (calendar) and start again.

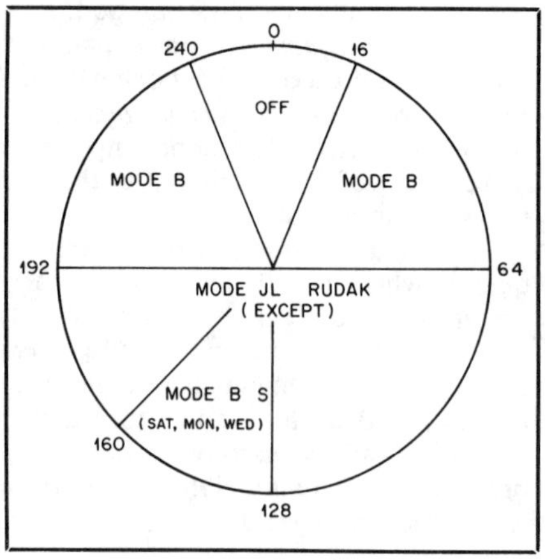

Fig 1—Sample Phase 3C operating schedule.

Let's complete the analogy now. Assume the Phase 3C satellite is the earth. Assume further that its year is defined as the time required for one complete orbit around its "sun," which in this analogy is really the earth. Let's assume that Phase 3C makes one circuit of its elliptical orbit in 11 hours; the satellite "year." Let's call it an S-year.

We could then divide the S-year into S-days (satellite days) of any convenient length. But, just as the rotation of the earth about its axis is unrelated to the movement of the earth around the sun, the rotation of the satellite about its axis is unrelated to its movement around the earth. So, it makes more sense to define an S-day in units that have some significance.[3]

What makes sense is to divide the S-year into 256 S-days. Many of you will recognize 256 as the number 2 raised to the 8th power, and powers of two are easily handled by computers. So, by "decree" alone, there shall be 256 S-days per S-year. Also by decree, the S-year is said to begin at the instant the satellite passes through its closest point to earth—its perigee. Conversely, halfway through its orbit, when the satellite is at its farthest from earth (apogee), the satellite is at S-day 128, or halfway to 256. Just remember, perigee equals "New Year"!

Now we can express a satellite operating schedule simply in terms of S-days, just as we earlier expressed the baseball season in terms of its start and end dates. We could say, for example, that Phase 3C Mode B will be on from S-day 82 to S-day 150.

In practice, the terms S-day and S-year aren't used, however. These terms are simply constructs for this column. In fact, users of amateur satellites use the term "phase," often designated by the Greek letter phi (ϕ), or the term "Mean Anomaly" (MA), to refer to the position of the satellite on its orbit (what we've referred to as S-day so far). When MA = 0, the satellite is at S-day 0—perigee. When the satellite is at MA = 128, the satellite is at S-day 128—apogee. Each of the points in between represents equal increments of time.[4]

That would make perfect sense if you had a clock by which to reckon what the MA time was. And, because most earthlings reckon time with clocks that synchronize with the sun (more or less), it sure would be handy to know how to set the alarm clock to rise for an early morning orbit!

Let's assume the orbital period is exactly 11 hours. Because the orbit is divided into 256 equal-time increments called MA units or MA ticks, each tick must be 11/256 = 0.043 hour, or 2.58 minutes long. Using our sample operating schedule, when we say Mode B begins at MA 82 and runs to 150, we can now figure out what that means in terms of time of day. Assume perigee occurred at 12:00. Recall that at perigee, MA = 0. To find the time when MA = 82, take 82 × 2.58 = 211.4 minutes = 3.52 hours. So, MA 82 occurs about 3½ hours after perigee, or at about 15:31. Now, find when MA 150 occurs. Take 150 × 2.58 = 386.7 minutes = 6.44 hours. So, MA 150 occurs about 6½ hours after perigee, or at about 18:27. We can now see that this Mode B episode lasted from 15:31 to 18:27, or a little less than 3 hours. To double check, take 150 − 82 = 68. Then 68 × 2.58 = 175.44 minutes = 2.92 hours.

Is there an easier way to correlate the

operating schedule to time of day? The easiest means by far is to let a computer be your clock. Many AMSAT tracking programs (those of which I'm aware) actually tell you what the exact MA is at that instant. Then, you plan your operating practices according to what the computer's MA clock tells you.

But suppose you don't yet use a computer. How can you tell what the phase or MA is? For this, you will need to know when perigee occurred. This information is available from many sources. AMSAT Nets or AMSAT Area Coordinators can often supply you with this information. When you know when the perigee occurred, you know when the MA clock started, and you can carry on from there.

Finally, Phase 3C will broadcast its own reckoning of the phase or MA in its telemetry. If you can read the PSK or CW telemetry, it will tell you exactly what the MA is. Thereafter, you can synchronize your reckoning with that of the IHU because *it* is the controlling element that determines when to turn on one transponder and turn off another. Thus, the IHU knows where the satellite is in its orbit, and the IHU's reckoning of that position determines what the MA is and what activities and configurations shall occur.

Next month I'll have a feature article on Phase 3C with an overall summary of the spacecraft and what's needed to operate it.[5]

Notes

[1]The on-board computer in the Phase 3 series of spacecraft is called the Integrated Housekeeping Unit, or IHU.

[2]Mode definitions were provided last month in Table 1. Even if there weren't frequency conflict problems with running Modes B and JL concurrently, the combined power consumption of the two would be prohibitively high.

[3]The spin rate (angular velocity) of Phase 3C will be set at about 35 r/min (3.67 radians/sec).

[4]Mean Anomaly, MA, normally refers to the angle that increases uniformly with time to indicate where the satellite is along its orbit. (Compare Mean Anomaly to True Anomaly.) Experts in the field will recognize that MA, as used in this context, clearly refers to a point *in time* rather than an angle. The period of the orbit is divided into equal "time" increments we call MA units. These *do* correlate to positions along the orbit as determined by the angle MA as used in the classical sense. That is, specifying the position in terms of time after perigee is equivalent to specifying the angle that increases uniformly at a known rate beginning at perigee. Thus, the only practical difference in expressing orbital position is the dimension of expression. In one case, degrees are used; in the other, the implied unit is time—perhaps in minutes. We have often referred to ticks of the MA clock, but this is a mere ad hoc construct. What may not be clear, however, is that the satellite's velocity changes during the course of its orbit. This can be described in terms of Kepler's second and third laws of planetary motion. So, although MA ticks are uniformly spaced in time, the distance traveled by the satellite between successive ticks varies dramatically.

[5]Free information about Phase 3C and how to get started in the satellite program is available from AMSAT, PO Box 27, Washington, DC 20044.

Conducted By
Vern "Rip" Riportella, WA2LQQ
PO Box 177, Warwick, NY 10990

New Russian Satellite Sparks Surge of Interest

Every once in a while, we get to share the great joy of celebrating a rare and wonderful event in Amateur Radio: The birth of a new OSCAR.[1] On June 23, our Russian colleagues in space successfully launched a new OSCAR. RS-10 and RS-11 are alive and well, some 620 miles aloft.

Unlike earlier RS satellites, which had gone up on a single launcher containing as many as six separate satellites,[2] COSMOS 1861 was a single spacecraft carrying two Amateur Radio transponders and one special navigation transponder. Here's how the story unfolded.

The Radio Moscow announcement said COSMOS 1861 had been launched earlier in the day. That was Tuesday, June 23. The announcement said COSMOS 1861 carried Amateur Radio communications relay equipment in addition to its primary scientific and communications research payload. The new RSs were aloft at last! Within hours, G3IOR had his first access and QSO, confirming that the new birds were up and running. Soon, WØCY was also reporting access and initial tracking information.

According to the best current information, RS-10 and RS-11 are identical except for operational frequencies. Each RS apparently uses *three* bands in various combinations to achieve *five* distinct modes of operation in addition to its auxiliary Robot repeaters. (A Robot is an automatic QSO machine that will engage you in a CW QSO when addressed properly.)[3]

On each RS, 15 meters is used exclusively as an uplink band, 10 meters is used exclusively as a downlink band and 2 meters can be employed as either an uplink or downlink band. The overall frequency scheme is delineated in the accompanying table.

The desired orbit was attained precisely. The nodal period is 105.0245 minutes; the orbital increment is 26.3824 degrees west per orbit. A reference orbit for Sunday, July 5, is 00:14:31 at 61.2 degrees West. Average height is close to 1000 km (621 miles).

Next month, we'll explore the fascinating RS-10 and RS-11 telemetry suite. Later, we'll return to the techno-sport theme begun last spring.

RS-10 and RS-11 Operating Frequencies

Summary for both RS-10 and RS-11:

Mode A	2 meters up and 10 meters down.
Mode K	15 meters up and 10 meters down.
Mode T	15 meters up, 2 meters down.
Mode KT	15 meters up, 10 and 2 meters down.
Mode KA	15 and 2 meters up, 10 meters down.

Beacons can carry telemetry or Robot downlink.

RS-10

(Note: All uplink and downlink frequencies are given in MHz.)

Mode A: 145.860-145.900 up yields 29.360-29.400 down.

Uplink	*Downlink*
	129.357 beacon
145.860	29.360 passband limit, lower
145.870	29.370
145.880	29.380 passband center
145.890	29.390
145.900	29.400 passband limit, upper
	29.403 beacon

Robot A:

Uplink	*Downlink*
145.820	29.357 or 29.403

Mode K: 21.160-21.200 up yields 29.360-29.400 down.

Uplink	*Downlink*
	29.357 beacon
21.160	29.360 passband limit, lower
21.170	29.370
21.180	29.380 passband center
21.190	29.390
21.200	29.400 passband limit, upper
	29.403 beacon

Robot K:

Uplink	*Downlink*
21.120	29.357 or 29.403

Mode T: 21.160-21.200 up yields 145.860-145.900 down.

Uplink	*Downlink*
	145.857 beacon
21.160	145.860 passband limit, lower
21.170	145.870
21.180	145.880 passband center
21.190	145.890
21.200	145.900 passband limit, upper
	145.903 beacon

Robot T:

Uplink	*Downlink*
21.120	145.857 or 145.903

Mode KT: 21.160-21.200 up yields 29.360-29.400 and 145.860-145.900 down.

KT Uplink	*K Downlink*	*T Downlink*
	29.357	145.857 beacon
21.160	29.360	145.860 passband limit, lower
21.170	29.370	145.870
21.180	29.380	145.880 passband center
21.190	29.390	145.890
21.200	29.400	145.900 passband limit, upper
	29.403	145.903 beacon

Mode KA: 21.160-21.200 and 145.860-145.900 up yields 29.360-29.400 down.

K Uplink	*A Uplink*	*KA Downlink*
		29.357 beacon
21.160	145.860	29.360 passband limit, lower
21.170	145.870	29.370
21.180	145.880	29.380 passband center
21.190	145.890	29.390
21.200	145.900	29.400 passband limit, upper
		29.403 beacon

RS-11

Mode A: 145.910-145.950 up yields 29.410-29.450 down.

Uplink	*Downlink*
	29.407 beacon
145.910	29.410 passband limit, lower
145.920	29.420
145.930	29.430 passband center
145.940	29.440
145.950	29.450 passband limit, upper
	29.453 beacon

Robot A:

Uplink	*Downlink*
145.830	29.407 or 29.453

Mode K: 21.210-21.250 up yields 29.410-29.450 down.

Uplink	*Downlink*
	29.403 beacon
21.210	29.410 passband limit, lower
21.220	29.420
21.230	29.430 passband center
21.240	29.440
21.250	29.450 passband limit, upper
	29.453 beacon

Robot K:

Uplink	Downlink
21.130	29.403 or 29.453

Mode T: 21.210-21.250 up yields 145.910-145.950 down.

Uplink	*Downlink*
	145.907 beacon
21.210	145.910 passband limit, lower
21.220	145.920
21.230	145.930 passband center
21.240	145.940
21.250	145.950 passband limit, upper
	145.953 beacon

Robot T:

Uplink	Downlink
21.130	145.907 or 145.953

Mode KT: 21.210-21.250 up yields 29.410-29.450 and 145.910-145.950 down.

KT Uplink	*K Downlink*	*T Downlink*
	29.407	145.907 beacon
21.210	29.410	145.910 passband limit, lower
21.220	29.420	145.920
21.230	29.430	145.930 passband center
21.240	29.440	145.940
21.250	29.450	145.950 passband limit, upper
	29.453	145.953 beacon

Mode KA: 21.210-21.250 and 145.910-145.950 up yields 29.410-29.450 down.

K Uplink	*A Uplink*	*KA Downlink*
		29.407 beacon
21.210	145.910	29.410 passband limit, lower
21.220	145.920	29.420
21.230	145.930	29.430 passband center
21.240	145.940	29.440
21.250	145.950	29.450 passband limit, upper
		29.453 beacon

Notes

[1] I use the word "OSCAR" in a generic sense here.

[2] The last RS launch was on December 2, 1981. Six satellites, RS-3, 4, 5, 6, 7 and 8, were launched by a single rocket at that time.

[3] RS-5 and RS-7 both had Robots aboard, but both are probably defunct. To address a Robot you simply send: "RS-10 de (your call) AR" on the Robot channel. RS-11 has a Robot, too, so you would substitute its call sign in your addressing transmission. For example, RS11 DE WA2LQQ AR should work fine. The Robot will reply with a signal report and the QSO serial number. In the past, special certificates were sent to Robot users by the sponsoring organization in the USSR, thought to be DOSAAF.

QST

Conducted By
Vern "Rip" Riportella, WA2LQQ
PO Box 177, Warwick, NY 10990

New Russian Satellite Sparks Interest Surge: Part 2

Last month, we looked at the two new Russian Amateur Radio transponders, RS-10 and RS-11.[1] This month, we'll look at the telemetry suite of RS-10 and RS-11 to see what it can tell us.

Telemetry means measurement from a distance. In the present context, telemetry indicates the situation in and around a satellite. Through careful monitoring of the telemetry, one obtains an interesting and informative appreciation of the goings-on within the spacecraft. There's a lot of enjoyment and education that can be derived from simply monitoring them on their easily heard beacon frequencies.[2,3]

The telemetry is sent in CW at 20 WPM. The information conveyed represents various status points and measurements. There are 16 status points and 16 measurements sent in a repeating cycle. The beginning and end of each cycle is indicated by the identifier "RS10" or "RS11." A complete cycle comprises the RS identifier, 16 "words" of telemetry, and the RS identifier. A complete cycle is called a *telemetry frame*.

Each of the 16 words is comprised of two parts: an *alpha* part and a *numeric* part. Both parts are two characters long. For example, take the telemetry word "IG45." "IG" is the alpha part, and "45" is the numeric part. From Table 1, we see that "IG" indicates channel 4 information is being sent.[4] The alpha portion of channel 4 codes the status of the 15-meter uplink receiver.

The first character in the alpha portion codes the state of the binary variable being sent (refer to Table 3, next page). The "I" in the "IG45" example indicates the 15-meter receiver is off. Had the first character been an "N," we would have known the 15-meter receiver was on.

The numeric part of each telemetry word gives a value for a parameter of interest. For example, the temperature of the 10-meter transmitter is coded in channel 9. The value of the numeric portion of the telemetry word can vary from 00 to 99. To convert the numeric value to meaningful units of current, voltage or temperature, process the numeric portion of each word through the equation for that word. The equations are given in Table 3.

Here's a complete analysis of our example, "IG45." The "IG" indicates the status of channel 4: 15-meter receiver on/off. The "I" means it's off. Taking the "45" portion of our example and dropping it into the equation for channel 4, we get AGC voltage, $V = n/5 = 45/5 = 9$ V.

When a command station is accessing the system, the telemetry format is modified slightly. The modification takes the form of an extra dot or dash attached as the first Morse element of the first alpha character of each word sent (see Table 2).

Logging trends in telemetry is one of the most fascinating and edifying aspects of OSCAR work. It especially prepares young minds for the discipline, organization and record keeping essential to engineers and scientists. Next month, I'll detail how you can try out the fascinating Robot QSO machines on RS-10 and RS-11.

Table 1

Summary Telemetry Matrix

General telemetry word form is: XY## where X is I, N, A or M (or may be modified as shown in Table 2); Y is a channel designator and can be S, R, D, G, U, W, K or O. ## is a two-digit number. Details are given in Table 3.

	X	*Y*	*Meaning of XY*	*Parameter "##" Indicates*
1	I/N	S	Telemetry sampling period	Power supply voltage over sample period
2	I/N	R	RX attenuation	2-m TX output power
3	I/N	D	RX attenuation	10-m TX output power
4	I/N	G	15-m RX status	15-m RX AGC voltage
5	I/N	U	2-m RX status	2-m RX AGC voltage
6	I/N	W	Command station channel	Command station AGC voltage
7	I/N	K	10-m service command	10-m beacon power output
8	I/N	O	2-m service command	2-m beacon power output
9	A/M	S	Status of 1st memory board	10-m TX temperature
10	A/M	R	Status of 2nd memory board	2-m TX temperature
11	A/M	D	Memory loading channel	20-V power supply temperature
12	A/M	G	Code Store memory status	9-V power supply temperature
13	A/M	U	Memory dump via channel	Control of backup 9-V power supply
14	A/M	W	15-m Robot RX atten.	IF voltage of 15-m Robot RX
15	A/M	K	2-m Robot RX atten.	IF voltage of 2-m Robot RX
16	A/M	O	Robot QSO counter where 00-32 QSOs logged is indicated as 00 and 33-128 QSOs is indicated by values in the range of 80-99.	Command channel 2-m power output

Table 2

Format Modification During Command Station Access

Channel Number	*X with No Command Station Access*	*X with Command Access Via 15 Meters (Add leading dot)*	*X with Command Access Via 2 Meters (Add leading dash)*
1-7	I or N	S or R	D or G
8-16	A or M	U or W	K or O

Explanation: The X character in the general telemetry word XY## normally indicates just a binary state, such as on or off. By substituting a different character set, the X character can indicate more. The first character is changed to indicate a command station is accessing the satellite through command channel. When X = I, N, A or M, the command station is *not* accessing the satellite. When X = S, R, U or W, the command station is accessing via the 15-m uplink. When X = D, G, K or O, the command station is accessing via the 2-m uplink. Thus, there are three character sets for use in the first, or X, slot. The first has two code elements; the other adds a leading dot or dash to make the new character sets, which use *three* code elements for each character.

Notes

1Both transponders ride along with the primary payload (a navigation system for ground users) on a "bus" called Cosmos 1861. All were launched from the Soviet Union on June 23, 1987.

2Many secondary schools have included telemetry analysis of OSCAR satellites, together with orbital analysis/prediction, in their science curricula. *The Satellite Experimenter's Handbook* (SEH), published by ARRL and written by Dr Martin Davidoff, K2UBC, was derived from an earlier book by Davidoff, *Using Satellites In the Classroom.* SEH is a good place to start for ideas on including telemetry analysis and tracking topics in the scholastic classroom.

3Beacons are (RS-10) 29.357, 29.403, 145.857, 145.903 MHz; (RS-11) 29.407, 29.453, 145.907, 145.953 MHz. A complete frequency list appeared in October 1987 *QST.*

4Similarly, NG would indicate channel 4 is being sent.

5Total receiver attenuation implemented is sum of channels 2 and 3. Attenuation can take values of 0, 10, 20 or 30 dB.

6AMSAT NA is the world's largest organization of Amateur Radio satellite operators. Free information is available for an SASE (or SAE with IRCs) sent to AMSAT, PO Box 27, Washington, DC 20044, tel 301-589-6062.

Table 3

Detailed RS-10/RS-11 Telemetry Analysis

Each channel is sent as a four-character word, eg, XY##, where XY is a two-character alpha indicator, ## is a two-character numeric value.

Ch No.	*"X" and its meaning*	*"Y"*	*Meaning of "XY" part*	
1	I = 90 minutes N = 10 minutes	S	Telemetry sampling period.	## = Power supply voltage over sample period where V = n/4 volts. Example: IS80. Sample period = 90 minutes; battery voltage = 20
2	I = 20-dB attenuator N = 0-dB attenuator	R	RX attenuation. [See note 5]	## = Power output of 2-m TX where W = n/10 in watts Example: NR25. 0 dB attenuation; power = 2.5 W
3	I = 10-dB attenuator N = 0-dB attenuator	D	RX attenuation. [See note 5]	## = Power output of 10-m TX where W = n/10 in watts Example: ID19. 10 dB attenuation; power = 1.9 W
4	I = Off N = On	G	15-m RX status.	## = 15-m RX AGC voltage, where V = n/5 in volts Example: NG45. 15-m RX on; AGC voltage = 9
5	I = Off N = On	U	2-m RX status.	## = 2-m RX AGC voltage, where V = n/5 in volts Example: NU45. 2-m RX on; AGC voltage = 9
6	I = Off N = On	W	Special command station channel	## = Special command station AGC voltage, where V = n/5 in volts Example: IW00. Command channel off; AGC voltage = 0
7	I = 1000 mW N = 300 mW	K	10-m beacon power output	## = Service command parameter, 10-m mode Example: IK00. 10-m beacon 1000 mW out; command mode off
8	I = 1000 mW N = 300 mW	O	2-m beacon power output	## = Service command parameter, 2-m mode Example: IO00. 2-m beacon 1000 mW out; command mode off
9	A = Off M = On	S	Status of 1st memory board	## = 10-m TX temperature, where T = n − 10 in °C Example: AS35. 1st memory board off; temp of 10-m TX = 25°C
10	A = Off M = On	R	Status of 2nd memory board	## = 2-m TX temperature, where T = n − 10 in °C Example: AR23. 2nd memory board off; temp of 2-m TX = 13°C
11	A = Open M = Closed	D	Special memory loading channel	## = 20-V power supply temperature, where T = n − 10 in °C Example: AD38. Memory channel open; 20-V supply temp = 28°C
12	A = Open M = Closed	G	Code store memory status	## = 9-V power supply temperature, where T = n − 10 in °C Example: MG31. Code store memory closed; 9-V supply temp = 21°C
13	A = 10 m M = 2 m	U	Memory dump via channel	## = Control parameter backup 9-V power supply, where V = n/5 volts Example: AU00. Memory dump via 10 m; backup 9-V supply control off
14	A = 10 dB M = 0 dB	W	Attenuator setting of 15-m Robot RX	## = IF voltage of 15-m Robot RX, where V = n/5 in volts Example: AW46. 15-m Robot RX attenuated 10 dB; Robot IF voltage = 9.2
15	A = 10 dB M = 0 dB	K	Attenuator setting of 2-m Robot RX	## = IF voltage of 2-m Robot RX, where V = n/5 in volts Example: AK46. 2-m Robot RX attenuated 10 dB; Robot IF voltage = 9.2
16	A = 1000 mW M = 300 mW	O	Special command channel 2-m power output	## = Robot QSO counter where 00-32 QSOs logged is indicated as 00, and 33-128 QSOs is indicated by values in the range of 80-99. Example: AO89. Command channel, 1000 mW out; Robot QSOs counted, 33<n<128

Conducted By
Vern "Rip" Riportella, WA2LQQ
PO Box 177, Warwick, NY 10990

New Russian Satellite Sparks Interest Surge: Part 3

In previous months, I have discussed the new Russian Amateur Radio transponders, RS-10 and RS-11, and their telemetry suite. This month you'll learn how to use the Robot QSO machines on these Russian birds.

A Robot, as the term is applied to the RS (Radio Sputnik) satellites, is an "auto-responder," or automatic QSO machine. In other words, it's a small computer on board the satellite that can engage you in a simple CW QSO, respond to your call, log it, and send you a radio QSL. Later, if the Soviet operators keep to the practice established years ago with the RS-5 and RS-7 Robots, you may get a QSL card in the mail, too.

As I explained in earlier columns, both RS-10 and RS-11 are on the same spacecraft, and have similar functions. However, they operate on different frequencies and cannot be in operation simultaneously. The frequencies that the Robots use are given in Table 1.[1]

Table 1

RS-10 and RS-11 Auto-Responder (Robot) Frequencies

Transponder	*Mode*	*Uplink Frequency, MHz*	*Downlink Frequency, MHz*
RS-10	A	145.820	29.357 or 29.403
RS-10	K	21.120	29.357 or 29.403
RS-10	T	21.120	145.857 or 145.903
RS-11	A	145.830	29.407 or 29.453
RS-11	K	21.130	29.407 or 29.453
RS-11	T	21.130	145.907 or 145.953

An experienced satellite operator, Ray Soifer, W2RS, explains the Robot access procedure this way: First, listen for the Robot on one of the downlinks indicated in Table 1. If the Robot is ready for action, it will tell you so by sending CQ DE RS10 or CQ DE RS11 and then indicate the frequency on which it will listen for your call. Then, all you need to do is call the Robot as follows, using your call in place of W2RS, in the following example:

RS10 DE W2RS AR

If the Robot has heard your signal, it will respond with something like this:

W2RS DE RS10 QSL NR 775 OP
Robot TU USW QSO 775 73 SK

It is not clear what "USW" means, but the rest should be evident to most amateurs. TU is Thank You, obviously. QSLs may be sent to the usual QSL address, ie, Radio Sport Federation, PO Box 88, Moscow, USSR.

The RS birds built and launched by Russian Amateurs have traditionally been simple, rugged devices designed primarily to serve Soviet-bloc nations, where modern VHF and UHF radio equipment is difficult to get and very expensive. Consequently, RS satellites have tended to exploit the high frequencies (HF) to a much greater extent than Western satellites have in the last decade.

This may change somewhat in the future as a result of several factors. For one, the next few years will see a rise in solar activity. That will result in increased ionospheric density. Of course, this is a boon to HF users of F2 propagation. But have you considered what it might mean to a satellite emitting, say, 15-meter signals on the outside of the F2 layer?

Leonid Labutin, UA3CR (left) and your column conductor met in Moscow last October to discuss joint Amateur Radio satellite projects.

Alexandr Papkov (left) and Viktor Samkov, of the Tsiolkovskiy Institute near Kaluga, are shown with the RS-10 and RS-11 transponders. (Reprinted from the cover of May 1987 *Radio.*)

Obviously, at the peak of the solar cycle, which will arrive in a few years, very little 15-meter energy will get through from satellites radiating from above the F2 layer. Indeed, during the last solar activity peak in the late 70s and early 80s, it was fascinating to listen to the 10-meter downlinks of various satellites such as RS-1, RS-2 and AO-8 play peekaboo through various holes in the ionosphere.

So, for their next generation of RSs, which will operate during the next peak of the solar cycle, our Soviet colleagues will likely plan more extensive use of VHF and UHF frequencies than they have in the past. This effort may be abetted by new cooperation that now seems possible between the RS builders and the builders of the OSCARs in the West.

I recently had the pleasure of meeting with Leonid Labutin, UA3CR, at the "Space Future Forum" in Moscow, and later at his home. Leo is widely recognized as the foremost Amateur satellite enthusiast in the Soviet Union. He has undertaken to form a new affiliate of AMSAT, AMSAT-UA, for the express purpose of facilitating joint spacecraft projects. This could, in turn, lead to more extensive use of VHF and UHF by RS builders and increase launch access for all the Amateur Satellite community.[2] The fruits of this new era of cooperation may begin to become evident by the time you read this column.

In general, cooperation in building and launching Amateur Radio satellites can have strong symbolic meaning as well as substantive benefits for Amateurs worldwide. Next month I'll begin to introduce you to the new AMSAT Phase 3Ç satellite due for launch in a couple of months.

Notes

[1]A complete list of frequencies employed by the RS-10 and RS-11 transponders was published in this column in October 1987.

[2]Launches are the rarest of all resources in the Amateur Satellite community. Launches are *so* rare that when one is identified and committed to, it can—and does—change the entire Amateur Satellite community. AMSAT and its affiliates try to obtain launches from all possible sources. We will accept a launch from virtually *any* dependable source. Against the existing background of a supreme appetite for launches (commercial, military, amateur), recognize that the USSR currently out-launches the rest of the world combined by a 10 to 1 ratio! In this context, it certainly makes sense to seek a symbiotic relation with the RS team.

Amateur Satellite Communications

Conducted By
Douglas A. Loughmiller, KO5I
PO Box 247, Brookston, TX 75421

A Look at the Easybird: RS-10/11

In recent columns, we've explored topics geared toward experienced satellite operators. So this month, let's take a look at amateur satellite communications from a beginner's perspective.

An often-asked questions on amateur satellites goes something like this: "I'm interested in operating via the amateur satellites, but the only equipment I have in the shack is my HF transceiver and an assortment of HF antennas. How can I get started on the birds?"

My suggestion to such inquiries is to use the Easybird: The Soviet RS-10/11.

RS-10/11 comprises two amateur satellite systems and six transponders. Launched in June of 1987, RS-10/11 was placed into a low earth orbit with an average height of 1000 km.

RS-10/11 is an ideal tool for investigating issues unique to amateur satellite communications. Once you've learned the lingo of satellite communications, practiced the art of tracking[1] and become acquainted with things such as Doppler shift, you'll be an experienced satellite operator before you know it! The basics learned from operating through RS-10/11 are applicable to all the other birds.

As with any special interest, having access to good information is necessary to gain maximum insight and enjoyment. Thanks to the hard work and dedication of Dr Marty Davidoff, K2UBC, *The Satellite Experimenters Handbook* is an excellent reference that every amateur interested in satellite communications should have on his bookshelf. Published by the ARRL, the second edition of the *SEH* has just been released. I highly recommend it to beginners and old-timers alike.

Table 1
RS-10/11 Transponder Frequencies

	RS-10	*RS-11*
Mode A:	Uplink: 145.860-145.900 MHz Downlink: 29.360-29.400 MHz	Uplink: 145.910-145.950 MHz Downlink: 29.410-29.450 MHz
Mode A Robot:	Uplink: 145.820 MHz Downlink: 29.357 or 29.403 MHz	Uplink: 145.830 MHz Downlink: 29.407 or 29.453 MHz
Mode K:	Uplink: 21.160-21.200 MHz Downlink: 29.360-29.400 MHz	Uplink: 21.210-21.250 MHz Downlink: 29.410-29.450 MHz
Mode K Robot:	Uplink: 21.120 MHz Downlink: 29.357 or 29.403 MHz	Uplink: 21.130 MHz Downlink: 29.403 or 29.453 MHz
Mode T:	Uplink: 21.160-21.200 MHz Downlink: 145.860-145.900MHz	Uplink: 21.210-21.250 MHz Downlink:145.910-145.950 MHz
Mode T Robot:	Uplink: 21.120 MHz Downlink: 145.857 or 145.903 MHz	Uplink: 21.130 MHz Downlink: 145.907 or 145.953 MHz

About the Bird

RS-10/11's ease of use stems in part from its sensitive receivers and powerful transmitters. The satellite's uplink and downlink frequencies are also important factors. Table 1 lists them all.

RS-10/11 can be accessed with truly simple equipment. The spacecraft utilizes an HF uplink or downlink for every transponder. Because most beginners have HF transceivers, they already have more than half of the equipment needed to work through the satellite. A wide variety of station setups are used. Low power and simple antennas are commonplace on the uplink, and receiving the downlink signals is easy, too.

Over the Thanksgiving weekend, my junior op, Dustin, and I rigged up temporary antennas to listen to the bands. After raising an 80-foot wire for HF and a discone antenna for VHF, we settled in for some "band scanning." As we scanned across 10 meters, we decided to put our modest setup to the test: working through RS-10/11.

A quick glance at the tracking data showed that a pass was a few minutes away. Running 10 watts into the discone and tuning the wire antenna with an antenna tuner, we "optimized" our station as the bird came over the horizon. A few minutes later, as we lost the signal on the other horizon, we counted a total of three enjoyable QSOs during the 15-minute pass. If we can do it, you can, too!

Another unique aspect of this bird is its novel "robot" system that allows ground stations to have CW QSOs with the spacecraft itself. The format for answering a robot CQ (RS-10 in this case) is: RS10 DE KO5I $\overline{\text{AR}}$. If you are successful, the robot will respond KO5I DE RS10 QSO NR 123 OP ROBOT TU FR QSO 73 $\overline{\text{SK}}$. The robot is capable of copying clean CW in the 10-30 WPM range. Frequencies for robot operation are listed in Table 1.

Because RS-10/11 uses popular HF frequencies, it sees a great deal of activity worldwide. And because of operational considerations aboard COSMOS 1861 (RS-10/11's host spacecraft), it's usually operating in Mode A. Mode A was a workhorse mode during the early days of amateur satellites. Thousands of amateurs have logged Mode A QSOs. And although great advances have been made in satellite technology, Mode A is still a valid place to start.

Because of this, AMSAT-NA is often asked why it no longer constructs Mode A satellites. The answer has to do with today's amateur satellite service itself. In the early days, satellite construction activities were centered around a single construction group comprised of technical volunteers from a small number of organizations. Fortunately, this is no longer the case. A number of viable groups have emerged from around the world, and the number of amateur satellite launches has soared over the past several years. The net result is a broader base of resources that can be applied to an *international* amateur satellite program. The arena in which we participate is, after all, a truly international one. Hams everywhere benefit from each new satellite, regardless of its origin.

This is exactly the case with regard to Mode A. Our Soviet colleagues have indicated that they intend to design, construct and launch Mode A birds well into the future. By consulting with various international groups, the needs of the amateur satellite service are discussed and planned.

All of the satellite groups believe that the amateur community is best served by this approach. This way, our resources are put to the best use possible.

LOS

If you're thinking about joining in the fun of amateur satellites, we'd be pleased to count you among our ranks. Give RS-10/11 a try. I'm sure you'll enjoy it!

If you'd like more information, write to AMSAT, PO Box 27, Washington, DC 20044.

See you on the birds! QST

[1]The subject of satellite tracking could take up a whole column of its own. Future columns will discuss this topic in detail. For the purpose of this overview discussion it should be pointed out that two basic satellite tracking systems exist: plotter boards, such as the *OSCARLOCATOR*; and computer software. A complete software catalog can be obtained from AMSAT at the address given at the end of the article.

Conducted By
Douglas A. Loughmiller, KO5I
PO Box 247, Brookston, TX 75421

More Mode A and a Look at Operating Etiquette

Proving just how dynamic the Amateur Satellite Service truly is, I had hardly handed off my February column, which included a detailed discussion of Mode A operation on the Soviet RS satellites, when I received word that the launch of RS-12/13, the replacement for the aging RS-10/11, was imminent.

Sure enough, at 0236Z on February 5, RS-12/13 was successfully placed into a low earth orbit (with an 82° inclination and an altitude of 983 km) as part of the COSMOS 2123 platform (a navigation satellite).

In my February column, I characterized RS-10/11 as the "Easybird" because of its strong downlink signals and its sensitive receivers. This combination bodes well for even the simplest ground stations, and early reports suggest RS-12/13 is living up to its predecessor's nickname.

A reader pointed out, however, that I had failed to include the beacon frequencies for RS-10/11. After reviewing my February column, I found (to my complete embarrassment) that I had indeed omitted the beacon information—an oversight of significant proportions!

Uplink Etiquette

Much like a lighthouse on the shore, satellite telemetry beacons serve as "navigational tools." The strong beacon signals are an easy-to-find indicator of the satellite's presence overhead.

More importantly, beacon signals from satellites that use linear transponders serve as standards to gauge necessary uplink power—one of the primary points of operating etiquette in the Amateur Satellite Service.

Linear transponders have a finite amount of power to distribute among the signals that appear in their uplink receivers. With multiple users, the power must be shared equitably.

That's where beacons come in. The universally accepted practice for gauging proper uplink power levels is to first observe the beacon and note its signal strength. When you transmit an uplink signal, adjust your transmitter output power so your downlink signal is never stronger than the beacon.

By monitoring the beacon and establishing your correct uplink power, you can successfully make QSOs via the bird and not exceed your fair share of available power.

Linked to the issue of uplink power is the transponder's automatic gain control circuit (AGC). If an exceptionally powerful signal is bouncing the AGC all over the place, this will undoubtedly prevent weaker signals from modestly equipped stations from being detected by the spacecraft's receiver.

Aside from proper operating etiquette (and not "elbowing aside" fellow satellite users with an overly powerful uplink signal), measuring your downlink signal against the beacon assures that you're not overtaxing the satellite's transponder in general.

This practice is valid for any of the linear transponders used in today's OSCARs. Future satellite projects such as Phase 3D, another wide-coverage OSCAR, may include improved transponder features to handle excessively strong uplink signals with a technology based solution. Until then, however, we must rely upon good operating practices to ensure that the amateur satellites are properly utilized.

Frequencies

Because I blew it in my February column and failed to include beacon frequencies for RS-10/11, I have included them this month in Table 1. Table 2 is a complete set of frequencies for all of the transponders aboard RS-12/13. Note that RS-12/13 employs a CW robot, much like RS-10/11.

LOS

That's it for this month. Until next time, 73, and enjoy the new birds. For information about the Amateur Satellite program and how you can help support this exciting aspect of our hobby, write to AMSAT, PO Box 27, Washington, DC 20044, for a free information packet. QST

Table 1
RS-10/11 Beacon Frequencies in MHz

	RS-10	*RS-11*
Mode A	29.357 or 29.403	29.407 or 29.453
Mode K	29.357 or 29.403	29.407 or 29.453
Mode T	145.857 or 145.903	145.907 or 145.953
Mode KT	29.357 or 29.403	29.407 or 29.453
	145.857 or 145.903	145.907 or 145.953
Mode KA	29.357 or 29.403	29.407 or 29.453

Table 2
RS-12/13 Transponder and Beacon Frequencies in MHz

		RS-12	*RS-13*
Mode A	*Uplink*	145.910-145.950	145.960-146.000
	Downlink	29.410-29.450	29.460-29.500
	Beacon	29.408 or 29.454	29.458 or 29.504
Mode K	*Uplink*	21.210-21.250	21.260-21.300
	Downlink	29.410-29.450	29.460-29.500
	Beacon	29.408 or 29.454	29.458 or 29.504
Mode T	*Uplink*	21.210-21.250	21.260-21.300
	Downlink	145.910-145.950	145.960-146.000
	Beacon	145.912 or 145.958	145.862 or 145.908
Mode KA	*Uplinks*	21.210-21.250	21.260-21.300
		145.910-145.950	145.960-146.000
	Downlink	29.410-29.450	29.460-29.500
	Beacon	29.408 or 29.454	29.458 or 29.504
Mode KT	*Uplink*	21.210-21.250	21.260-21.300
	Downlinks	29.410-29.450	29.460-29.500
		145.910-145.95	145.960-145.000
	Beacons	29.408 or 29.454	29.458 or 29.504
		145.912 or 145.958	145.862 or 145.908
Robot	*Modes*	*A, K, KA, KT*	*A, K, KA, KT*
	Uplinks	21.129 and/or 145.830	21.138 and/or 145.840
	Downlinks	29.454 and/or 145.958	29.504 and/or 145.908

Conducted By Jeff Ward, GØ/K8KA
The Flat, Flexford House
Guildford Surrey, GU3 2JT, England

UoSAT-OSCAR-22 in Orbit

At 02:05:51 UTC on July 17, 775 km above Nova Scotia, UoSAT-F became UoSAT-OSCAR-22 when it was released into orbit by an Ariane launch vehicle. Compared with the traumatic events during testing reported in May *QST*, the UoSAT-F launch campaign was safe, but not uneventful.

Harold Price, NK6K, hand-carried three solar panels in two suitcases from Los Angeles to London without difficulties. He arrived on Saturday, March 30, and over the weekend UoSAT engineers added connectors and temperature sensors to the basic panels. Tuesday and Wednesday the panels were vibrated, baked and flash tested. Thursday at lunchtime the launch team left for the airport and a few hours later the shipping company picked up the satellite and took it away. Fourteen days later—just a month after our thermal-vac episode—the satellite was safely mounted on the Ariane Structure for Auxiliary Payloads (ASAP)...

...but not for long. The initial May 7 launch date came and went. A problem with the third stage of the Ariane launcher caused a string of delays that spun out week by week until late May. At one point it was rumored that the launch wouldn't be until October! Finally, Arianespace told us that the launch would be July 16 "at the earliest."

Seizing the opportunity to make a few final adjustments, Martin, G3YJO, and Alex, G7GLY, set off to Kourou to retrieve UoSAT-F. Despite French air traffic controllers' strikes, they made it to South America and back in only three days. The satellite returned to Surrey on June 11...

...but not for long. Three days later we got the news that the launch was definitely on for July 16, and the satellite would have to be mounted to the ASAP on June 28! The team spent 10 hectic days reconditioning the batteries, checking the RF links and generally tweaking things up. Then, four days before the ASAP mate, the shippers came to take UoSAT-F back to Kourou again.

The next time UoSAT-F left Kourou it was on the launch vehicle, heading for orbit. The launch went smoothly, and eight hours later we got our first UoSAT-OSCAR-22 passes over the UK. The worst happened: we heard nothing when the wake-up commands were transmitted. The 90-minute wait for our next pass was tense and filled with speculation about causes and cures. On the second pass, a short snatch of telemetry was heard on the downlink, and the 20 or so kibitzers in the control room cheered. Then nothing.

The fourth pass was somewhat better, although we could still only coax a few short transmissions from the redundant transmitter. At 1320, when the satellite was on the other side of the globe, we were put out of our misery; Graham Ratcliffe, VK5AGR, phoned to say that he was receiving strong, healthy telemetry from UO-22. (UoSAT RF engineers believe that a partial vacuum had developed in the transmitter output filter, causing arcing at high RF voltages.)

For the next week we operated UO-22 on every pass over the UK. By the end of day 1, the main onboard computer operating system was loaded and running. On day 2, the file-transfer protocol software (the same program that runs on AO-16 and LO-19) and some attitude-control software were loaded. The first task of the attitude-control program was to get the satellite spinning so that the sun would heat all of the solar panels evenly. Then (day 4), maneuvers were initiated to make the satellite point toward the earth. Saturday morning (day 5), we fired the explosive bolt holding the gravity gradient boom, and the boom extended to its full 5-meter length. This boom helps keep the satellite pointing toward the center of the earth.

Image of Success

With the boom out and the satellite pointing down, it was time to try the camera. Sunday morning—after one cloud-filled, overexposed image—we were glued to our computer screens looking at UO-22's first *picture* of the earth: Italy and the Mediterranean basking in the summer sun.

As the photo of the Red Sea shows, UoSAT's 10-year commitment to OSCAR cameras has finally paid off. The Amateur Satellite Service now has a remote imaging satellite with image quality that can compare with existing low-earth-orbiting weather satellites. Unlike the NOAA and Meteor satellites, however, UO-22 pictures can be taken anywhere, stored on the satellite and downloaded in your shack. Apart from the military, there are only two organizations in the world (SPOT and Landsat) that can take images with this flexibility. Now, for a fraction of the cost, AMSAT has joined this elite group.

Any amateur station capable of receiving 9600 bits/second FSK on 435.120 MHz can download pictures from UO-22. The signal is strong, and you won't necessarily need steered satellite arrays. The picture files are transmitted using AX.25 frames and the PACSAT Broadcast Protocol, which is already familiar to hundreds of PACSAT users. With more than 150 users on the UO-14 BBS and great pictures being transmitted by UO-22, the time is right to get a 9600-baud satellite station operating.

Contributing to the Advancement of the Art

Some 20 radio amateurs work at UoSAT, and we're always trying to build satellites that carry on the "AMSAT tradition" of education and technical quality. Somebody, nevertheless, has to pay the bills. UO-22 cost more than $1.5 million and we have to raise that from somewhere—without compromising the Amateur Satellite Service.

Some of the UO-22 bills were paid by a nonamateur humanitarian organization called SatelLife, formed by 1985 Nobel Prize winner Dr Bernard Lown. SatelLife

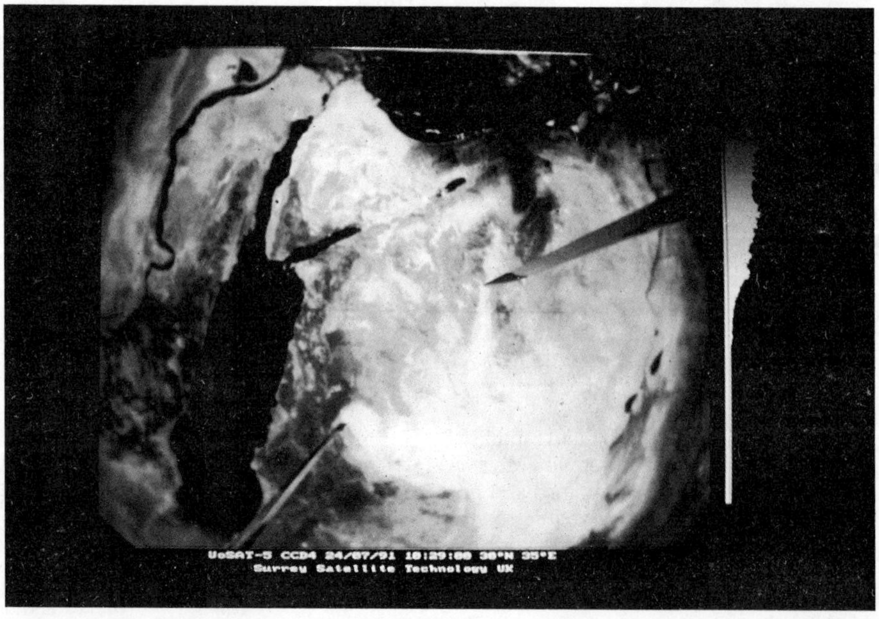

The Red Sea as seen by UoSAT-OSCAR 22. This image was received and processed at the University of Surrey.

will use a store-and-forward transponder on UO-22 to start a nonprofit electronic mail network for medical students. Initially, five African medical schools will use this "HealthNet" to exchange electronic mail and receive up-to-date medical literature.

HealthNet *will not* operate in the Amateur Satellite Service. It has an uplink outside the amateur bands, and a downlink in a shared portion of an amateur band. UO-22 memory, power, and orbit time will be shared between AMSAT and HealthNet, with AMSAT getting roughly 40% of the satellite's time. HealthNet illustrates how techniques developed in the Amateur Service (store-and-forward, packet-radio satellites) are applied to other problems, fulfilling our obligations under FCC Part 97. It also shows how the Amateur Satellite Service can continue to have interesting, state-of-the art missions without going broke.

LOS

UoSAT-OSCAR-22—like UoSAT-OSCAR-9 and UoSAT-OSCAR-11 before it—will not be a *communications* satellite. It will transmit bulletins, pictures, telemetry and other experimental data. Radio amateurs have traditionally used this information to increase their own understanding of radio, satellites, communications and the physical sciences. Interest in satellite imaging has been demonstrated by a series of popular articles in *QST*. We're looking forward to long and interesting service from UO-22 in this experimental niche.

Conducted By
Vern "Rip" Riportella, WA2LQQ
PO Box 177, Warwick, NY 10990

NEXT Generation Satellites on the Horizon

Despite the enjoyment derived in tracking satellites, there are circumstances when it's inconvenient to wait for OSCAR to appear. To the beginner, moreover, it's unclear why the satellite need move at all. "Hummingbirds and balloonists remain motionless, don't they?"

A satellite needs motion to stay in orbit. Without a velocity component away from earth, it would plummet.[1] When a satellite's motion away from earth and gravity are in balance, the trajectory closes on itself to become an "orbit."[2] The higher the satellite, the less velocity it need have to remain in orbit.[3] Today's "stationary" geosynchronous satellites are in orbits 22,300 miles over the equator. But even though they appear stationary, they too have a significant velocity component directed away from earth.

After two decades of experimenting in lower orbits, AMSAT is now charting new conceptual grounds for the next-generation OSCARs. Will they be Phase 4 geosynchronous satellites? What could a Phase 4 satellite system do?

You're motoring down the San Bernardino Freeway. You pick up your radio, punch in a few numbers and instantly you're in contact with your cousin, who's also motoring down the highway. Not really exciting, you say. You already do that? Did I mention that your cousin was motoring down the Trans-Canada highway west of Montreal? A satellite gateway in the San Gabriel mountains and another in the Gatineaus has linked these two motorists through an AMSAT geosynchronous satellite high over Ecuador.

You're sitting at your computer whacking out a reply to an electronic-mail QSL card. You hit the return key and a "MSG DELVD" advisory appears on your screen. The QSL card now resides in an accountable processor in Tucson. When the addressee, a Boston amateur, comes on frequency, the QSL will be forwarded automatically. The 9.6-kbit/s channel is provided by AMSAT's AMSTAR, placed high over the Andes.

A severe earthquake hits coastal Mexico. Normal communications are obliterated. Soon a portable AMSTAR terminal at the site is on the air and a high-quality channel is available from the disaster site to every capital in the Western Hemisphere. Voice and packet data flow continuously for days.

Sitting in the canoe you avoid making any sharp movements. The lake is calm; anchors are positioned to hold the canoe steady. The small dish clamped to the bow rail is pointed right at Orion's belt where, you figured out earlier, AMSTAR would be. Your digital watch beeps in the dark to announce the hour. Donning your headset, the cosmic noise of innumerable stars supplants the din of an apparently equal number of katydids. As you fiddle with the squelch, your lake transforms to a tranquil, 75-acre hamshack. The voice in your ear announces, "Here are tonight's Amateur Radio bulletins via AMSTAR."

These four examples typify system capabilities being considered for the next generation of OSCARs. But to get there will require a much larger support base—a base comprising a larger portion of the Amateur Radio community than is now involved.

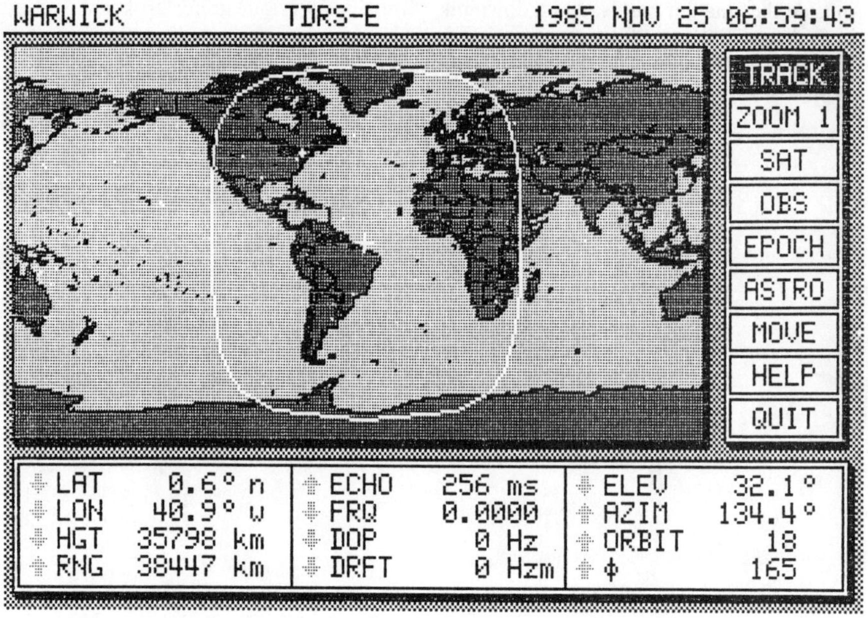

Geosynchronous satellite coverage is typified by this plot of the footprint of TDRS East. It is positioned just north of the coast of Brazil. Areas within the curve can intercommunicate via the satellite.

The motions of OSCARs are determined by physics. In confrontation with Newton and Kepler, user convenience is subordinate. For amateur satellites to reach their full service potential, however, they must serve the much larger community which, surveys indicate, places a premium on access convenience. Furthermore, while those currently on OSCAR often have an abiding interest in the medium itself, i.e., OSCAR, many others would prefer to ignore the medium entirely and get on to the matter of communicating. They seem to be saying, "One needn't get into the clockworks to be interested in the time of day!"

In response, AMSAT is engaging in some healthy introspection. Many are coming to feel what is needed now is a "utility satellite" system. In this line of thinking, advanced capabilities are provided through simple, convenient access enabled by superior engineering. In the months to come, AMSAT will weigh concepts for the next generation of satellites. It will study tentative goals for spacecraft design, user capability, financial resources, and others.

It is timely for current OSCAR user and potential user suggestions. Those experienced on OSCAR have a special perspective since they've conquered the beast; done it the hard way. But those who've never worked OSCAR also have something to say here. It would be helpful to have your ideas, too. How would you like OSCAR to perform, and how much would you be willing to put into your current station to achieve that new capability?

Amateur Radio will have geosynchronous satellites sooner or later. Given their druthers, many would have it sooner rather than later! If you would like to participate in the next-generation OSCAR planning, we'd be glad to hear from you. Meanwhile, AMSAT's Project Linkup will demonstrate the feasibility of bulletin delivery both directly and through gateway repeaters. Concept validation will lead to possible regular service before the end of 1986 using current-generation Phase 3 satellites. Want to be a part? An SASE will bring you information on getting started now. Avoid the last minute rush!

Notes

[1]Similarly, a hummingbird *sans* aerodynamic lift and a balloonist without buoyancy would plummet.

[2]On the other hand, some situations result in starkly different trajectories. A particularly rude one on the low end of the velocity scale ends with a rather direct path to Mother Earth—reentry the hard way . . . at Mach 25. At the other end of the scale, we find trajectories that are described by unique S parameters: Space Sayonara Syndrome, aka escape velocity.

[3]Very low satellites, i.e., about 100 miles, orbit in about 1.5 hours. At 900 miles, orbital periods are about 2 hours. At 22,300 miles, geosynchronous altitude, the orbital period is 24 hours. That's why it's "geosynchronous." At 230,000 miles, the moon's orbital period is about 28 days.

W1AW Schedule

MTWThFSSn = Days of Week   Dy = Daily

W1AW code practice and bulletin transmissions are sent on the following schedule:

UTC	Slow Code Practice	MWF: 0300, 1400; TThS: 000; TThSSn: 0300
	Fast Code Practice	MWF: 000, 2100; TTh: 0300, 1400; S: 0300; Sn: 0000
	CW Bulletins	Dy: 0100, 0400, 2200; M-F: 1500
	Teleprinter Bulletins	Dy: 0200, 0500, 2300; M-F: 1600
	Voice Bulletins	Dy: 0245, 0545
ET	Slow Code Practice	MWF: 9 AM, 7 PM; TThSSn: 4 PM, 10 PM
	Fast Code Practice	MWF: 4 PM, 10 PM; TTh: 9 AM; TThSSn: 7 PM
	CW Bulletins	Dy: 5 PM, 8 PM, 11 PM; MTWThF: 10 AM
	Teleprinter Bulletins	Dy: 6 PM, 9 PM, 12 PM; MTWThF: 11 AM
	Voice Bulletins	Dy: 9:45 PM, 12:45 AM
CT	Slow Code Practice	MWF: 8 AM, 6 PM; TThSSn: 3 PM, 9 PM
	Fast Code Practice	MWF: 3 PM, 9 PM; TTh: 8 AM; TThSSn: 6 PM
	CW Bulletins	Dy: 4 PM, 7 PM, 10 PM; MTWThF: 9 AM
	Teleprinter Bulletins	Dy: 5 PM, 8 PM, 11 PM; MTWThF: 10 AM
	Voice Bulletins	Dy: 8:45 PM, 11:45 PM
MT	Slow Code Practice	MWF: 7 AM, 5 PM; TThSSn: 2 PM, 8 PM
	Fast Code Practice	MWF: 2 PM, 8 PM; TTh: 7 AM; TThSSn: 5 PM
	CW Bulletins	Dy: 3 PM, 6 PM, 9 PM; MTWThF: 8 AM
	Teleprinter Bulletins	Dy: 4 PM, 7 PM, 10 PM; MTWThF: 9 AM
	Voice Bulletins	Dy: 7:45 PM, 10:45 PM
PT	Slow Code Practice	MWF: 6 AM, 4 PM; TThSSn: 1 PM, 7 PM
	Fast Code Practice	MWF: 1 PM, 7 PM; TTh: 6 AM; TThSSn: 4 PM
	CW Bulletins	Dy: 2 PM, 5 PM, 8 PM; MTWThF: 7 AM
	Teleprinter Bulletins	Dy: 3 PM, 6 PM, 9 PM; MTWThF: 8 AM
	Voice Bulletins	Dy: 6:45 PM, 9:45 PM

Code practice, Qualifying Run and CW bulletin frequencies: 1.818, 3.5815, 7.0475, 14.0475, 18.0975, 21.0675, 28.0675, 147.555 MHz.

Teleprinter bulletin frequencies: 3.625, 7.095, 14.095, 18.1025, 21.095, 28.095.

Voice bulletin frequencies: 3.99, 7.29, 14.29, 18.160, 21.39, 28.59, 147.555 MHz.

Slow code practice is at 5, 7½, 10, 13 and 15 WPM. Fast code practice is at 35, 30, 25, 20, 15, 13 and 10 WPM.

Code practice texts are from *QST*, and the source of each practice is given at the beginning of each practice and at the beginning of alternate speeds. For example, "Text is from August 1990 *QST*, pages 16 and 80" indicates that the main text is from the article on page 16 and the mixed number/letter groups at the end of each speed are from the contest scores on page 80.

On Fridays, UTC, a DX bulletin replaces the regular bulletin transmissions.

On Tuesdays and Saturdays at 2330 UTC, Keplerian Elements for active amateur satellites will be sent on the regular Teleprinter frequencies.

Teleprinter bulletins are 45.45-baud Baudot, 110-baud ASCII and 100-baud AMTOR, FEC mode.

CW bulletins are sent at 18 WPM.

W1AW is open for visitors Monday through Friday from 11 AM to 11 PM ET and on Saturday and Sunday from 4:30 PM to 11 PM ET. If you desire to operate W1AW, be sure to bring a copy of your license with you. W1AW is available for operation by visitors between 1 and 4 PM Monday through Friday.

In a communications emergency, monitor W1AW for special bulletins as follows: voice on the hour, teleprinter at 15 minutes past the hour, and CW on the half hour.

For more information...

Publications

The Satellite Experimenter's Handbook, 2nd edition, ARRL (Order #3185, $20). This is *the* book to have. It's a complete guide to amateur satellites.

The AMSAT Journal comes with your membership in AMSAT ($30 in the United States, $36 Mexico and Canada and $45 in all other areas). Contains news, technical articles and commentary. Available from AMSAT, PO Box 27, Washington, DC 20044.

OSCAR Satellite Report, a semimonthly newsletter, contains late-breaking satellite news, current Keplerian elements and commentary. *Satellite Operator*, a monthly newsletter, contains feature articles and news reports, plus Keplerian elements for nonamateur satellites. Both are available from R. Myers Communications, PO Box 17108, Fountain Hill, AZ 85269-7108.

A Beginner's Guide to OSCAR 13 ($7) and *The PACSAT Beginner's Guide* ($10) walk you through the process of setting up your station for OSCAR 13 or the PACSATs, respectively, then show you how to operate these satellites. Available from AMSAT.

Computer Bulletin Boards

DRIG Datalink BBS (214-394-7438)
Celestial RCP/M BBS (513-427-0674)
N8EMR BBS (614-895-2553)

AMSAT Information Nets

Area	*Day*	*Time*	*Frequency*
International	Sunday	1800 UTC	21.280 MHz
International	Sunday	1800 UTC	14.282 MHz
International	Saturday	2200 UTC	21.280 MHz
US East Coast	Tuesday	2100 EST/EDT	3.840 MHz
US Central	Tuesday	2100 CST/CDT	3.840 MHz
US West Coast	Tuesday	2100 PST/PDT	3.840 MHz

ABOUT THE AMERICAN RADIO RELAY LEAGUE

The seed for Amateur Radio was planted in the 1890s, when Guglielmo Marconi began his experiments in wireless telegraphy. Soon he was joined by dozens, then hundreds, of others who were enthusiastic about sending and receiving messages through the air—some with a commercial interest, but others solely out of a love for this new communications medium. The United States government began licensing Amateur Radio operators in 1912.

By 1914, there were thousands of Amateur Radio operators—hams —in the United States. Hiram Percy Maxim, a leading Hartford, Connecticut inventor and industrialist saw the need for an organization to band together this fledgling group of radio experimenters. In May 1914 he founded the American Radio Relay League (ARRL) to meet that need.

Today ARRL, with more than 160,000 members, is the largest organization of radio amateurs in the United States. The League is a not-for-profit organization that:

- promotes interest in Amateur Radio communications and experimentation,
- represents US radio amateurs in legislative matters, and
- maintains fraternalism and a high standard of conduct among Amateur Radio operators.

At League headquarters in the Hartford suburb of Newington, the staff helps serve the needs of members. ARRL is also the International Secretariat for the International Amateur Radio Union, which is made up of similar societies in more than 100 countries around the world.

ARRL publishes the monthly journal *QST*, as well as newsletters and many publications covering all aspects of Amateur Radio. Its headquarters station, W1AW, transmits bulletins of interest to radio amateurs and Morse Code practice sessions. The League also coordinates an extensive field organization, which includes technical information for radio amateurs and public-service activities. ARRL also represents US amateurs with the Federal Communications Commission and other government agencies in the US and abroad.

Membership in ARRL means much more than receiving *QST* each month. In addition to the services already described, ARRL offers membership services on a personal level, such as the ARRL Volunteer Examiner Coordinator Program and a QSL bureau.

Full ARRL membership (available only to licensed radio amateurs) gives you a voice in how the affairs of the organization are governed. League policy is set by a Board of Directors (one from each of 15 Divisions). Each year, half of the ARRL Board of Directors stands for election by the full members they represent. The day-to-day operation of ARRL HQ is managed by an Executive Vice President and a Chief Financial Officer.

No matter what aspect of Amateur Radio attracts you, ARRL membership is relevant and important. There would be no Amateur Radio as we know it today were it not for the ARRL. We would be happy to welcome you as a member! (An Amateur Radio license is not required for Associate Membership.) For more information about ARRL and answers to any questions you may have about Amateur Radio, write or call:

ARRL
Educational Activities, Dept B
225 Main Street
Newington CT 06111
(203) 666-1541

Notes

Notes

Notes

Notes

The ARRL Satellite Anthology

PROOF OF PURCHASE

FEEDBACK

Please use this form to give us your comments on this book and what you'd like to see in future editions.

License class:

□ Novice □ Technician □ Technician with HF privileges

□ General □ Advanced □ Extra

Name

____________________ Call sign __________

Address ____________________

City, State/Province, ZIP/Postal Code ____________________

Daytime Phone ( ) __________ Age __________

If licensed, how long? __________ ARRL member? □ Yes □ No

Other hobbies ____________________

____

Occupation ____________________

For ARRL use only

Edition 2 3 4 5 6 7 8 9 10 11 12

Printing 1 2 3 4 5 6 7 8 9 10 11 12

From ______________________

____

____

Please affix postage. Post Office will not deliver without sufficient postage.

Editor, The ARRL Satellite Anthology
American Radio Relay League
Newington, CT 06111

please fold and tape